EDUCATING THE CHILD WITH CANCER

A Guide for Parents and Teachers

Edited by Nancy Keene

Candlelighters™
Childhood Cancer Foundation

Educating The Child With Cancer: A Guide for Parents and Teachers
Edited by Nancy Keene

Copyright © 2003 Candlelighters Childhood Cancer Foundation
Printed in the United States of America

Published by Candlelighters Childhood Cancer Foundation

Production Editor: Ruth Hoffman

Copy Editor: Ruth Hoffman

Cover Design: Trevor Romain

Interior Design: Shannon Schaffer

Interior layout: Ruth Hoffman

Printing History: Novermber 2003 First Edition

ISBN 0-9724043-3-3

...because kids can't fight cancer alone!

Candlelighters™
Childhood Cancer Foundation

Table of Contents

Preface

Childhood cancer is one of modern medicine's greatest success stories. Forty years ago, almost all children diagnosed with cancer died. Now, many of these children are cured. It is not all good news, however. The diagnosis of cancer in a child hits families like a nuclear bomb. All parts of life—including school—dramatically change after diagnosis.

One of the first things that the family learns is that the treatment, regardless of the kind of cancer, will probably be brutal and it may take a very long time. Most children with cancer have surgery, chemotherapy and/or radiation. They miss weeks, months and sometimes years of school. There are many reasons for these absences—hospitalizations, illnesses at home, contagious diseases at school, fatigue, low immunity, and many more. In addition, the end of treatment does not always signify the end of difficulties, particularly regarding education. Many children face lasting effects of the treatments that saved their lives and these effects may have a significant impact on their education.

This book was written to help families and teachers cope with all aspects of educating the child with cancer. It covers learning issues from infancy through adulthood. It combines the best information from researchers and the wisdom of parents who have "been there" to help parents and educators provide the best possible education for children who have, or had, cancer. A good education provides hope for the future.

Who Wrote the Book

The creation of this book defines community. Candlelighters Childhood Cancer Foundation asked researchers, physicians, psychologists, speech and language therapists and other experts in educating children with cancer, to donate their time and knowledge to this project. Every expert who was asked agreed to participate. Their clear explanations and descriptions of current research provide parents and teachers with a roadmap to what is known about educating children with cancer. The authors really care about our kids, and it shows.

Explaining the issues and describing the research doesn't tell the whole story, however. Parents of children with cancer quickly become experts on their own child and local schools. To portray the rest of the story, a section called "Parent Perspectives" follows every chapter. In these sections, parents share the disappointments and triumphs of advocating for their children's educations. They tell, with great emotion, the obstacles they faced and how they overcame them. Their stories provide a lifeline to those just stepping onto the hard road of childhood cancer treatment and lessons for professionals who may not have considered the emotional aspects of this hard journey. Each story is true, however in some cases names have been changed to protect children's privacy.

How the Book is Organized

This book is divided into six major parts. Part I "Understanding Childhood Cancer," contains two chapters that describe the different types of childhood cancer and how cancer and treatment can affect children's education.

Part II describes educational issues during treatment. These include education in the hospital and at home, school re-entry programs, neuropsychological testing, speech and language difficulties, and advice for educators.

Part III reviews educational issues after treatment, including cognitive, physical, and psychological late effects. The role of the comprehensive late effects clinics is described, and new research on cognitive remediation is described.

The essential role of advocacy is explored in Part IV. Parents sometimes struggle to choose the best educational setting for their child: public education, private schools, home schooling, or charter schools. Learning about special education laws and how to best use them looms large in the lives of parents of children with temporary or permanent disabilities. And planning for high school and beyond is the future of every survivor.

Part V, "Special Issues," deals with three very important topics: Sports and physical education for children with cancer, helping the siblings, and coping with grief in the classroom.

Four appendices comprise the last section of the book. Appendix A contains a sample letter about communicable diseases to send home with the classmates. Appendix B defines dozens of educational terms that parents may hear at school. The next appendix lists hundreds of accommodations that students used at school to help them obtain the best possible education given their unique circumstances. The accommodations are divided into categories to help parents find what might best help their child. For instance, there is a general category for accommodations that help all children with cancer, followed by many other sections, including ones for children with hearing or visual impairments, social problems, or processing difficulties. Appendix D lists dozens of resources—books, websites, and organizations—that provide additional information on educating children who have, or had, cancer.

How to Use this Book

This book was written for two audiences—parents and teachers. Parents do not need to read the book straight through. In fact, that can be overwhelming. It is probably most helpful only to read the chapters that apply to a child's stage of treatment. For instance, if a child has just been diagnosed, it might help to read chapter 2 for an overview of the issues, then chapters 3 through 7 on educational issues during treatment. For long-term survivors with learning or physical disabilities, chapter 2 and chapters 8 through 12 might be most appropriate.

Teachers should all start with chapter 1, which briefly explains childhood cancers and the methods used to treat it. Then, they can pick and choose the chapters that most apply to the student in their class who has or had cancer. Many of the parent stories describe caring actions that teachers took that helped their child succeed in school.

At the end of each chapter is a shaded box containing "Key Points." These give readers an overview of the material in the chapter and may help readers choose the most appropriate chapters to read.

Other Resources

This book grew quite large because the educational needs of children with cancer are great. Some special resources are not listed in the appendices. Instead, they were put on the Candlelighters' website where they can be updated regularly. Both teachers and parents might want to review the technical bibliographies on specific topics contained in this book. Parents of high school-aged survivors might be especially interested in the list of scholarships for college. To view these educational resources, visit Candlelighters' national website at *http://www.candlelighters.org*.

Parents of Preschoolers

Because education does not start the first day a child walks into kindergarten, this book covers issues for infants and preschoolers with cancer. Developing the tools to succeed starts in infancy, when children use their eyes, ears, and brains to learn to speak and interact with others. Cancer can derail normal development in infants and preschoolers.

Helpful chapters for parents of wee ones to read are Chapter 6, *Speech, Language and Hearing Difficulties* and the two chapters on the law (Chapters 14 and 15). Federal laws mandate free services to children at risk for developmental delays or disabilities. Parents who avail themselves of these free services may help keep their child developmentally and physically on track.

Acknowledgements

This book would not exist without the generous support of the Davenport Family Foundation. Their passion and financial support for educational resources help to ease the tremendous difficulties faced by families of children with cancer. Thank you from the heart.

This book is a true collaboration between parents of children with cancer and medical professionals. We are so very thankful to the chapter authors who answered numerous emails, endured editing, and volunteered their time to write such wonderful chapters. Your time, effort, expertise, and caring will help thousands of families find the best and most helpful education for their children. Thank you so very much: F. Daniel Armstrong, PhD; Ernest R. Katz, PhD; Laurie Leigh, MA; Deryk Beal, MHSc; Donald Mabbott, PhD; Eric Bouffet, MD; Kathryn H. Wissler, MS; Raymond K. Mulhern, PhD; Shawna L. Palmer, PhD; Debra L. Friedman, MD; Mary T. Rourke, PhD; Anne Kazak, PhD; Barbara Anne Hieb, CRNP; Susan K. Ogle, CRNP; Wendy L. Hobbie, CRNP; Donna R. Copeland, PhD; Robert W. Butler, PhD, ABPP; Loice A. Swisher MD; Grace Powers Monaco, JD; Gilbert P. Smith, JD; Kathryn Smith, RN MN; Carol Dean; Cecily Betz, RN, PhD, FAAN; Kathy Ruble, RN, PNP, AOCN; Cindy Schwartz, MD; Kathleen A. Ingman, PhD; Avi Madan-Swain, PhD; Heather Austin, MS; Patricia Taylor-Cook.

Stories from parents form the soul of the book. Over 100 people took time to share snapshots of their children's school experiences. This process generated both smiles and tears. We thank you for sharing, and for helping those who will follow in your footsteps. Because survivors of childhood cancer are often discriminated against when trying to obtain employment and insurance, we chose not to publish the names of parent contributors. You know who you are though, and we give you our deepest thanks.

Many, many parents donated time, energy, and enthusiasm to this much-needed project. We would like to thank each and every one of you who helped transform an idea into this special book. Special thanks to Trish DeWitt, Ruth Ehrlich, Ruth Hoffman, Karen Morehouse, and Catherine Woodman MD, who slogged through draft after draft, and made remarkably helpful and gracious comments. This book is much better because of their efforts. Lynne Rief collected stories from bereaved parents and reviewed chapters. Her input was invaluable. Loice Middleton MD, donated countless hours to this project. She collected stories from families of children with brain tumors, reviewed the organization of the book, encouraged inclusion of material for families of preschoolers, and read and reread the text. Creating this book has long been her dream, and she helped bring it into the world. Thank you!

Trevor Romain whipped up a warm and wonderful cover for the book. Trevor, aka "Dr. Mischief," is a life-long friend to children with cancer. We so appreciate his donation of time and talent to make the cover so special.

Shannon Schaffer donated untold hours to design the interior of the book. His talent, good cheer, and patience are very much appreciated.

Ruth Hoffman, the Executive Director of the national office of Candlelighters Childhood Cancer Foundation, spent an enormous amount of time laying out the interior of the book so that it is beautiful to look at and easy to read.

Several chapters used selected text from other books with permission from the publisher:

Chapter 14, *"Special Education: The Law,"* Chapter 15, *"Special Education: Navigating the System"* and Chapter 17, *"High School and Beyond,"* used some material from *Childhood Leukemia*, 3rd edition, by Nancy Keene and *Childhood Brain & Spinal Cord Tumors* by Shiminski-Maher, Cullen, and Sansalone.

It has been a pleasure to work with so many dedicated professionals and such caring parents to create this resource. Together, we can help survivors of childhood cancer make the most of the lives they fought to save. They can't do it alone.

Nancy Keene, Editor

Unity

I dreamed I stood in a studio

And watched two sculptors there.

The clay they used was a young child's mind,

And they fashioned it with care.

One was a teacher; the tools he used

Were books and music and art.

One a parent with a guiding hand,

And a gentle loving heart.

Day after day the teacher toiled

With a touch that was deft and sure,

While the parent labored by his side,

And polished and smoothed it o'er.

And when at last their task was done,

They were proud of what they had wrought.

For the things they had molded into the child

Could neither be sold nor bought.

And each agreed he would have failed

If he had worked alone

For behind the parent stood the school,

And behind the teacher, the home.

Author Unknown

Chapter 1

Introduction to Childhood Cancer

Nancy Keene

Every day in the United States, approximately 50 children—two classrooms full—are diagnosed with cancer. Forty years ago, almost all children and teens diagnosed with cancer died. Today, cure rates have dramatically improved for many types of childhood cancer. Treatment for childhood cancer is one of the great success stories of modern medicine.

While celebrating the good news, all families of children with cancer know that there is more to the story. A sizable percentage of children still die from the disease. In fact, childhood cancer kills more children than any other disease in the United States. During and after treatment, children often suffer from numerous short-term and long-term difficulties. The surgery, radiation, and chemotherapy used to cure children can affect growing bodies and developing minds. Both short-term and long-term problems can create challenges at school.

When teachers hear that one of their students was diagnosed with cancer, they often think of adults they know with cancer. Childhood cancer is an entirely different beast. Therefore, this chapter provides a short introduction to childhood cancer for the educator. It covers how childhood cancer differs from adult cancers, and then describes the most common cancers diagnosed in children. It ends with a brief overview of treatments.

Childhood Cancer is Different

Millions of adults are diagnosed with cancer each year, but only about 13,000 children under the age of 20 are diagnosed annually. Because of the rarity of childhood cancer, misconceptions are common. Often, people

Nancy Keene is a writer, editor, and mother of two daughters, one of whom is an 11-year survivor of high-risk acute lymphoblastic leukemia (ALL).

assume that childhood cancer is similar to adult cancers. However, childhood cancer is different from adult cancer in several significant ways.

Screening tests

Adults often take screening tests to help catch cancer early, when it is more treatable. For instance, adults over the age of 50 have routine examinations to check for colon cancer. Women have periodic mammograms and do monthly self-examinations to check for breast cancer. This is not the case for childhood cancer. There are no routine screening tests done for most childhood cancers.

Symptoms

The signs and symptoms of childhood cancers are non-specific and often mimic those of common childhood illnesses. Fever, headaches, nausea and loss of appetite usually indicate minor illnesses in children. Because of this, and because most pediatricians see few cases of childhood cancer, diagnosis is sometimes delayed.

Types

The most common types of adult cancers are cancers of the breast, skin, and lung. These are almost never diagnosed in children. The most common cancers in childhood are leukemia and tumors in the brain and spinal cord. Some cancers are diagnosed almost exclusively in children, for example, retinoblastoma (a cancer of the eye) and neuroblastoma (a cancer of the sympathetic nervous system). Some children are even born with cancer.

Risk factors

Many adult cancers are linked to genes inherited from parents. For instance, genes that predispose women to develop breast cancer have been identified. Other adult cancers, for example lung cancer, are related to behaviors such as smoking cigarettes. The vast majority of childhood cancers are not inherited or caused by behaviors. They just happen, and the causes are not understood. This is often hard for families, friends, and teachers to accept.

It is important for families and educators to understand that cancer is not contagious; people cannot "catch it" from other people. Adults need to make sure that brothers, sisters, and classmates are told this and understand it.

Treatment

Most adults with cancer are treated by oncologists in their local community or nearby city. Childhood cancer is different. Treatment is given at major medical centers that specialize in treating children. Some families live close to large children's hospitals, and travel time to the hospital is brief. Many families, however, travel great distances to obtain treatment for their child, creating additional strain and disruption. In many cases, one parent stays with the ill child at the distant children's hospital, while the other parent tries to work (essential in order to maintain insurance to cover expensive treatments) and care for the brothers and sisters, if any. In addition, treatment for many childhood cancers is lengthy, lasting from months to years.

Late effects

Children are especially vulnerable to powerful chemotherapy and radiation, in most cases, far more than adults. More children are being cured these days because multiple therapies are given simultaneously. This creates difficult short-term problems (baldness, nausea, weight loss) and many known long-term effects (learning problems, short stature, heart damage). Because a new generation of survivors of these toxic therapies is just reaching adulthood, the very long-term price they paid for survival is unknown.

Types of Childhood Cancer

Following are brief descriptions of the most common childhood cancers, listed in alphabetical order. To learn more about a specific kind of cancer, visit the National Institute of Health's Physician's Data Query (PDQ) website at *http:// www.cancer.gov/cancerinfo/pdq/pediatrictreatment.*

Acute leukemias

Leukemia is the most common cancer in children less than 15 years of age. Eighty percent of children diagnosed with leukemia each year in the U.S., approximately 3,000 children, have acute lymphoblastic leukemia (ALL). Childhood ALL is most commonly diagnosed in children between ages 2 and 7, most commonly around the age of 4.

Another form of acute leukemia is acute myelogenous leukemia (AML), a cancer of the granulocytes (a type of white cell). Approximately 500 children are diagnosed with AML in the U.S. each year.

Acute leukemias begin in the blood-forming tissues of the bone marrow—the spongy center of the bones that produces blood cells. The bone marrow creates too many immature white blood cells that cannot perform their normal function of fighting infection. As the bone marrow fills with abnormal cells, the production of healthy white cells, red cells (which carry oxygen), and platelets (which form clots to stop bleeding) slows and stops. The blood carries the leukemic cells to other organs such as the lungs, liver, spleen, kidneys, and testes. The cancer can also cross the blood-brain barrier and invade the central nervous system (brain and spinal cord).

Brain and spinal cord tumors

Primary brain tumors are the most common solid tumors occurring in children. Approximately 2,200 children younger than age 20 are diagnosed with brain and spinal cord tumors in the U.S. each year. There are many different kinds of brain tumors. The most common pediatric brain tumors are astrocytomas, medulloblastomas, brain stem gliomas, ependymomas and optic gliomas. The number of children diagnosed with each particular type is small.

Although brain tumors can be considered benign or cancerous, all are considered "malignant" because of the location within the brain. Benign tumors can be located near or within critical brain tissue making surgical removal impossible. Radiation and/or chemotherapy used for benign and cancerous brain tumors can result in numerous late effects.

Ewing's sarcoma

Ewing's sarcoma gets its name from the physician who first described it in 1921, Dr. James Ewing. For many years it was believed that Ewing's sarcoma occurred only within the bone, however, other tumors within soft tissues were determined to be similar under the microscope. These include extraosseous Ewing's sarcoma (EES) and peripheral primitive neuroectodermal tumor (PNET). Together, these malignancies are called the Ewing's sarcoma family of tumors (ESFT).

Each year, about 200 children and adolescents under 20 are diagnosed in the U.S. with an ESFT cancer. Eighty-seven percent are diagnosed with Ewing's sarcoma of the bone. ESFT tumors can occur from ages 5 to 10, but they are most common in teenagers.

Hodgkin's disease

Hodgkin's disease, first described by Thomas Hodgkin in 1832, is a type of lymphoma—a cancer of the lymph system. This system is made up of vessels throughout the body that carry a colorless liquid called lymph. Throughout this network are groups of small organs called lymph nodes that make and store lymphocytes—cells that fight infection. Lymph tissue is found throughout the body, so Hodgkin's can be found in almost any organ or tissue, such as the liver, bone marrow, or spleen.

Approximately 850 children and teens are diagnosed with Hodgkin's disease in the U.S. each year. The disease, very rare in children under 5, is most commonly diagnosed in teenagers and young adults.

Neuroblastoma

Neuroblastoma is cancer of the sympathetic nervous system—a network of nerves that carries messages from the brain to all parts of the body. Primary neuroblastoma is a solid, malignant tumor that usually first appears as a mass in the abdomen (most often in the adrenal gland) or near the spine.

About 650 children are diagnosed with neuroblastoma each year in the U.S. The average age at diagnosis is 2, and 25 percent of newly diagnosed children are under 1 year of age.

Non-Hodgkin's lymphoma (NHL)

Lymphomas are cancers of the lymph system. This system is made up of lymph vessels throughout the body that carry a colorless liquid called lymph. Throughout this network, groups of small organs called lymph nodes make and store lymphocytes—cells that fight infection. Lymph tissue is found throughout the body, so NHL can be found in almost any organ or tissue, such as the liver, bone marrow, or spleen. Hodgkin's and non-Hodgkin's lymphomas are differentiated by cell type, and require different treatments.

Approximately 800 children under the age of 20 are diagnosed with NHL in the U.S. every year. It is rare in very young children.

Osteosarcoma

About half of all bone tumors diagnosed are osteosarcoma, most of which occur during the adolescent growth spurt. It typically appears at the ends of the long bones, usually at the knee. Other, less common sites are the upper arm (close to the shoulder), the pelvis, and the skull. Approximately 400 children and teens are diagnosed each year in the United States.

Retinoblastoma

Retinoblastoma is a malignant tumor of the retina in the eye. Retinoblastoma is usually found in very young children, and may be present at birth. Although it may occur at any age, 95 percent of children with retinoblastoma are diagnosed before the age of 5. Approximately 300 children are diagnosed in the U.S. each year.

Rhabdomyosarcoma

Rhabdomyosarcoma (RMS) is a malignant soft tissue tumor of primitive muscle cells called rhabdomyoblasts. Instead of maturing into muscle cells, the rhabdomyoblasts grow out of control. Because muscles are located throughout the body, the tumors can appear at numerous locations. RMS is most commonly found in the head and neck, genitourinary tract, extremities, and chest and lungs.

Rhabdomyosarcoma is the most common childhood soft tissue sarcoma. Approximately 350 children are diagnosed with rhabdomyosarcoma in the U.S. each year. Two-thirds of those diagnosed are under the age of 5.

Wilms tumor

Wilms tumor is a cancer of the kidney. It accounts for 5 to 6 percent of all childhood cancers in the U.S.—approximately 500 children are diagnosed each year. Wilms tumor occurs most commonly in children under 5 years of age. Only 1 to 2 percent of Wilms tumors are believed to be inherited. In cases where the disease is inherited, there is a higher incidence of bilateral (in both kidneys) disease.

Rare cancers

Other cancers occur in children, but rarely. Following are brief descriptions of chronic myelogenous leukemia, liver cancers, melanoma, nasopharyngeal carcinoma, and soft tissue sarcomas.

Chronic myelocytic leukemia (CML) is common in adults but rare in children. In CML, mature white cells become cancerous. Children or teens with CML get very big spleens and have a high number of white blood cells in their blood.

Tumors in the liver are rare in children. The two cancers that are sometimes diagnosed are hepatoblastoma and hepatocellular carcinoma. Most children who are diagnosed with hepatoblastoma are younger than 3. Hepatocellular carcinoma shows up in children from birth to 4 and from 12 to 15.

Melanoma is a cancer of the skin that is common in adults but sometimes grows in children or teens. Melanoma can spread from the skin to other parts of the body through blood or lymph.

Nasopharyngeal carcinoma is a cancer in the area behind the nose and the top and back of the mouth. It is most common in children between the ages of 10 and 15.

There are several rare soft tissue sarcomas that sometimes are diagnosed in children or teens. The ones found most often in children are synovial sarcoma, fibrosarcoma, malignant peripheral nerve sheath tumor (also called neurofibrosarcoma or malignant schwannoma), and malignant fibrous histiocytoma.

Treatment for Childhood Cancer

The most common treatments for childhood cancer are surgery, radiation, chemotherapy, and stem cell transplantation. Surgery and radiation are directed treatments—affecting one part of the body. Chemotherapy and stem cell transplantation are therapies aimed at cancer cells throughout the body. This section briefly describes each treatment and the possible effects on children's education.

Surgery

Surgery has a vital role in treating most types of childhood cancer. For children with leukemia or lymphomas, it is used only to insert a catheter (central line) in the chest. This allows doctors and nurses to put medicine directly into the bloodstream and to take blood samples without having to put a needle in the child. Children with solid tumors usually have surgery to implant a catheter as well as one or more surgeries to diagnose, treat, or remove the tumor. Some of the most commonly used surgeries of children with cancer are:

- **Biopsy:** During a biopsy, a tiny sample of the tumor is taken through a small incision to help determine the diagnosis and to plan treatment options.

- **Debulking:** Sometimes a tumor is too large or too close to vital structures for the surgeon to remove it safely. Debulking the mass (removing as much of the tumor as possible without removing it entirely) can have several benefits. The child is often more comfortable after the mass has been debulked and chemotherapy and radiation are sometimes more effective on a smaller tumor.

- **Tumor removal:** Surgery to remove an entire tumor is called maximal surgical resection. In this type of operation, the surgeon attempts to remove the whole tumor and, in some cases, a small margin of healthy tissue around the tumor.

- **Limb salvage:** This surgery removes the tumor and the bone in which it is growing, and replaces the bone with a metallic device or donor bone.

- **Amputation and enucleation (removal of the eye):** For some children with retinoblastoma and sarcomas, surgery includes the removal of all or a portion of a body part. With the advances being made in childhood cancer treatment, amputation and enucleation are less frequently necessary.

- **Shunt insertion:** Sometimes children with brain tumors develop hydrocephalus—a build up of fluid in the brain caused when a tumor, scar, or clot blocks the normal flow of fluid in the brain. A tube, called a shunt, is surgically inserted to divert the excess fluid from the brain into the abdomen, chest, or a large vein in the heart.

Short-term and long-term effects from surgery depend on the age of the child and the location and extent of the surgery. Children who have a kidney removed usually have few effects from surgery other than a large scar that is normally covered by clothing. In contrast, teens who need to have a leg or part of the pelvis removed have multiple effects in function and appearance. A huge constellation of problems can occur after surgery for a tumor in the brain.

Radiation

Radiation treatment, also called irradiation or radiotherapy, is the use of high-energy x-rays to kill cancer cells. A large machine called a linear accelerator directs x-rays to the precise portion of the body needing treatment. In some cases, the radiation is shaped to the contours of the tumor to protect as much healthy tissue as possible. In other situtations, such as children with a brain tumor called medulloblastoma, cancer cells can migrate throughout the central nervous system. Radiation to the entire brain and spine is then performed. Total body irradiation (TBI) is sometimes used to prepare a child for stem cell transplant. Children with tumors in weight-bearing bones are sometimes treated with radiation to prevent fractures.

Not all childhood cancers respond to radiation treatments. For those tumors that may respond, radiation treatment is usually given daily (on weekdays) for several weeks. When side effects occur, it is often hard to differentiate those caused by radiation from those caused by the high-dose chemotherapy that is sometimes given at the same time. The severity of the side effects depends on the sensitivity and the size of the area being radiated. Possible short-term side effects are:

- Loss of appetite
- Nausea and vomiting
- Mouth sores and/or sore throat
- Fatigue
- Reddened or itchy skin

- Hair loss
- Low blood counts
- Changes in taste and smell
- Sleepiness (somnolence syndrome) from radiation to the brain

These side effects can affect the way children look, how much energy they have, and their susceptibility to illness. All of the short-term side effects can create difficulties in school. In addition to side effects, the need to travel to and from the hospital every day usually interferes with school attendance.

While short-term effects appear and subside, long-term side effects may not become apparent for months or years after treatment ends. Specific late effects depend on the age of the child, the dose of radiation, and the location of the radiation. The effects of radiation on cognitive functioning, hair regrowth, bone growth, soft tissue growth, teeth and sinuses, puberty, and fertility, range from no late effects to severe, life-long impacts. The late effect that has the biggest impact on education is learning disabilities after radiation to the brain. This commonly occurs in survivors of brain tumors and leukemia who were treated with radiation to the brain.

Chemotherapy

The word chemotherapy is derived from the combination of "chemical" and "therapy" or treatment. It means using drugs, singly or in combination, to destroy or disrupt the growth of cancer cells.

Normal, healthy cells divide and grow in a well-established pattern. When normal cells divide, an identical copy is produced. The body only makes the number of normal cells that it needs at any given time. As each normal cell matures, it loses its ability to reproduce. Normal cells are also preprogrammed to die at a specific time. Cancer cells, on the other hand, reproduce uncontrollably and grow in unpredictable ways. They invade surrounding tissue and can travel in blood or lymph to lodge in other parts of the body. All chemotherapy drugs work in some way to interfere with the ability of the cancer cells to live, divide, and multiply.

Chemotherapy causes a large number of side effects, depending on what drugs are used and the dosages. Some of the short-term common side effects that affect children at school are:

- Hair loss
- Nausea and vomiting

- Fatigue
- Weight loss
- Weight gain (especially a moon face and big belly from corticosteroids)
- Low numbers of infection fighting cells in the blood
- Inability to concentrate
- Emotional swings
- Uncoordination
- Diarrhea or constipation

Long-term effects from chemotherapy that most commonly affect school are:

- Changes in cognitive functioning (usually from chemotherapy to the brain)
- Chronic fatigue
- Hearing loss

Blood stem cell transplantation

Stem cell transplants, which includes bone marrow transplants, are complicated procedures used to treat cancer and some blood diseases that were once considered incurable. There are three sources of stem cells: blood, bone marrow, and umbilical cord blood. In these procedures, the child is given high-dose chemotherapy, with or without radiation. Normal stem cells are then infused into the child's veins. The stem cells migrate to the cavities inside the bones where new, healthy blood cells are then produced.

Transplants, although frequently life-saving, are expensive, technically complex, and potentially life-threatening. Recovering from a transplant can take a very long time, which frequently disrupts schooling.

Side effects after a transplant can be severe. Some common complications after a transplant are:

- Infections
- Mouth and throat sores
- Fatigue
- Low numbers of infection-fighting white cells
- Low numbers of blood clotting cells (platelets)

Long-term late effects that affect education include:

- Changes in cognitive function

- Early or late puberty
- Altered growth and development
- Cataracts (if the eyes were irradiated)
- Changes in the appearance of the skin
- Fatigue

Other tests and therapies

In addition to the treatments described above, children with cancer undergo a host of other medical treatments that cause absences from school. Examples are:

- Tests to monitor the health of body parts (hearing tests, heart tests, blood tests)
- Tests to monitor the disease (MRIs, second look surgeries, bone marrow aspirations)
- Meetings with nutritionists, social workers, child life workers
- Therapies to lessen side effects (physical therapy, occupational therapy)

The above is a brief overview of the types of cancer that affect children, the treatments used to eradicate the disease, and some of the more common effects from treatment. Each child is unique, and his or her response to treatment depends on many individual factors. It helps if parents, teachers, administrators and school counselors discuss the disease, the treatment, and possible impacts on school. Together they can craft a plan to help the child maintain contact with friends and keep up with schoolwork to the extent possible. Working together, they can help the child have as normal and rewarding a school experience as possible during the months or years of treatment and beyond.

KeyPoints

- Every day, approximately 50 children are diagnosed with cancer.
- Childhood cancer is different from adult cancer:
    - There are no screening tests
    - Symptoms are non-specific
    - Children get different types of cancer than do adults
    - Most childhood cancers are not inherited or caused by behaviors
    - Children usually travel to major medical centers for treatment
    - Because children's minds are developing and bodies are growing, toxic treatments can cause difficulties months or years after treatment
- Despite improvements in cure rates, treatment is usually difficult and often lengthy. Short- and long-term side effects can impact education.
- The most common treatments for childhood cancer are chemotherapy, surgery, radiation, and stem cell transplantation.

Parent Perspectives

We have a tree called Hope. The anniversary of Matt's diagnosis is a painful day for us; there was no happiness so we do not celebrate it. Instead, we celebrate the anniversary of his completion of treatment. So for his anniversary we planted a tree and Matt named it Hope. We picked a flowering apple tree and it grows outside our living room window. When I look at our tree it reminds me how the cycle of the tree reflects our journey with cancer.

When the tree is bare in winter it reminds me of when we were diagnosed and how dead and empty we felt inside. We feel like we have lost hope. But slowly a bud begins to form in our hearts and we again begin to feel hope. We hear a bird sing, a child laugh and smile again, the warmth of the sun. Suddenly that bud bursts forth into a blossom and we begin to have hope in the future. As the tree is in full bloom, we are filled with hope as we have completed treatment and are warmed by the satisfaction that we have survived. The tree will provide nourishment and protection for other creatures just as we will offer nourishment and support to others who are on this journey.

The branches of the tree aren't all perfectly formed any longer but there is strength and beauty in its imperfection as we remember what that tree has had to overcome just to survive. Sometimes we enter a fall in this battle with cancer and just as the leaves fall from the tree, so do our tears. The winds blow us sometimes to our breaking point and some will have to again face winter. We need to remember that when the tree looks bare and void of life, there is a bud of hope just waiting to burst forth. As I watch Hope grow skyward, I watch my son reaching also, for the sky is the limit for him.

✛ ✛ ✛

My 8-year-old daughter loves babies. She is two years off-treatment for standard risk ALL. One day we went in for her regular follow-up and she proudly told our oncologist that when she grew up she planned to be an obstetrician. He laughed and fired back: "No way. You could never do the math." I won't go into how insensitive and crushing this comment was or how I "enlightened" him out in the hallway. The sad fact is, he is quite possibly correct in his assessment. But he had no right to rip her dream from her.

When educators read this book, I hope they will understand not just that childhood cancer is devastating. I also want them to know that these battered children have profound strengths and they might be able to move the earth if we can just help them build the right lever to move it with. It is so easy for an adult in power to crush a child's dream with an off-hand comment based on a preconceived notion of the child's limitations. Yes, cancer is a vicious disease and the children who survive it often pay a very high price. But no one knows how far they can go if they are treated to an education that encourages them to find their strengths, build that lever, and move the Earth.

Chapter 2

Childhood Cancer and Education

F. Daniel Armstrong, PhD

At the time a child is diagnosed with cancer, the last thing on the minds of most parents is what effect this will have on school and their child's education. The focus is understandably on whether the child will live, and at what cost. Once the initial shock wears off, however, educational issues begin to emerge. Should my child return to school? What if she is exposed to chicken pox? What if the other children tease him? Will it really matter if he doesn't learn his multiplication tables this year? So what if she graduates from high school a year or two late? Is this treatment going to interfere with his success for the rest of his life? These are but a few of the thoughts that parents may face as they absorb the information about the diagnosis and treatment plan. As treatment starts and the child and family settle into a routine, these educational concerns become real, and most families struggle for answers to their questions.

Educational issues arise at many points in the treatment. Initial concerns about keeping up while starting treatment give way to struggling with how to educate a child who sometimes feels fine and then becomes ill as blood counts change between treatment cycles. When the child is well enough to return to school, concerns about appearance, teasing, and school re-entry emerge. Once in school, exposure to infections carried by other children becomes a major concern, as does keeping up with the pace of work. As treatment moves along, new concerns about how best to educate the child in the face of acute and long-term side effects of treatment begin to creep in. Finally, treatment stops, but some of the long-term learning consequences do not, launching children and parents into what can be a frightening struggle for normal life.

The purpose of this chapter and this book is to help parents, teachers, physicians, and

Dr. Armstrong is professor and associate chair of the department of pediatrics and director of the Mailman Center for Child Development at the University of Miami School of Medicine, FL.

children understand some of the common challenges, learn what is known about these challenges, and develop plans for dealing with the educational challenges faced by the child with cancer.

Research over the past 20 years has consistently pointed to the importance of school-related issues for children's quality of life. When we look closely at this research, we find several consistent themes. These include a focus on:

- How to help children return to school and school-related activities after treatment has started (school re-entry).

- How to help parents learn to advocate for their children.

- How to educate teachers and physicians about common school-related problems.

- How to deal with the long-term consequences (late effects) of cancer and its treatment long after treatment has stopped.

Educational Issues While On Treatment

Just because a child is diagnosed with cancer does not mean learning stops. School is a child's work environment, and learning to read, write, do math, draw, jump, create, and plan are the career activities of childhood and adolescence. Unfortunately, the demands of treatment often lead parents, physicians, teachers, and other adults to decide that education is secondary, something to be addressed when things are better. The consequence of this approach is that learning needs are neglected, leaving children at a disadvantage when treatment is finished.

There are a number of things that may make attending to school-related issues difficult for parents and children. The stress of diagnosis and the initial phases of treatment often force school to the back burner. Medical complications, or acute side effects, like low blood counts, infection, or severe nausea and vomiting point many to hospital or home-bound educational approaches. Understandably, parents are sometimes unwilling to have the child return to school because of fear for the child's safety (e.g, exposure to infections) or distress over being separated from the ill child. Both parents and children/teenagers may worry that other children will tease because of appearance changes. Teachers may be hesitant to have the child return to school because of lack of understanding of childhood cancer, or because of a feeling of incompetence in dealing with both health and educational needs in the classroom. Educational systems may be challenged by the in-and-out nature of attendance required by clinic visits or hospitalization, and the challenge of working this out in the face of state laws related to school attendance and performance on mandated standardized testing. There are a lot of reasons to avoid attending to school issues.

However, research suggests that regular school attendance by children while on treatment is associated with better quality of life nearly 10 years after completing therapy. This is true for children with specific learning needs, as well as those who have no identified learning problems. Children who return to school are more quickly reintegrated into typical social activities, and they do not fall (as far) behind because of missed opportunities for learning. For these reasons, it is increasingly clear that parents, members of the pediatric oncology team, and educators need to work together to develop plans that can practically and effectively help children return to a school environment as soon as possible. Some strategies for doing this are described in the next sections.

Medical complications

Pediatric oncologists can work with parents and schools to address medical issues that interfere with school attendance. Admissions for chemotherapy can sometimes be scheduled to lessen interference with school (e.g., scheduling admissions to include weekend days). Aggressive supportive care (e.g., use of granulocyte colony stimulating factors to boost blood cell counts; prophylactic antibiotics; anti-nausea medications) combined with good communication about events that may be dangerous for the child (e.g., chicken pox exposure) can also make it possible for the child to attend school as often as possible. Likewise, pediatric oncologists and other pediatric specialists can provide evidence-based guidance about limitations and non-limitations on physical activity, including competitive sports participation. These strategies do need to vary, since no two children are alike in their response to treatment, but careful planning by oncologists, parents, and educators can substantially lower concerns and risks in most cases.

Teacher and educational system concerns

Members of the pediatric oncology team can meet with teachers and school personnel to discuss concerns related to the health of the child with cancer. Brochures related to childhood cancer treatment describe most of the known side effects, and several have been written specifically for teachers. Parents and teachers can work out plans for dealing with unexpected medical problems, and good communication between parents and teachers about expected absences because of clinic visits or hospitalization can avoid most difficulties related to missed work and assignments.

Educational systems are in place in many areas to address the needs of the child with cancer. For some, a period of hospital/home-bound education may be necessary because of risks associated with very aggressive treatment. In these cases, it is important for the hospital/home-bound teacher to be in on-going communication with the child's regular classroom teacher, so that the hospital/home-bound curriculum matches the classroom curriculum as closely as possible. For the child who has periods of time when he/she is well, dual enrollment plans can be developed. In these situations, children attend regular class whenever possible, but are shifted to hospital or home-bound instruction during times when they are not able to attend class. There are procedures established under federal law that permit these types of arrangements. Parents and educators working together can usually develop an educational plan that meets both state law and the needs of the child.

Acute learning concerns

The child on active treatment for cancer, even if well enough to attend school, is likely to have some limitations that healthy children do not have. Some medications (e.g., steroids) have acute side effects that interfere with the ability to stay focused or produce physical behavior changes (e.g., hyperactivity, emotional mood swings). Others affect the ways that the nervous system works (e.g., vincristine), resulting in slower reflexes and problems with fine motor coordination. Fatigue may be a problem in both physically active and quiet settings, and children treated with cancer may require time to rest at school. Parents should be sure that teachers are aware of the medications that the child is taking at any given time, and of the effects these medications can have on behavior and learning.

Parent and child emotional concerns

Anticipating a return to school can be very stressful for children, adolescents, and their parents. Physical changes (e.g., hair loss, weight gain, surgical scars) often lead to worries that the child will be teased or even socially ostracized by peers, and that school administrators will be insensitive to needed modifications in school policies (e.g., letting a child wear a hat in class). In most cases, the worries far exceed the realities. A meeting between the parent and the child's teacher prior to a return to school can often resolve all the issues that parents have. In some cases, however, something more may be needed. A variety of educational materials (e.g., brochures, videotapes) are available to educate teachers about childhood cancer, and these should be provided soon after a child is diagnosed. Many helpful materials are listed in Appendix D, *Resources* at the end of this book. In addition, in-school sessions that teach classmates about childhood cancer often reduce classmates' worries, teasing, and may lead to an easy transition back into school. Many of these school re-entry programs actively involve the child with cancer as a leader of the session; one outcome of this approach is that the child with cancer is seen as competent and highly knowledgeable rather than sick and weak. Parents can be invited to observe these sessions. Many parents report that their own worries decrease a great deal upon seeing the positive response of teachers and classmates to the returning child with cancer.

Once a child has successfully returned to school, regular contact between the parent and the teacher is very important. Parents should request teacher observations of any difficulties with learning, social relationships, emotions, or behavioral control, so that these difficulties can be addressed before they become problems. Likewise, teachers should know that parents welcome feedback on how the child is doing. Parents may have access to information about a potential problem commonly experienced by children with cancer, while teachers may overlook early signs of later difficulties because of lack of knowledge. Both parents and teachers need to work together to develop expectations that recognize limitations imposed by the disease and treatment. They also need to develop agreement about how to provide positive discipline that can help children to manage their own behavior and emotions and continue positive all-around development.

Late Effects of Disease and Treatment

Aggressive treatment of childhood cancer has resulted in most children surviving cancer. As these children survive, we are becoming aware of long-term effects of this successful treatment that we did not recognize before, often because most children did not survive long enough to have them. Learning problems that emerge over the years after treatment ends represent a growing area of concern.

Mechanism for learning problems

We do not fully understand why learning problems develop in children treated for cancer. Injury from a tumor or complications of surgery, exposure to radiation therapy of the brain, and some kinds of chemotherapy that affect brain development have all been linked to later occurring learning problems. In these cases, damage to a specific structure of the brain (e.g., surgery or tumor) or damage to small blood vessels (calcification) or to nerve cells that grow and develop after treatment, are believed to be the main causes of learning late effects. Problems associated with damaged structures are seen almost immediately; problems associated with brain development after treatment are often not recognized until the child reaches the age at which other children demonstrate an ability, but they do not.

Other things may be involved in whether a child experiences learning late effects or not. Pre-existing learning disabilities, lack of opportunity to learn because of prolonged hospitalization, genetic factors that increase or decrease the effects of treatment, and things like poverty, malnutrition, or accidents unrelated to cancer can have an effect on a child's ability to learn. Parents should make sure that their pediatricians and psychologists are aware of any of these other factors that may affect learning over time.

What children are at greatest risk?

- **Brain tumors:** Almost all children treated for brain tumors, even those treated only with surgery who show no immediate signs of difficulty, have a significant risk for learning problems in the years after treatment. Those treated with surgery, radiation therapy, and chemotherapy are at greater risk, and children who are treated at a younger age (e.g, less than 6 years) are at the greatest risk.

- **Acute lymphoblastic leukemia (ALL):** Children with ALL who were treated with radiation therapy to the brain who also received methotrexate have a significant risk of learning problems. Today, few children with ALL are given radiation therapy to the brain. Instead, some children receive medications using spinal taps (triple intrathecal chemotherapy) combined with higher doses of methotrexate given in the hospital. Others are given higher doses or more frequent doses of intrathecal methotrexate. Many of these children experience brain injury following this treatment, but not all. Right now, we do not have a way to know which children will have problems, and which will not.

- **Children treated with radiation to the head:** A number of tumors of the face and head require radiation therapy, and the radiation may penetrate into the brain. Children with these tumors (e.g., rhabdomyosarcoma, Histiocytosis X, osteosarcoma of the orbit) share similar risk with those treated in this way for brain tumors. Likewise, some children receive low-dose radiation to the brain prior to bone marrow transplant. If these children have relapsed following treatment for ALL, they may have a combined risk from the previous chemotherapy and radiation therapy. Low dose radiation therapy (less than 1200 cGy, sometimes given before bone marrow or stem cell transplants) alone has not been linked to major learning late effects.

- **Others:** There are other groups of children that may be at risk, but there is no evidence to be sure. These children include those who have tumors that may affect learning, such as neuroblastoma, but poor survival in the past has not allowed us to learn whether there are learning late effects or not. Another group of children with potential risk are those treated with intensive therapy that requires many long and repeated hospitalizations, particularly at a very young age. For these children, learning difficulties are likely related to missed opportunities for learning.

Common learning late effects

While some children may experience significant problems in almost every area of ability, most demonstrate patterns of strength and difficulty that occur for many children. These problems are often not seen right away, but instead show up when they reach the age when healthy children would acquire the ability, but they do not. General intelligence may be affected, but more often the difficulties are those associated with the structures of the brain that grow after treatment. Formal neuropsychological testing, parent and teacher observations, and children's reports point to a number of common problems:

- For many children, the most notable late effect is that it takes longer to process information and complete tasks. Children appear slower in their social interactions, they appear to learn things more slowly, and completion of academic work often takes two or three times longer that it does for healthy children.

- Difficulty sustaining attention and inconsistent attention is common. Hyperactivity is not common, but some impulsivity and "spacing out" are frequently reported by parents and children.

- Memory difficulties are also commonly seen. In general, memory for verbal information and meaningful information is usually not a problem. However, memory for visual information and novel, non-meaningful information is frequently impaired, and children may encounter difficulties with memory for sequences of information.

- Difficulty with fine motor ability may be encountered. Children may have problems translating things that they think or see into a motor response (e.g., writing). This may translate into handwriting that is either accurate but very slow, or quickly done but illegible. One consequence of this late effect is that children are not able to transfer the quality of their thinking into written form because of a performance, but not knowledge or creativity, deficit.

- Difficulty with planning, organizing materials, or solving abstract problems may occur, particularly as children reach the teenage years. These types of problems are also called problems of executive functioning, and can be quite frustrating for the child, parents, and teachers. Children may need additional help with organizational aids, beginning with organization of school papers, assignments, and planning projects that are due in the future.

These neuropsychological deficits may also be related to specific school performance problems. In general, memory and attention difficulties can be associated with problems in basic math calculation skills, particularly multiplication and division, but a child's ability to apply math concepts is not seriously affected. Likewise, difficulties with organizing visual information can affect basic reading abilities. Children are often able to learn to recognize words, but lag behind in their ability to comprehend what they are reading. Sometimes, if there are problems with visual-spatial difficulties, the child may also lose his/her place on the page. As academic work in both math and reading becomes more complex, the difficulties become much more evident, and begins to affect learning in all content areas (e.g., social studies, science, etc.).

Fortunately, abilities associated with brain development that takes place before treatment seem to be preserved in most cases. Therefore, a child's ability to listen (process information that is heard and efficiently remember that information) and express him/herself verbally are usually areas of strength in both learning and showing what has been learned.

Strategies for Intervention

While there has been a lot of research that describes the problems that children treated for cancer may face, there has not been as much on how to help children with these problems. Fortunately, we are beginning to see some studies that focus on how best to help, and the early results from these studies appear promising.

- **Tutoring:** The first step in helping a child with learning problems is to provide extra attention from an adult or peer who may be able to help work through problems. This approach is most often helpful if the difficulties are related to missed opportunities for learning and not to effects of treatment on brain development.

- **Cognitive rehabilitation:** Some researchers are exploring whether having the child engage in activities that strengthen the development of the brain by practicing skills over and over (called "massed practice") can be helpful.

This is a very experimental area and information is not yet available about whether the approach is helpful, for what type of problems it might be helpful, what children may best be helped, or whether there is a best time for this type of intervention.

- **Medication:** Another group of researchers is evaluating whether medications used for attention problems may be helpful for children who experience slow processing speed, problems with sustaining attention, and some memory problems. These studies are being conducted very carefully, since children who have received brain radiation and chemotherapy may respond to the medications and dosages in different ways than children who have not been treated for cancer.

- **Compensatory intervention:** Another group of researchers are investigating whether using accommodations (e.g., using books on tape for reading, calculators for math, and voice recognition software and computers for producing written work) can help children work around the cognitive late effects of treatment. This approach uses existing special education resources in the schools with modifications that address performance. The focus of the intervention is on listening and speaking rather than reading and writing.

KeyPoints

Learning problems are real for children treated for cancer. It is difficult for parents to think about school and learning issues at the time their child is diagnosed and treated for cancer. Improvements in treatment and growing numbers of children who will be cancer survivors make this an area that needs to be more aggressively discussed and addressed by parents, physicians, nurses, psychologists, and teachers. While there is a lot more research that needs to be done, a great deal has been learned that helps us understand the common risks, the common problems, and some effective strategies for helping. Advocacy for increased and improved research in this area, followed by education of parents, children, teachers, and pediatric oncology teams are the activities that will likely lead to children's quality of life being the "second life" saved in our battle against childhood cancer.

Parent Perspectives

The topic of neurocognitive late effects and physical late effects, always provokes such passionate responses from parents. To learn that one's child has cancer is devastating, and the world cries with you. To learn that one's child has life-long late effects from the treatment intended to cure him of his disease, is equally devastating, yet somehow the world doesn't understand this. It is almost worse than diagnosis because these effects can be life-long challenges for our children, and those who love them. When we were looking down the barrel of two years of chemo/radiation, there was an end. When does it end for our kids after treatment? A friend and parent of a child with cancer likes to say, "For those in the trenches...stand strong."

✦ ✦ ✦

I never know if I should be pleased that Ethan is doing well enough to "pass" as a non-impaired kid, or cry when something is overlooked so grossly that I want to scream. I am trying to opt for optimism but find it a challenge some days.

✦ ✦ ✦

Chemotherapy can really zap some kids, leaving them a pale, tired version of themselves. Other children can have chemo and still have lots of energy to participate in school. Some children have always gotten every little bug they are exposed to—others are never sick.

We were one of the lucky ones. My son continued to attend school, do karate, and play baseball. He had few hospitalizations and rarely even had a cold. Cancer was pretty much just a reason he had to go to the doctor every once in a while. We didn't dwell on it, but we also didn't deny it. He still had to make his bed every morning and do his homework and behave in an acceptable manner.

✦ ✦ ✦

My son Jamie has leukoencephalopathy (changes in the brain) from his chemotherapy and radiation treatment for T-cell ALL. I'm getting ready for

Jamie's neuropsych testing this week. I've read through each and every paper and was quite mesmerized by all the changes that have occurred over the past 4 ½ years in terms of Jamie's education since his cancer diagnosis. It's been a real learning experience for me. I never dreamed I'd one day have to fight like hell for one of my kids to get a good education.

This year we've made several tough decisions about high school and are satisfied (and relieved) with the program Jamie will be placed in for grade nine in September. He is also finishing up a 'Learning Strategies' course tomorrow and we have seen significant improvements in his work. Tomorrow he/we are meeting with an Acquired Brain Injury Facilitator at his school. Her plan is to observe Jamie in the classroom and then give us some (hopefully) useful insights.

I've come a long way in terms of coping with brain damage. I remember being told at the beginning of Jamie's treatment that neurotoxicity was a rare side effect of some of the chemo and radiation he was going to have. I didn't give it much thought at the time as I was completely focused on helping Jamie beat leukemia. I never thought it would happen to us.

When we discovered Jamie did in fact have neurotoxicity about eight months into treatment, I was devastated. I wasn't sure I would ever be able to handle this terrible diagnosis. I remember with crystal clear clarity the day our favorite oncologist told us, "Your goal for Jamie should be to have him learn to balance a check book and grow up to be an independent adult." To say I was crushed would be an understatement.

But here we are 4 ½ years later, and while I'm certainly not blind to the learning/social disabilities my son has, he has shown me over and over again that goals that his doctors once thought were insurmountable for him, can be accomplished.

He struggles daily in school and has to work much, much harder than most kids to learn. What amazes me more than his ability to learn though, is his ability to remain happy and positive each and every day. He never, ever complains. I could count on one hand how often this kid has been grumpy— not including steroid days of course!

Tomorrow is going to be tough. I'm not happy about having to meet with a brain injury facilitator but I'm going to face it with a positive attitude like my son would. I've learned more from Jamie than anyone/anything else in my whole 42 years.

Chapter 3

Education in the Hospital and at Home

Ernest R. Katz, PhD

When a child or teenager is diagnosed with a life threatening illness like cancer, school often takes a back seat to the immediate medical crisis at hand. With so much new and stressful medical information to absorb, complex treatment decisions to make, and an overwhelming range of emotions to go through, children and parents may feel that school is not very important at this critical time. And yet, especially for the child or teen whose world is turning upside down because of a frightening illness, thinking about normal life experiences like school can help a young person feel hopeful and optimistic about the future.

School is to kids what work is to adults. Both are necessary for people to feel they are part of the mainstream and still like everyone else in spite of a serious illness. Even with the focus of attention on the diagnosis and treatment of disease, talking about school and friends is an important way to remind the child that normal life will continue. During the initial phases of treatment, while undergoing intensive medical interventions like chemotherapy, surgery, and/or radiation therapy, it is not unusual for a child to miss weeks or months of school. For a child undergoing a bone marrow transplant, the time away from school may be even longer. It is of great importance to the child's overall quality of life and adaptation to illness that school continue during periods of hospitalization or when homebound because of health issues. Home and hospital instruction provided by hospitals and local school districts is available to help.

Hospital Teaching

Under the federal laws known as the Individuals with Disabilities Education Act

> Dr. Katz is the director of behavioral sciences and clinical professor of pediatrics at the Childrens Center for Cancer and Blood Diseases, Children's Hospital Los Angeles and the Keck School of Medicine, University of Southern California, CA.

(IDEA) of 1997, and Section 504 of the Rehabilitation Act of 1973, stipulations are made for the continuation of educational programs for young people who are not able to attend a regular school because of health concerns. Each individual state also has educational laws and regulations that follow the federal guidelines to help implement these services across the country.

Children are often treated at medical centers far from home. Most children's hospitals and large pediatric departments of general medical centers employ permanent hospital teachers who teach children hospitalized for five or more days.

Hospital teachers usually identify the new patients who need to be enrolled and they will come and meet you and your child. If you haven't met the hospital teacher and your child will be in the hospital for an extended stay, ask a nurse or your child's doctor to connect you with the teacher. If the hospital does not have a full-time teacher, the hospital social worker, child life specialist, or nurse coordinator will help you contact the local school district to arrange for an appropriate teacher to work with your child.

In order to begin teaching your child in the hospital, the hospital teacher may need a statement from your child's doctor that identifies the medical diagnosis and provides an estimate of the length of time the child will be hospitalized. Make sure your child's doctor says that the child will be hospitalized the minimum number of days necessary to start hospital teaching (usually 5 school days) or a teacher may not be assigned. If your child is able to leave the hospital before the estimated time has been completed, this is generally not a problem; your child will be able to transfer to a home teacher or return to school if medically able. The minimum number of days in the hospital is generally required because the child is technically "transferred" from the regular school to the hospital school for that period of time, after which he will be transferred back to the school or he will be transferred to home teaching (see next section).

As part of enrolling your child in hospital teaching, the hospital teacher will meet with you and your child and collect information about your child's regular school program and teachers. The hospital teacher will contact the regular school and coordinate the lessons with the home school teacher. Unfortunately, hospital teaching is usually limited to about one hour per day, but that is often all an ill child can tolerate.

The hospital teacher will accommodate her teaching schedule to the medical needs and hospital schedule of your child. Teachers may not be able to cover every subject, especially for middle and high school students with numerous classes and teachers. However, school credits are still earned during hospital teaching, and this can help children feel a sense of normalcy in their lives. It is also desirable for children and teens in the hospital to have contacts with their friends at school by phone, email, or visits, whenever possible.

If hospital teaching will be done by teachers from outside the hospital, it can be more complicated. Parents should contact their child's school district and request hospital instruction as soon as possible after diagnosis and treatment planning is completed. The child's physician should write a letter stating that the treatment, hospitalizations, clinic appointments and side effects will cause the child to miss a substantial amount of school and that hospital and home instruction will be necessary. The child's home school district is responsible for providing hospital and home instruction for their students under the Federal laws 94-142 and Section 504. They may provide their own teachers or contract with an agency, hospital or another school district to provide the instruction. Individual states determine minimum guidelines for instruction but school districts have discretion to provide more than the minimum if the child can benefit from additional instruction. It is in the school district's best interest to keep the child up to date with schoolwork so that they won't have to repeat the grade, a costly alternative for school districts.

Homebound Instruction

When your child is discharged from the hospital but still is unable to return to a regular school campus because of health concerns (e.g., low blood counts causing susceptibility to infections), your child's regular school district must provide a homebound teacher to come to your home to teach your child on a regular basis. Some districts provide telephone teaching, in which a teacher works with a small group of students on a conference call. Telephone teaching may work with a group of homebound students at the same time, giving students the benefits of a group experience and a chance to interact with other kids. Some children and parents find "teleteaching" to be a little less personal than a teacher coming to the home.

Individual states and school districts vary on how long a child must be expected to be out of school in order to qualify for a home teacher, but 3 to 4 weeks is generally the minimum time required. States also differ in the minimum weekly number of home instruction hours that are provided, but one hour per day is the general rule. Home instruction is usually delivered in two or three weekly meetings, when the teacher brings the student work, teaches and reviews material, collects homework, and assigns new homework for the next meeting. Parents and students need to understand that home teaching provides less teaching time than occurs in a regular classroom, but the student is able to earn most of the credits she will need to stay current with her class. Gifted students in accelerated or advanced placement classes may need extra accommodations (see later section).

If your child's hospital is in your home school district, the hospital teacher can easily transition the child to the home teaching staff. If your home school district, is different, you will need to send a new request for a home teacher to the district that includes a letter from the doctor stating the diagnosis and time expected to be out of school. The hospital teacher or health care team at the hospital can assist you in the transition to a home teacher.

Larger school districts have teachers assigned to homebound instruction who have specialized training in teaching young people with health challenges. Smaller districts may recruit a teacher to work with a homebound child from their pool of regular or substitute teachers. Recruited teachers may or may not have extensive experience and/or training for working with a homebound student. Smaller districts may take a longer time finding a teacher for the homebound student, and may need encouragement to find a teacher as quickly as possible. If your child has not been assigned a home teacher within two weeks of the paperwork being filed with the district, you may want your child's physician or health care team to help expedite this request.

When the home teacher comes to meet you and your child for the first time, be sure to interview him and make sure that he understands your child's illness, treatment, and schedule for outpatient medical appointments and/or hospital stays. Help the teacher contact members of your child's healthcare team to get the information he needs to effectively work with your child (e.g., the schedule of chemotherapy drug administration and if certain drugs effect energy, attention, or concentration). Be sure to determine that the teacher has experience with the grade level of your child and his or her academic requirements. Help the teacher understand unique cultural or religious traditions of your family so he can be respectful and appropriate in his dress and interactions when he comes to teach.

If you or your child feels that the home teacher is not able to work with your child effectively for any reason, you have the right to discuss this situation with your district's director of home instruction and explore the available options. If you are having difficulty getting the director to respond to your concerns, be sure to enlist the support of your hospital's medical team and school advocates.

It is the home teacher's responsibility to contact your child's regular classroom teachers and coordinate the teaching materials and course of instruction so that it is similar to that covered in the regular classroom. It will not be possible for the home teacher to cover all of the material, but she should be expected to help your child with the basics of the instructional program. The home teacher will assign grades at regular report card times, and the credits earned will be credited to your child in his cumulative school record.

What About the Child Who Goes Back and Forth Between Home and the Hospital?

If your child is in and out of the hospital for many short admissions, maintaining a consistent educational program can be a real challenge. When your home school district is different than the hospital's school district, it may not make sense to transfer the child's school program back and forth between districts, as each transfer requires paperwork and time to implement. In such cases, it may be best to leave the child enrolled in her home school district, and ask the hospital teacher to provide educational supervision and limited assistance, as needed, during relatively brief hospital stays. Hospital volunteers may also be available to help with educational support during brief hospital stays.

If the hospital and home school districts are the same, it can be relatively easy to switch the child back and forth between hospital and home teaching. Sometimes a home teacher will come and work with her students during brief hospitalizations, especially when distance is not a major factor.

Special Education and Home Teaching

If your child was receiving special education services prior to her illness because of a learning disability, a developmental delay, speech and language problem, or any other reason, the Individual Education Plan (IEP) team should be reconvened to make sure the home teacher is capable of working with your child, and to determine if special education services beyond academic home teaching are necessary (see Chapter 14, *Special Education: The Law*). If your child needs additional services like speech therapy, this may not be available at home but could be made available at a local public school campus where the child might be brought for brief periods of time. The IEP team and special education staff can help monitor educational progress during home instruction.

If your child has special educational needs because of his diagnosis and treatment of cancer (e.g., having a brain tumor that effects thinking or communication skills), it may make sense to have him qualify for special education services even before he returns to the regular school campus. Being eligible for special education may enable the child to take advantage of additional services during home instruction and will also be helpful when returning to school.

Gifted or Advanced Placement Classes

Students in gifted or advanced placement classes before getting ill present unique challenges when on home instruction. Discuss your child's special needs for creative work with the home teacher, and explore ways to get work from school that will be at the appropriate level of interest and difficulty. Because home teaching is limited in the number of instruction hours available per week, advanced students may need extra tutoring or participation in Internet instruction courses. Check with your child's teachers at school to explore all available options.

Maintaining Friendships and Social Relationships

It is extremely important that children receiving home teaching maintain friendships and connections with peers at school. This kind of social support helps children feel more optimistic and hopeful, and will help with the school re-entry process. Unfortunately, it can be very challenging for healthy, busy children to continue calling and visiting, and they may need assistance in order to keep up these connections. The ill child may also withdraw from normal relationships because he might feel self conscious about his appearance (e.g., being bald or skinny) or fear being ridiculed. If your child resists interacting with healthy peers, he may benefit from professional guidance from hospital staff or a pediatric psychotherapist to help him remain connected to his friends.

Regular teachers may need help reaching out to the homebound child. The home teacher and hospital staff can help classroom teachers consider different ways to comfortably keep the ill child connected, through visits of the child to the school campus, and visits of friends to the home.

Internet connections at home are often a very effective tool to help children and teens maintain relationships with friends through e-mail. There are also some wonderful monitored Internet sites for children with chronic illnesses to communicate with each other and healthy peers around the country and world (e.g., *www.starbright.org*).

Videoconferencing is available on some sites, and a small number of school districts are experimenting with helping homebound students remain connected with their regular classrooms through this medium.

School Re-entry

The goal of home and hospital instruction is to keep your child connected to school, both academically and psychologically, so that she can return to regular school as easily as possible once the medical team determines that it is safe to do so. Elementary school children can generally reintegrate back into school anytime during the school year. Middle and high school students may find it very hard to return to regular school if only a short period of time remains in the school year. It is very important to evaluate the best time to help your child successfully reintegrate back into school after a prolonged absence.

The home teacher and the health care staff can assist you and your child in the transition to a more regular routine of attending school. Young people, who have been out of school for a prolonged period, as well as their parents, often need some time to adjust to the child no longer being so medically fragile. The transition back to regular school is a highly significant marker in the road to recovery and adjustment.

Conclusion

Home and hospital instruction are critical links in the recovery and adjustment of children with cancer who are unable to attend regular school programs. Continuing active learning and connections to peers at school during periods of fragile health is vital to the recovery process. Home and hospital instruction is not only important for maintaining and enhancing learning skills: it is vital to a child's overall quality of life and hopefulness for the future.

Key Points

- Your child is eligible for teaching in the hospital if he or she will be hospitalized for a minimum number of days (depending on state and school district rules).

- Home Instruction should begin as soon as your child returns home if she will not be medically ready to return to school for a period of weeks or months. The home teacher should be informed about your child's illness, treatment, schedule, and special family and cultural issues.

- During hospital and home teaching, efforts should be made to help your child maintain connections to his or her peers at school. Visits to the campus or classroom should be encouraged even while on home teaching.

- Hospital staff can be helpful in supporting home teachers with the information they need to be successful with your child.

- Special education services already in place should continue for children who have received them before getting ill. If the child will need special assistance when they return to school, the special education qualifying process (known as the IEP) should be started during this period of home instruction.

- Gifted or advanced students may need additional enrichment, beyond home teaching alone, to maximize their potential.

- Consider academic and social enrichment experiences for all children and teens receiving home teaching.

Parent Perspectives

I found the whole schooling issue very overwhelming. Because my daughter was born 14 weeks early in August, we had decided to use her projected birthday in November so she would start kindergarten at age 6. She had surgery, chemotherapy, and radiation for her brain tumor the spring before kindergarten was to start. The social worker suggested homebound schooling. At first I didn't understand that homebound was different than home schooling. Once I was told that the district would provide a tutor for homebound therapy, I was shocked that this would be only three hours a week. This never happened.

My girl fell through the cracks because kindergarten was not required in our state so the district refused homebound therapy. We felt peer interaction was very important and hoped to do a combination homebound/in-class year depending on her health and blood counts. The school district would not help us for kindergarten telling us "just start her in first grade next year." A social worker told us to hire a lawyer. There was no way I was going to deal with cancer and fight the school to have my child in kindergarten. I wanted a place that wanted her. We found a private kindergarten that would work with us. She missed 40% of the year but they sent worksheets home and she had friends.

✛ ✛ ✛

Ethan stayed in school (1st grade) the year he was in treatment for medulloblastoma, so he was in and out of the classroom frequently. His teacher was very supportive. When Ethan was still mute, the teacher had kids read to him. The teachers made him feel included and also cut him the slack he needed so his self-esteem was not damaged. For example, the teacher came to visit in the hospital and brought some work to do together. My child had no interest in doing work with the hospital teacher, but would work with his own teacher. His teacher also organized work into "must do," "could do," and "okay to never do" categories. This allowed us a way of deciding what to focus on—new concepts had priority, solidifying those concepts came second, and we never ever got to the last category.

Our son was diagnosed with medulloblastoma when he was 2 years old. He was inpatient for most of the first six months, then on outpatient chemo for 18 months. He had intensive rehabilitation while in the hospital. When we were at home, I accessed the school early intervention program. He had physical therapy, occupational therapy, speech therapy, and an itinerant teacher twice a week until he was five years old when he became ineligible. Now we get the services he needs through the school system.

+ + +

My 16-year-old son, Steven, had a brain tumor and was treated at a well-known and well-funded institution. He and my wife lived there for about six months while he underwent surgery, radiation, and chemotherapy (with four stem cell rescues). Our hospital schooling experience was mostly positive. The negative experiences originated from the school's end, not from the tutor or hospital. Much of it the result of a first time experience for us and lack of communication and understanding on the home school's part. Steven maintained a 93 | GPA for the year and cumulative through high school stands at over 95%. So his age and aptitude contributed to his successes. He did however miss some concepts by not being with his class in the physics and advanced math areas (these are his strengths).A more determined effort to acquire a tutor in that specific area may have helped. We struggled with how hard to push because of the intensity of the protocol—one week inpatient out of every four and clinic visits everyday. He had daily appointments with the tutor and she was a great advocate for Steven. She helped us navigate the 504 plan for him when we got home. It has worked out well so far and we have not needed an IEP. The education department at the hospital handled most of the correspondence with our school and if someone wasn't hearing, she spoke louder until they had no choice but to listen.

+ + +

Here are a few things my daughter's school did during and after her illness that were meaningful or helpful. My daughter Olivia was 6 and a first grader when diagnosed with an inoperable brain tumor. We left our home in Saint Louis and travelled to another state for treatment. While we were gone her teacher would send her work, along with notes from her and from the children in the class. The teacher also encouraged Olivia to call, which she did frequently. The notes and phone calls really lifted her spirits. When we got home, Olivia showed a movie to the class that she had filmed, which showed the Ronald McDonald house, the hospital, Olivia pretending to get her radiation treatment, and sights around town that she particularly enjoyed. The kids in her class loved this and Olivia was so proud to show off where she had been. She also was allowed to read a book aloud to both the first grade classes "Oncology, Stupology, I Want to Go Home!" We donated a copy of this book to the school.

By the start of second grade, sadly Olivia could not attend (wheelchair, partial paralysis etc.) so the school district provided a tutor. This was very important to Olivia because she loved school. The tutor came daily for a few hours and Olivia kept up with her classmates easily. Olivia's teachers came to see her several times, and the school bought her a teddy bear with a school shirt, which all the teachers signed.

✦ ✦ ✦

My daughter Julia was diagnosed with T-cell ALL when she was in 2nd grade. We had her tutored at home by a district-sponsored, certified teacher and it was a great experience. She received the tutoring right through the end of the school year (she started around mid-January with the tutoring and it continued through June). The teacher we had was fabulous and Julia stayed caught up (and even ahead of) her class. Our school district has everything in place for kids who for medical reasons need to be tutored at home. I think it was much less stressful than trying to get into school for a day or two at a time and not being able to keep track of homework, etc., plus we didn't have to worry about all the germs floating around. It was hard being home all those months (I took a leave of absence from work) but we managed and actually I believe our relationship really deepened during the time home— I have a closeness with Julia that is really special. When Julia went back to school last year, she had no adjustment problems and did very well.

✦ ✦ ✦

Jon's doctor considered him (a 6th grader) too immunosuppressed to attend school. Our school district provided a tutor (a retired school teacher) to come to the house once a week. She stayed usually about one hour. It was hardly enough time. Yet Jon was so weak and ill that he didn't have much strength for more than that. One thing we did do was to have Jon's local school assign him to a classroom. His teacher gave him a desk and included his name on the bulletin board etc. When he felt well enough and his blood counts were high enough he would go to school and participate as he could. He was only able to do this a couple of times but it made him feel like he was a part of the classroom. The school was also very open with the other students about leukemia and many of Jon's classmates visited him regularly after school.

His absences made re-entry hard, especially when he entered 7th grade (middle school). I asked for an individual education plan (IEP) and got one. It became useful when his art teacher wanted to give him a D for missing too much school. We never were able to get his PE teacher on board, however. She insisted that he was lazy when in fact he was anemic and still suffering from a low red blood cell count.

Today Jon is a junior in high school. He takes college prep classes: honors english, honors chemistry and precalculus. He is also co-captain of his high school's varsity swim team. He recently won an award for having the highest scores at Leadership Academy. He still has problems with memory and he has lapses in attention so that sometimes we have to say something twice. He also has difficulties with test taking. Generally we ask the teachers to remind him of homework assignments, and to give him an extra day when he forgets to bring the assignment to class. Jon is real good with this and tries really hard not to forget.

✦ ✦ ✦

We had a unique situation I wanted share about my son's schoolwork. He went to a parochial school. We did have the option of having a public school teacher tutor him at home, but we chose not to go this route. There was also a teacher at the hospital who tried to get my son to work with him. This man really rubbed him the wrong way, and we did not use that option either. His school sent home all his books and work books, and offered to send his teacher over a few times during the month. Again we did not have the teacher come to us. I am a certified teacher, so the school allowed me to home school my son. I was told by the assistant principal to allow him do what he felt up to doing. I was not required to send any work back to school. He received a blank report card at the end of the year stating only that he was promoted to the next grade.

My son's personality during treatment changed dramatically. He was angry most of the first three months, and especially when taking prednisone. He was never really himself during the entire first nine months. And looking back I now believe he was battling some form of depression. He lost contact with all his friends and sports buddies. He spent a lot of time alone at home with a little sister (a bright joy during a grim time) and Mom.

So when I tried to get him to do school work it was just not a pleasant experience. He would refuse to do many of the things I tried. I finally gave up on formal schoolwork. Of course he was learning all kinds of science with all the blood draws, metric medicine doses and the function of white blood cells, platelets, and red blood cells. He would watch documentaries on TV and he would read. Thank God for all those Harry Potter books; they were a lovely escape from treatment. I read them too, and it gave us something to talk about. Someone gave us the audiotapes and that helped when he was too sick to read.

My son is very bright, and even though he missed six months of school he still moved on to the next grade. Except for a few things in math, we never noticed any concepts that were truly missed. He still talks about how he did not do the big Native American project that everyone else did in fifth grade. He did miss so much socially, as I think boys really bond at this age and he still is not as close to his school pals as he once was.

I share this with you because I want other parents to know that if the schoolwork does not happen, not to feel too guilty. I felt the biggest job he had was to fight the cancer and everything else was a distant second. Looking back, I may have handled it a bit differently, but I cannot say that for sure. Uncertainty about the future was always part of every decision.

✝ ✝ ✝

Cami, 5, was out of school about six weeks when a couple of kindergarteners had chicken pox, and I home schooled with the help of the kindergarten teacher. Cami and I had a great time, and were actually sorry to see our time together end.

We stuck to a loose schedule, which started with her sleeping in as late as she needed to. Then we'd do a little "gym," which, because it was winter, consisted of learning ballet poses, throwing and catching balls, and jumping on a little trampoline. Then we'd practice violin before settling into the work the teacher provided. We just loved going at our own pace, enriching what was easy and taking extra time with stuff that was hard. After lunch, we'd lie on her bed and read aloud before she rested. (More than a few times Mom "rested," too.). Because we'd usually gotten the work done in the morning, we could do some fun stuff—puzzles, games, playing with dolls—in the afternoon.

We'd drive to school a couple of times a week. I'd leave Cami in the office and run down to the classroom to pick up and deliver work. The teacher called regularly and spoke to Cami, as well. Cami got notes home from the class, of course, but what really helped her stay connected was that we wrote in about our doings, too. Our favorite "letter" was a poster-sized card showing Cameron's day in Polaroids: her gym, her homework spot, her dog as her lunch partner. When Cami went back to school, the transition was easy.

✝ ✝ ✝

Shoshana (who is now 24 years old) did incredibly well psychologically while being treated for osteosarcoma, and then two recurrences to the lungs and chest wall. She kept up with school (tutors at home and hospital for 10th and 11th grade). She also took the SATs and went for a college interview (bald and on crutches). She wrote a research paper using a college library (she was the brains and I was her legs) that blew them over at the interview. She also helped to create a multimedia project for patient information at the hospital.

Shoshana was back in school for her senior year. It was a big adjustment socially. Some kids didn't remember her; some thought she was a transfer student. She was still recovering from the side effects of chemo (lower counts, weight loss, low energy). Shosh was determined to put it all behind her and made college plans. She interned in a research lab and won an award from our community called Courage to Come Back. She won a full scholarship to our local university (Distinguished Honor Scholar) and moved into the dorm in the fall of '97. She finished treatment in May of 1999. She has now graduated from college, and is a pediatric physical therapist and engaged to be married.

Chapter 4

School Re-Entry

Laurie D. Leigh, MA

This chapter presents a plan for school re-entry for children with cancer. This generic plan can be used as a template with the understanding that each child's school re-entry plan should be individualized to meet his or her specific needs. It is important for children and adolescents with cancer to return to school as soon as medically possible. School is a normal part of life for them and a return to school means a return to some aspect of normalcy while in an abnormal situation. It also gives them an avenue to continue social interaction with peers.

During Hospitalization

The process of school re-entry ideally begins at diagnosis. Shortly after diagnosis, there are certain essential issues that, if taken care of, will help make the actual school re-entry process easier.

Identify a hospital-school liaison

Shortly after diagnosis, a hospital staff member should be identified as the child's hospital-school liaison. This will provide school personnel with access to medical information they need and will assure parents that someone will help school personnel understand what is happening to their child. The liaison can also advocate when necessary for any assistance the child may need upon re-entry and afterward. Hospital professionals who may function as a liaison include: nurse, social worker, hospital school program staff or child life specialist. A contact person at the school (school nurse, guidance counselor, principal) should also be identified, and all information should go to the school contact person. Parents need to give the hospital written permission to provide information to the school.

Activate hospital or home education

Plans should be made as soon as possible after diagnosis for continuation of the child's education through home or hospital services.

Ms. Leigh is director of the school program at St. Jude Children's Research Hospital in Memphis, TN.

This is discussed more fully in Chapter 3, but it deserves mention here as well due to the importance of this to school re-entry. How well the child is able to keep up academically during his time away from school will affect his attitude about school re-entry.

Inform classmates

Once information is verified about the child's diagnosis, expected length of treatment, and length of time out of school, accurate information should be given to classmates. It may be a few weeks to a few months before the child returns to school, so it is best not to wait until the re-entry presentation to provide information to classmates. Children will probably hear bits and pieces of information from teachers and parents and it may be inaccurate information.

The only experience that many children have had with cancer is with an adult relative who may have died. They will make assumptions based on that experience. Also, children tend to make up explanations if their questions go unanswered. This may include the use of magical thinking such as "Johnny was bad the day before he went to the hospital, so that is why he got cancer" or "Jane read a book about cancer the day before she went to the hospital and she got cancer from the book." The hospital-school liaison can give school personnel written materials to help them provide accurate information to classmates.

The school liaison can also help classmates keep in contact with the ill child. The child's perception that she is still a part of her class is also important to school re-entry. Classmates should be encouraged to write letters and send cards and posters to the child. They can also e-mail, call, and visit the child in the hospital or at home if possible. This continuing contact with classmates will alleviate fears that peers will forget about the child and reduce anxiety about rejection by peers upon return to school.

Make communicable disease plan

Children with low blood counts need to avoid exposure to communicable diseases. To prevent exposure, the school liaison and parents need to work closely with the school to develop a chicken pox, shingles, and measles outbreak plan if the school does not already have a disease notification plan in place. One way to let other parents know of the need for quick communication about outbreaks is to send a letter home to parents of children in the classroom. Appendix A contains an example of such a letter.

The school needs to let the parents know when illnesses are spreading through the school, so the child can stay at home to avoid the outbreak. Parents need to be notified immediately if their child has been exposed to chicken pox, so that the child can receive the varicella zoster immune globulin (VZIG) injection within 72 hours of exposure.

Preparation for School Re-entry

Once school re-entry time is known, a more specific plan can be developed. Going back to school can be done on a part-time basis. Many children, after being out of school for a long time, may not have the stamina for a full day of school and will need time to get used to the routine of going to school again. Even if the child can only go once a week or for two half-day sessions, that is okay. Most school systems allow supplementary homebound services to continue until the child can return to school full-time.

The hospital-school liaison or other hospital professional, school guidance counselor, school nurse, and teacher are all professionals who may assist with planning school re-entry. The following is an example of a school re-entry plan.

Discussion with the child/adolescent

First, the professional who is planning the school re-entry should talk with the child about his feelings regarding going back to school. Ask what he is looking forward to at school and what his fears or concerns are about returning to school. This will lead to a general discussion with the child about the school re-entry presentation. Most younger children want someone to talk with their classmates, but many adolescents do not. If the child/adolescent does not want a presentation to classmates, talk with her about the advantages of giving the classmates accurate information, but do respect her choice to not have the presentation. If the child or adolescent does want the presentation, start with a discussion about the following information:

- **Content:** Go over the information presented later in this chapter about the content of the presentation. Talk with the child about things he does and does not want discussed.

- **Audience:** The parent or child may want only his class or all the classes in his grade to attend the presentation. If the choice is for all children in his grade to hear the presentation, only talk with 1 to 2 class groups at a time. Children in smaller groups are more likely to remember the information and they will feel more comfortable asking questions.

- **Presence of child during the presentation:** Some children don't want to be in the class during the presentation, whereas others want to actively participate in talking about their experience in the hospital. This is purely a personal preference for the child and his choice should be respected.

Discussions with school personnel

Information to discuss with school personnel about the presentation includes the following:

- Date of re-entry.
- Where presentation will be done (classroom, library, etc.).
- Who will receive the presentation (one classroom or whole grade of students).
- Hospital staff who will attend.
- General content of the presentation.
- Child's presence at the presentation.

The school liaison should also discuss any special accommodations or services in school the child will need. These accommodations depend on each child's special circumstances. Any child diagnosed with cancer has a right under federal law to receive certain services and accommodations. These federals laws are discussed in Chapter 14. *Special Education: The Law.* Accomodations may include:

- A second set of books so that the child will have a set of books at home and in each class so he does not have to carry a heavy backpack. This will save precious energy for doing schoolwork.
- Extra time to do class work, homework, and tests.
- Getting out of class a few minutes early to have time to navigate the hallway, staircase, or use the elevator.
- Decreased homework/class work.

The teacher, school nurse, and principal need to fully understand any medical issues and should have all medical information in written form. Parents can talk with the hospital-school liaison about any information school personnel will need such as medications taken in school, side effects of treatment, and anticipated school absences. Consider asking the child's physician to write a letter containing all of this information. Check to see if a communicable disease plan, as discussed earlier, has been developed. If not, work with school personnel to develop this plan. All of this information can be given to the teacher and other school personnel to insure that everyone receives the same accurate information.

Other information that the teacher should have prior to the child's return to school is material from the homebound/hospitalbound teacher. It is important for the teacher at school to know what the child has accomplished while out of school. There should also be a discussion with the teacher about appropriate expectations for the child's academics. The teacher should have realistic expectations of what the child can do given treatment and side effects. A lack of expectations can be just as bad as expectations that are too high.

Classroom Presentation

The classroom presentation should be given at an age-appropriate level. The amount of information and content should be adjusted for the age and grade level of the classmates. Classroom presentations typically include the following information.

General information about cancer

Many presentations begin by defining cancer and how it grows. Explain how cancer cells are different from regular cells because they grow "out of control." One example for young children is to say that healthy muscle cells grow to be the correct size, and do the work of muscles. If muscle cells become cancerous, they keep growing and growing until they make a big lump, and they don't stay put in the muscle like they are supposed to. Next, facts and myths about cancer are shared. It is extremely important to explain that cancer is not contagious and students cannot "catch it." Explain that children do not get it from bad behavior. Ask students if there is something they have heard about cancer that they have a question about. The presenter honestly answers all questions and then explains that there has been a lot of research in the last 20 years that has lead to treatments getting better and better.

Specific information about the child's diagnosis and treatment

Classmates need to understand about the child's type of cancer and treatment. The presenter will usually include the following information:

- **Type of cancer:** Describe where the cancer is and again talk about cells in the body. Use of visual aids such as posters, dolls, or videos is very helpful. You can usually find posters with pictures of different body systems in any large school supply store.

- **Treatment:** Give a specific description of the treatment the child received which may include chemotherapy, surgery, and radiation. Chemotherapy is described as "very strong medicine" to get rid of the cancer and to keep it from coming back. Explain the type and location of surgery that their classmate had. When talking about surgery, it is important, especially with younger students, to tell them how children are given special medicine so they will sleep through the surgery and not feel anything, and that this is different from regular sleep because of the special medicine they give to make you feel sleepy. For children or teens with osteosarcoma, discussion of surgery should include a discussion of the limb-sparing procedure. Present enough detail to give a good overview of the procedure without getting too technical. Radiation therapy can be described as invisible beams of radiation that are directed at the tumor. Sometimes a laser pointer can be used to demonstrate and explain radiation therapy.

- **Hickman line/Port-a-Cath:** During the discussion of chemotherapy, the presenter should also discuss the use of the Hickman line or Port-a-Cath, if the child wants to share this information. Some children will go back to school with a central line and the outline of the dressing may be visible under clothing causing other children in the class to be curious about it. If the child does not want this to be a part of the primary presentation, you will need to explain that someone may ask how the chemotherapy is given during the question and answer session and the presenter and child should discuss options on ways to answer this question.

  When demonstrating the Hickman line or Port-a-Cath, it is very helpful to have a doll with the appropriate line in place to show exactly what the line looks like and how it is placed on the body. It is also helpful to have a bag of saline to demonstrate how the line is hooked up to the chemotherapy. Some children who wish to participate in the presentation may want to show their Hickman line or Port-a-Cath. If the child feels comfortable doing this, it can be a very positive affirmation of the "child as expert" about what has happened to him.

- **Other medical appliances:** Many children use other technologies that need to be discussed with classmates. Examples are nasogastric tubes (tube through the nose to the stomach), shunts (tube leading from the brain to the abdomen), and feeding tubes (tube the goes from outside the abdomen into the stomach). These technologies are sometimes obvious (bump on the side of the head, a tube coming out of the nose and taped to prevent movement, etc). The presenter should discuss any technologies that the child will use after returning to school.

Effects of cancer and treatment

An important part of the presentations is discussing the effects of cancer and its treatment on the ill child.

- **Appearance:** The most obvious change in appearance brought about by treatment is loss of hair. When discussing hair loss, stress that the hair will grow back. Other changes in appearance caused both by the cancer and the treatment include:

  - Changes in weight
  - A weakness on one side of the body
  - Loss of an eye or other facial changes due to surgery
  - Use of crutches or wheelchair
  - Loss of a limb

- **Energy level:** Fatigue is a big problem for many children returning to school. It is important for classmates to know that there may be days when the child may feel very tired from the effects of the treatment and that this may also be a reason the child may not be in school every day.

- **Suppressed immune system:** Treatment for cancer makes children more likely to catch illnesses like colds, flu, and chicken pox. Explain the need to wash hands often to prevent spreading illnesses. For older students, the presenter can also talk about white blood cells, what their purpose is in the body and how they are affected by the chemotherapy. Tell the students that this may be a reason that the child maybe absent from school some days, especially in the winter.

- **School absences:** The child may be coming back to school on only a part-time basis and it is important to explain this to his classmates. Discuss this as a normal part of the routine for a child who is in treatment or has just finished treatment and let them know there will be a time when the child will return to school full-time.

What classmates can do to assist the child

Depending on the age of the classmates, you can solicit suggestions from the group about things they think that may help the child when he is back in school. For older elementary-age students and adolescents, ask them how they would like to be treated after coming back to school and how they would want their friends to react. Talk about how the child is the same person he or she was before the diagnosis of cancer. For younger children, the discussion will have to be more guided.

The following ideas may be helpful:

- Make sure the child is included in games.
- Have a "Hat Day" at school on the day of the child's return to show support.
- Get homework or notes for the child while he or she is absent at clinic visits.
- If you hear anyone giving wrong information about the child's illness, tell him or her the truth.
- Stand up for the child if anyone tries to tease him or her and explain to others why they should not tease.

Answering questions

Answering questions is a very important part of the presentation because they can give you some insight as to how some of the students processed the information that was presented. You have an additional opportunity to clear up any misconceptions or misinterpretations. Students may ask such questions such as "Can he die?" or "Can the cancer come back?" It is important in these situations to be optimistic but to answer the questions honestly.

Using videos

There are two types of videos that are frequently used during the presentation:

- Commercially prepared videos about a specific child going through treatment and going back to school. This may be a real child or a cartoon such as "Why, Charlie Brown, Why." There are many good videos available through the American Cancer Society, the Leukemia & Lymphoma Society and Cancervive.
- Videos made by the child describing a typical day at the hospital. The child may show the doctors, nurses, child life specialists, and teachers that describe how she spends her time at the hospital.

Use of videos and other visual aids and demonstrations are extremely helpful in getting and keeping the classmates' interest. Contact nurses, social workers, and child life specialists at the hospital to see if they can assist in getting such materials.

Key Points

- After diagnosis, designate a hospital/school liaison; obtain hospital/bound/homebound educational services for the child; and give accurate information regarding diagnosis to classmates.

- When preparing for school re-entry, have a discussion with the child/adolescent and contact school personnel to plan.

- The classroom presentation for school re-entry should include general information about cancer and the child's diagnosis and treatment, effects of cancer and treatment, and what classmates can do to assist the child. All questions should be answered in an honest, age-appropriate manner.

Parent Perspectives

The child life specialist and Brittany's primary nurse from the hospital came and talked to Brittany's class when she returned to school (kindergarten) and when she started 1st grade the next year. They brought the Charlie Brown movie along and answered questions. It really seemed to work well for her. She was very shy and she was glad she wouldn't have to answer as many questions.

✦ ✦ ✦

My daughter was treated at a very large, very famous children's hospital. Over 200 children were on treatment when she was. During the 2 years and 3 months of treatment, we never saw a social worker but I found out later that there was one. I heard that she spent her time helping the families that had completely fallen apart (e.g., sometimes didn't bring their kid in for treatment) but the rest of us had no services other than medical. They had no child life program or school liaison. They provided no help for school reentry: You were on your own.

✦ ✦ ✦

Andrew was returning to Kindergarten in the spring of '99 after his diagnosis the previous fall. At the time he had dramatic separation anxiety and was so worried about returning without his hair. The clinic's child life specialist and his primary nurse came and performed a wonderful puppet show for his class. The school sent out invitations for parents to attend, and Andrew was delighted to learn that his principal and school nurse would be attending as well. They explained to Andrew's class that while cancer is very serious, you cannot catch cancer like you do a cold. They also explained why he lost his hair and "wouldn't your head get cold if you didn't have any hair to keep it warm?" That was in answer to a child's question about why Andrew could keep his hat on in class.

For many of these children, it was the first time they had ever heard the word cancer. When they explained to the class how Andrew received his chemotherapy, Andrew was so pleased that he just stood up, raised his shirt and showed everyone his port. They used appropriate detail about cancer, and emphasized how brave Andrew was. By the end of that session the children who were seated on the floor, were scooting over to sit closer to Andrew. It made an enormous difference in easing his anxiety, and I just sat in the back of the class with my husband and daughter with tears spilling down my face (pregnancy hormones were also coursing through my system). It was such a happy day.

We still had tearful good-byes, and Andrew was called baldie on the bus, but Andrew knew the children were not afraid of him, and he in turn was somewhat less afraid as well. I cannot emphasize enough how important this kind of program is for children returning to the classroom after extended absences. My son had just one week of kindergarten before his diagnosis, so he did not know his classmates well at all. He felt unsure and awkward, and I don't know if I would have returned him to school without the re-entry program to support him. He was being tutored at home, and I may have continued with it exclusively. It gave us almost as much peace as it gave our child.

✛ ✛ ✛

Jamie was just about to enter 4th grade when he was diagnosed. The interlink nurse visited with us several times while inpatient and then visited us at home once Jamie was discharged to discuss whether or not we wanted her going in to speak to Jamie's class about his illness. We agreed so she told Jamie what she would be talking to the kids about and asked him what he wanted to share with the kids. For example, what will you tell the kids the worst thing about having cancer is? "The mouthwash." After the class discussion she let Jamie and I know what had transpired. We did not attend as Jamie was too ill. She also asked my other two children if they wanted her to go into their classrooms and tell the kids about their brother. They passed on her offer.

What was important in our case was that the classmates and teacher needed to be aware of what Jamie was going through. The teacher was VERY much against the interlink nurse going in to talk to the kids. I called her myself and told her how important this was to us and she allowed it and in the end I believe she learned the most from the session! While this teacher did not impress me in the beginning, I grew to respect and admire her.

+ + +

We utilized a school re-entry program when Brianna returned to 1st grade after being out almost two months. The Leukemia & Lymphoma Society provided the Charlie Brown movie and some materials that helped prepare the teachers (the kids watched the movie ahead of time). Then the child life worker and the oncologist came into school with "Buddy," the doll with removable hair, changeable facial expressions, port and hickman. They were great about explaining her disease in an age appropriate way and answering questions. They also met with the teachers/staff separately to explain/answer any questions they might have. They gave the school nurse a medical info sheet on Brianna's treatment, possible side effects and the clinic's phone number to call anytime with questions or concerns. Great program!

+ + +

Elizabeth was in preschool at the time of her diagnosis. The manager did a wonderful job of integrating her back into the fold. All of the other children at the school were taught what was happening to Elizabeth and what would be happening (such as hair loss). They learned that they had to be gentle with her when playing. The manager was a former home health nurse, so I was very confident that she would be able to take care of my daughter in the event of an emergency. She was already familiar with central lines and side effects from chemotherapy. She was a gem!

+ + +

I still feel unbelievable gratitude when I think of the school principal and my daughter's kindergarten teacher that first year. The principal's eyes filled with tears when I told her what was happening, and she said, "You tell us what you need and I'll move the earth to get it for you." She hand-picked a wonderful teacher for her, made sure that a chicken pox notification plan was in place, and kept in touch with me for feedback. She recently retired, and I sent her a glowing letter which I copied to the school superintendent and school board. Words can't express how wonderful they were.

+ + +

Jimmy's kindergarten teacher was the pits. Jimmy was on chemotherapy, and she told Jimmy not to wash his hands, as it took too long. I was disappointed that even after the nurse came to class and gave a presentation, the kids still teased my son. They would say things like, "You've got Jimmy germs, you are going to catch cancer," and "You can't get rid of cancer, you always die." During his kindergarten year, Jimmy needed to have surgery. I called the teacher to let her know, but my son did not hear from anyone in his class, not one card or phone call, even from the teacher. She didn't even tell the class why Jimmy was absent.

✝ ✝ ✝

My son was diagnosed at age 14. He was starting 9th grade, the last year of junior high. He missed about a third of that year. He was able to keep up, thanks to some terrific teachers and a very cooperative administration, not to mention being a really motivated kid. He hated missing school and would go even when he didn't feel very good, just to say he'd been to school that day, even if only for two periods. Our oncologists gave him the okay to be in school, saying that infection in kids his age was usually from bacteria they were already carrying around, so other kids were not a big threat, provided they weren't sick.

✝ ✝ ✝

We did our school re-entry by ourselves. My daughter needed a two and a half month stay for inpatient rehabilitation after surgery for her cancerous brain tumor, and when we were ready to go home no one mentioned anything about school re-entry. We did not know that there were school re-entry videos in the family library and we didn't know about hospital personnel who might be able to assist us. Instead my husband, a PhD candidate in psychology, got on the Internet and found "Why, Charlie Brown, Why?" We watched the video with our daughter and she was engrossed, even though it was not the same cancer. We talked about what she wanted other kids to know and then set up a time to go into the class to talk as a family.

It was very draining as young children can be so honest. One little girl kept saying, "The back of her head gives me the creeps" and another said, "She was like a snowman melting." My almost bald girl had three surgical scars on her head, a bump from the shunt, a feeding tube, tattoos from surgery, and significant right-sided weakness. It was hard to focus on the children and to support our daughter at the same time—especially when the events were still so raw and emotional for us.

I am proud of what we did since I think we did it well. However, if I was to do it again I would have searched out resources from the hospital and I would have taken a friend along to specifically watch our daughter so that if it became too much, she could have been taken out of the class.

Chapter 5

Neuropsychological Testing

F. Daniel Armstrong, PhD

Over the past 20 years, we have learned a great deal about how children treated for cancer learn and perform in school. Perhaps the most important thing we have learned is that there are patterns of abilities that occur after successful treatment that are different from those seen with more common learning problems that are often call "learning disabilities." This difference is importance, since the understanding of learning, and the approach to evaluating learning in children treated for cancer, needs to be different as well. For this reason, some of the standard approaches to testing children with cancer that occur in the school and other private settings may not be adequate for identifying problems and planning ways to help.

Common Approaches to Evaluation of Learning Problems

In the public schools, and in many private settings, a child's ability to obtain special education services for learning problems is based on his or her performance on a group of tests of intellectual ability and academic achievement. Commonly, children are administered a standardized IQ test, along with tests of school-based skills, and often a measure of adaptive function.

IQ tests

IQ tests are individually administered to the child and are made up of a number of subtests of specific abilities. A child's score is based on his/her performance compared to other children of the same age. Three scores from an IQ test are considered.

Dr. Armstrong is professor and associate chair of the department of pediatrics and director of the Mailman Center for Child Development at the University of Miami School of Medicine, FL.

- A verbal IQ score, which is an index of 5 to 6 different tests of verbal or language-based skills.
- A Performance IQ score, which is an index of 5 to 6 tests of visual, motor, speed, and perceptual abilities.
- A Full Scale IQ score, which is a combination of all the tests included in the Verbal and Performance IQ scores.

Academic achievement tests

The academic achievement tests are also individually administered, and may involve tests of reading (word recognition and comprehension), arithmetic (math calculations and applied math abilities), spelling, and writing. The child's scores on these tests are based on his or her performance compared to other children of the same age or in the same grade.

Tests of adaptive function

Tests of adaptive function are usually administered in the form of an interview with the parent or caregiver. These tests typically provide information about a child's communication, daily living, socialization, and motor skills compared to other children the same age, as observed by the parent or primary caregiver.

Use of tests for classification

Determination of a learning problem is usually based on several criteria. Children may be classified because their scores fall within a certain range, or because there are discrepancies between test scores in identified areas. Some of these classifications include:

- **Impaired cognitive abilities:** Children who score below 70 on an IQ test, have academic achievement scores in this same range, and have scores on a standardized measure of adaptive function (e.g., a parent report of the child's communication, daily living, socialization, and motor skills) that are also below 70 may meet criteria for diagnosis of impaired cognitive abilities or mental retardation.
- **Specific learning disability:** Children who score above 70 on an IQ test, but have a significant discrepancy (usually more than 15 points) between their IQ score and measures of academic achievement (Reading or Math) may qualify for services for the learning disabled. Usually some indication of a processing deficit (e.g., visual-motor or auditory processing) is also necessary for this classification.
- **Varying exceptionalities:** Children whose test scores indicate learning

problems, but who also have other sensory deficits (e.g, hearing, vision), physical movement problems, or speech difficulties, may be classified in the category of varying exceptionalities, and may receive a range of both educational and therapeutic services.

- **Other health impaired:** Children who experience problems in school that can be attributed to a chronic health condition (including cancer) may fall under the 504 regulations that permit services for children who do not otherwise meet special education categorization. However, many may also be eligible for Individual Education Plans (IEPs) and access to a full range of special education services.

Neuropsychological Testing

As noted in Chapter 2, *Childhood Cancer and Education*, the late effects of treatment of cancer in children often involve very specific disabilities, including visual perception, memory, processing speed, and sequencing. Problems in these areas are not commonly seen in children not treated for cancer. Over the past 20 years, investigators and parents have observed that the types of testing done for school problems do not include tests that identify the kinds of problems faced by children with cancer and are not helpful in determining the kinds of assistance that is needed. For these reasons, clinicians and parent advocacy groups are increasingly recommending that children treated for cancer receive a battery of tests that focus specifically on the patterns of difficulties that may be experienced. This kind of testing is commonly referred to as neuropsychological testing.

What is neuropsychological testing?

Neuropsychological testing involves giving a child a number of tests that provide information about how the brain works in the areas of memory, speed, language, visual processing, auditory processing, integration of information, emotional and behavioral regulation, and planning and organization. The tests are administered by a trained professional (either a licensed psychologist or someone supervised by the psychologist). The purpose is to provide a comprehensive, detailed assessment of a person's ability to encode, process, store and express information. Interpretation of the various test results allows strengths and weakness to be uncovered. From this evaluation, recommendations can be made for accommodations to assist learning and functioning.

The tests that are used are developed for children, and the tests that are given are selected to match the skills expected for children of specific age ranges. The child's scores are based on how he or she performs compared to other children of the same age. Neuropsychological tests of specific abilities may vary, depending on the age of the child at the time of diagnosis and treatment, the age at the time he or she is tested, and what kind of treatment he or she received.

What is a neuropsychologist?

A neuropsychologist is a licensed psychologist (PhD or PsyD) who has special and advanced training in evaluating the relationship between the brain and behavior in a number of areas. A pediatric neuropsychologist is a licensed psychologist who has training and experience in understanding the relationship between the brain and behavior in children. This requires the additional skill of understanding how this relationship changes over time as the child's brain grows and develops.

Most states do not specifically license "neuropsychologists," although the American Board of Professional Psychology does provide a board certification for advanced skills in the area. There is not a separate certification for pediatric neuropsychology. For these reasons, parents and referring physicians should determine whether the psychologist has obtained training in brain-behavior relationships, neuropsychological testing, neuro-rehabilitation, or other similar area, and whether he or she has experience evaluating children with complex medical problems that affect the brain. Knowledge about the disease process and the effects of chemotherapy and radiation may be critical to evaluations that are helpful. If parents are unsure of the qualifications of a psychologist to perform this type of evaluation, they should discuss this with their child's oncologist to be sure that a knowledgeable person is available to perform the evaluation. Most pediatric oncology programs that participate in the Children's Oncology Group (COG) have identified a qualified professional in this area.

The neuropsychologist can help parents and teachers:

- Understand how treatment has affected thinking, learning, and behavior.
- Identify what services and accommodations may be needed in the educational setting.
- Recommend interventions.
- Advise on potential or likely improvements, problems and changes.

Who needs neuropsychological testing?

Neuropsychological testing is usually indicated for children with:

- Tumors of the central nervous system (CNS), especially those requiring cranial radiation, but including those who were treated with surgery only.

- Acute lymphoblastic leukemia, particularly those treated with cranial radiation and those on more recent protocols that involved triple intrathecal chemotherapy and higher dose methotrexate during consolidation.

- Diseases requiring radiation to the head, including those receiving total body irradiation prior to bone marrow or stem cell transplantation.

- Very young children who receive intensive chemotherapy and require prolonged hospitalizations because of treatment and side effects.

- Other children who are identified by the pediatric oncologists because of specific concerns about that child's school performance, learning, or development.

Because the effects of cancer treatment appear to emerge over time, a single testing will usually not be adequate to address the child's needs as he or she develops. Obtaining an evaluation during the first year after diagnosis will help address immediate difficulties that may occur because of medication side effects or school absences, and will also provide a "baseline" for determining whether there are "late effects" when the child is a survivor. Re-evaluations every 18 months to 3 years (shorter intervals during the elementary years, with longer intervals in adolescence and young adulthood) are usually recommended to assess changes due to treatment and revise recommendations for intervention.

Preparing the child for testing

When the word "test" is used with a child treated for cancer, it inevitably brings up thoughts of needles, painful procedures, or confining spaces. For this reason, special care should be taken when talking with a child about neuropsychological testing. Both parents and the psychologist should be sensitive to this issue. There are several strategies that may be helpful:

- Explain to the child that no needles or painful procedures are involved in this kind of testing. Neuropsychological testing is a "no stick zone."

- Explain that these are not tests that you pass or fail. They are tests that help the psychologist, parents, and child understand how the child's brain works and how he or she best learns. The tests will hopefully identify areas where learning is difficult, but will also identify areas where the child does well.

- Explain that some of the tests may be really easy, some may be very hard, and some may be in-between. No one is expected to be able to know or do everything perfectly, but each child should do his or her very best. However, if there is something that is too hard, after giving a good try, or there is something that the child has never heard before, then the best answer may be "I don't know."

- Give the child a chance to ask questions, both of his/her parents before the testing session, and of the psychologist before and at appropriate points during testing.

- Explain that the results of the test will be used to find ways to help make learning and doing well in school a bit easier and more successful.

Parents should also prepare the child and themselves for the fact that neuropsychological testing requires time, a positive relationship between the child and the person administering the tests, and sensitivity on the part of the psychologist about special issues for the child with cancer (e.g., increased fatigue). In some cases, the psychologist may recommend conducting the evaluation over several sessions to be sure that the child's performance is the best possible, and not influenced by fatigue. This kind of evaluation is not something that can be rushed, so parents and children should approach the testing session with patience.

Parts of a neuropsychological evaluation

The neuropsychological evaluation involves more than just giving a few tests. It is designed to provide a comprehensive picture of the way the child learns and develops, and therefore includes a number of important parts. Most neuropsychological evaluations include:

- A detailed interview with the parents about the child's medical, developmental, learning, behavioral, and social history, with specific attention to the type of disease, treatment involved, and results of any hearing, vision, and neuroimaging evaluations that have been done. A review of past and current medications should be included in this interview.

- A brief family interview about family history of learning, attention, emotional, or behavioral problems.

- Tests of IQ, academic achievement, and adaptive behavior.

- Specific tests of visual and verbal memory, sequential memory, attention and concentration, visual-spatial-motor integration, processing speed, language ability (expressive and receptive), social perception, and executive function (planning, organization).

- Other special tests may be included if there are sensory deficits (e.g., vision or hearing), motor impairments, or a history of learning problems prior to diagnosis of cancer.

- Screening for social, behavioral, or emotional difficulties.

Many of the tests used in neuropsychological testing are not included in the typical evaluation provided in the school system, although there may be some overlap on some tests.

Interpretation of results: the report

Often, parents and teachers view the neuropsychological evaluation as being primarily focused on what tests are given. However, the real benefit of a neuropsychological evaluation is the interpretation of the patterns of test scores, which leads to recommendations that may be helpful. The interpretation and recommendations rely on the knowledge and experience of the psychologist related to normal brain development, an understanding of the effects of disease and treatment on the developing brain, and an awareness of the multitude of complex educational, developmental, medication, and therapeutic interventions available. There are two common types of interpretations that usually come from a neuropsychological evaluation:

- **Current functioning:** This type of interpretation provides information about how the child is performing at the time of testing compared to other children his or her same age. The psychologist also examines the patterns of these scores to determine if there are any inconsistencies between abilities, or if there are obvious delays. This point is important. What has been learned about late effects in childhood cancer is that IQ does not tell the story. Some areas of brain function do not seem to be at as great a risk for problems as others. For this reason, the absolute scores on any given test are not the major concern. Instead, the neuropsychologist examines patterns of abilities (e.g., visual vs. verbal memory, language vs. non-verbal problem solving). The neuropsychological evaluation often detects patterns of clearly defined strengths, as well as weaknesses. The IQ score may seem okay to parents, but the pattern of difficulties may represent a significant set of problems that need to be addressed, and may help parents and teachers anticipate problems that may be encountered in the future. This interpretation of the pattern is a major focus of the evaluation.

- **Functioning over time:** This is a more complex interpretation, but one that can provide major benefit. This interpretation examines how scores on the various tests have changed over time. Functioning over time can only be done if there are previous neuropsych results for comparison. Based on knowledge about normal brain development, the type of treatment, and the age of the child at treatment, this type of interpretation may permit some limited predictions about future functioning. More importantly, it may also allow the development of interventions that can prevent or lessen new problems down the line.

Parents should expect that the report and personal feedback session with the psychologist will provide them with a clear summary of the test results, an interpretation of what these results mean, and specific recommendations about how to address any problems that testing may have identified. Sometimes recommendations involve:

- Additional testing by developmental specialists (e.g., speech and language, audiology).
- Specific suggestions for how a child can be taught to read, do math, or write.
- Suggestions for "accommodations" in the school setting (e.g., extra time to complete work, use of books on tape, use of calculators).
- Consideration of evaluation for medications that may be helpful (e.g., stimulant medications for attention problems).
- Referrals for counseling, therapy, or behavioral management to address behavior or emotional problems that were identified during the evaluation.
- Suggestions about special school programs for the child with complex difficulties.

If these recommendations are not provided, or if they are provided but don't make sense, parents should always feel free to ask the psychologist to provide more information and explanation so that the information can be understood.

Key Points

- Neuropsychological testing offers information that is typically not obtained in a standard school evaluation.

- The results of the evaluation should be interpreted by a professional who has extensive training in interpreting complex test results.

- Parents of children whose cancer or treatment involved the brain should discuss neuropsychological testing with their child's oncologist. Repeated evaluations (conducted every 2 to 3 years or if there are new, specific concerns) may be needed through high school, and perhaps into college.

Parent Perspectives

My son Brian had triple intrathecals for 3¼ years to treat leukemia. Because he did not have cranial radiation, I think there was some hesitancy to even do testing. The school brought to my attention some issues with attention and focusing and that led me to find the appropriate resources (neuropsych testing to begin with and then later a private educational consultant specific to school learning). We repeated neuropsych testing 3 years off treatment and then again 3 years later. We wanted to know if things had changed since the first testing and we also wanted to help determine his needs for middle school.

I sought the resources and treatment and was able to get our medical insurance to pay for it (we paid a fairly large deductible however). In retesting this spring, they said that if they bill as "medical" and not "mental health services" we have a better chance of getting the testing covered. Insurance did not pay for the private consultant, but she was especially valuable for the school issues.

Having done all this, it has led to very little change in the school. Perhaps this was because the issues are more subtle, but also because we are at a private school that isn't required to follow federal regulations for IEPs, 504s, etc. It's been a very frustrating experience to expect a higher level of individual accommodation and to not receive it.

Our experience has left a few impressions:

- *Do whatever you can to be your child's advocate, no matter how severe or mild the issue is at hand.*

- *Pursue testing if you want more insight into specific behaviors or issues, but also use it as evidence for motivating the school to accommodate your child's needs. But be prepared for resistance (no one at our school seems remotely aware of "auditory processing disorders").*

- *Don't give up on the insurance coverage. File an appeal if you need to.*

- *Testing is one tool. Also collect concrete examples of your child's problems and how the faculty did or did not handle them.*

- *Don't expect private schools to offer more resources than public ones.*

Brian is in 5th grade and has difficulty with organization, short-term memory, and following verbal directions. He's bright; he is learning to compensate and he is keeping his grades up and is good at masking problems at school, but he takes his frustration out at home! So it becomes our problem and not the school's.

✝ ✝ ✝

The psychologist who did my son's neuropsych report did a thorough job and wrote an excellent report. Unfortunately, she included paragraphs on family functioning and sections on my son's psychological history. Since I wasn't asking the school system to provide counseling, I didn't want them to have access to that information. I didn't want that to travel with my son throughout his elementary and high school career. We need the labels to get the services, but I also wanted to protect his privacy as much as possible. So, I covered those sections, and copied the report. I only gave the school the parts that I wanted them to have.

✝ ✝ ✝

When Samantha was diagnosed at age 6 with pre-B cell ALL, she was finishing her first year of kindergarten. When she entered first grade, I made sure to keep her teacher and the school counselor aware of what was going on with her treatment plan, what problems might arise because of her treatment, and made sure the line of communication was always open between home, school and the doctor's office.

At the end of treatment, our oncologist suggested that Samantha have neuropysch testing done. The doctor's office arranged for everything, and we were very lucky that a local foundation for pediatric cancer paid for the testing. Samantha scored very well on the testing in all areas. We were very happy knowing that all the methotrexate she had during treatment did not cause any damage. We gave a final copy of the test results to the school, so they would have it for Samantha's school file. I'm happy to say that today at the age of 12, 3 ½ years off treatment, Samantha is finishing the 6th grade with excellent grades—all As and one B. She takes extreme pride in doing her schoolwork.

✝ ✝ ✝

What the school system offers in North Carolina is not neuropsychological testing. When we requested (private) neuropsych testing for our son who had a brain tumor, the insurance company wanted to know the purpose. All we knew to say at the time was "educational purposes" and that is why they declined covering it. If we had said "medical" then they would have covered it. My advice is don't say educational. Get a letter from the doctor verifying the medical necessity to evaluate damage to the brain.

✛ ✛ ✛

My daughter had 1800 cGy of radiation the week she turned 4. The hospital did not even mention neuropsych testing, but I'd done a lot of research on late effects and requested that we get baseline neuropsych testing done. They tried to talk me out of it but I insisted. They referred us to the psych dept at the children's hospital. A psychology intern tried to administer the tests. She said my daughter was not "compliant" and she wanted me to come in to try to "keep her on task." I think that people who administer these tests need to be warm, engaging, and experienced!

I did more research and hired a PhD neuropsychologist who did testing half time and research half time. She was splendid at giving the tests and very knowledgeable about which sub tests to give, based on results of the more general tests. We had all subsequent testing (every two years) done by her. She also wrote very long, detailed reports with excellent recommendations sections for the educators. Most teachers won't wade through the report so you need not only good testing, but a good summary with recommendations to help you get the services you need.

The other thing that I really appreciated about the psychologist was how warm and helpful she was. Hearing about brain damage is overwhelming for parents. I cried throughout the whole first results session. After dealing with the terror of treatment, having to face a lifetime of disabilities is so very hard. But, the psychologist was wonderful about explaining strengths as well as the weaknesses, and in providing reassurance about methods to develop strategies to compensate for the losses. She was truthful, but hopeful.

✛ ✛ ✛

The neuropsych testing was done after Andrew concluded treatment. It consisted of two three-hour days, and he was wiped out from it both days. More prep/info needs to go out to the parents so they can better prepare their child physically and emotionally. The testing was administered by the treating hospital's department of psychiatry. Part of his therapy included triple intrathecals and hyperfractionated cranial radiation (1890 rads) when he was 5 years old.

After referral, we had to wait almost a year for the tests to be administered. The oncologists just said, "It takes forever to get an appointment." What we do not understand, is why not take a baseline, especially with high-risk protocols? It would have been useful for gauging and comparison purposes.

The feedback session with the neuropsychologist was brutal. We were not prepared for the results, and it was like a big kick in the gut, it hurt so much. We felt blindsided just like we did at diagnosis. Our little boy who could dribble a basketball before he could barely walk, who loves any and all sports, was now being advised to play solitary sports because of the processing of directives necessary for team sport. Golf and tennis were suggested. He would need a counselor for the anxiety and frustration that results from the inability to complete work on time. He also has enormous difficulty communicating what is clearly in his head out to the rest of the world. The difficulty in keeping up with his peers would only become more intense as he advanced in grades. He should also learn to type as quickly as practicable, as it is exhausting for him to write.

Our child who just got through two years of difficult treatment now has life-long learning challenges from his treatment. More information should be given to parents so that they can better understand the true price of treatment. It's a very high price. Counseling should be given to parents before the feedback session, and if possible a staff member of the psychosocial department should accompany them.

✢ ✢ ✢

Gabriel had 1800 rads of cranial radiation and neuropsych testing was never mentioned because he was 14 at the time. Our oncologists don't worry about teenagers having any effects from radiation. Looking back I wish we had done the testing anyway even though the risk is lower for older kids who are irradiated. Gabriel does complain of having short-term memory loss that he says was not an issue before treatment. If he is learning a new math concept or memorizing something for an English test, in a couple of days he has forgotten what he learned and has to go over it again. He also has a hand tremor that makes his writing slow. I am going to buy the Mavis Beacon tutorial so he can learn to type in hope this will help him.

✦ ✦ ✦

William was 24 months old when he was diagnosed and he was given neuropsych testing during induction as part of his protocol (they are specifically looking for neurotoxicity). The results were "within normal limits." A year and a half later, we decided to have more neuropsych testing done, this time at our own expense ($1,400) because I felt I needed some guidance as to what to do with preschool. His preschool was putting him with younger kids because he still wore diapers sometimes and used a bottle, but I thought he was very bright and should be with an older group.

The testing was very valuable for us. The doctor said "definitely no" that he should not be with younger kids. She also reported that he was very, very smart, but had very poor fine motor skills. (Thank you, vincristine). I too, had noticed this, but she was able to document it and warn me about potential problems if the disparity in his intelligence and motor skills continued. He grips a pencil poorly and avoids drawing and coloring. His mental skills tested consistently in the 90th percentile and above, yet his fine motor skills were in the 16th percentile.

We have started occupational therapy (insurance is paying) and have seen an improvement. The key thing I learned about occupational therapy is that it is FUN! At least for a 4 year old. He considers it playtime.

Chapter 6

Speech, Language and Hearing Difficulties

Deryk Beal, MHSc
Donald Mabbott, PhD
Eric Bouffet, MD

Children with cancer may experience difficulty with speech, language or hearing function at various stages during their course of treatment. The aim of this chapter is to define speech, language and hearing, describe the potential deficits experienced by children with cancer and outline the role of the speech-language pathologist working with children with cancer. Suggestions for supporting speech, language and hearing development in children with cancer are provided.

Understanding what is meant by speech, language and hearing and appreciating the differences among these three areas is essential before we discuss the impact of cancer and its treatment on their function. Collectively, speech, language and hearing constitute communication.

What is Speech?

Speech refers to the noise we make when we produce sounds and words. Speech is the result of a complex series of muscle motor movements and is produced when the brain sends signals to the muscles of the speech mechanism including the lungs, vocal cords, tongue, lips and jaw.

What is Language?

Language refers to the ideas we express or comprehend when we speak, write, read text or hear other people talk. There are two main areas of language:

- Receptive language (comprehension)

> Mr. Deryk Beal is a speech-language pathologist with the Pediatric Brain Tumor Program and a project director in the Brain and Behavior Program at the Research Institute at the Hospital for Sick Children in Toronto, Ontario, Canada.

refers to how we understand the content of what we hear or read.

- Expressive language (expression) refers to how we formulate the content of what we speak or write.

What is Hearing?

Hearing is the perception of sound. In a normal hearing ear, acoustic information travels through the outer, middle and inner ear to the auditory nerve. The auditory nerve sends information to the brain for interpretation.

How are Speech, Language and Hearing Impacted by Cancer?

There are many different kinds of cancer and many different locations where cancer may occur in the body. Depending on the type of cancer, where it is in the body and the type of treatment given, there may be an impact on speech, language or hearing functions.

Who are the Children at Greatest Risk?

Children with brain tumors are at risk for changes in speech, language and hearing depending on the location of the tumor or other complications such as hydrocephalus and increased intracranial pressure. The most frequent occurring changes in children with brain tumors are slurred speech, difficulty finding the right words to use in conversation and ringing in the ears. Children with other types of cancer who require surgery or radiation to the head or neck may also experience problems with hearing and/or speech. Certain types of chemotherapy (vincristine, cisplatin) can also affect speech and hearing. The possible acute and late effects of treatment are discussed below.

How can Surgery Affect a Child's Communication Skills?

Whether or not a child is at risk for changes depends on where the cancer is in a child's body and the operation used to remove it. The surgeon will explain if there is a risk for changes in speech, language or hearing as a result of surgery.

Dr. Donald Mabbott is a psychologist with the Pediatric Brain Tumor Program, a project director in the Brain and Behavior Program in the Research Institute at the Hospital for Sick Children and an assistant professor of pediatrics at the University of Toronto, Canada.

Children who have surgery to remove a brain tumor may be at risk for speech, language or hearing changes depending on the location of the tumor. The most common location of a brain tumor in children is in the back part of the brain called the posterior fossa. Approximately 25% of children with a posterior fossa tumor will stop talking, or become mute, for a period of time after surgery. Children who experience mutism eventually talk again but the way that they talk may change. It may take several weeks or months before some children will begin to talk again.

The period during which children are mute can be a very frightening time for them and their families. Often the mutism is accompanied by other changes such as irritability, frequent screaming or moaning, swallowing and vision problems and difficulties moving the body. Children with mutism still understand what is said to them. Children may be frustrated that they cannot easily express their wants or needs or ask questions that are important to them. Encouraging children to talk at this time is not advised, as they are not ready to talk. Talking is the easiest way to communicate and the motivation to talk is natural. If children could talk postoperatively it is likely that they would.

A speech-language pathologist may help children with mutism. A speech-language pathologist can develop a different way of communicating using gestures (e.g., head nods and shakes, hand squeezes, or other body movements) or pointing to pictures. Children can then communicate to family and staff on a basic level.

Surgery to remove some tumors (e.g., posterior fossa, brainstem, and neck) may result in damage to vocal cord function and changes in children's voice quality. If you notice that your child has difficulty talking or has a breathy voice after surgery be sure to inform the surgeon. There is treatment available to repair vocal cord function and improve voice quality.

How can Chemotherapy Affect Speech, Language or Hearing?

Some chemotherapy drugs may damage how the brain controls the muscles for speech and voice production. Vincristine and vinblastine can cause unilateral or bilateral vocal cord palsy. This results in a weak and breathy voice with pitch changes and sometimes an associated swallowing problem. Your oncologist may consult an

Dr. Eric Bouffet is the director of the Pediatric Brain Tumor Program and an associate scientist in the Brain and Behavior Program in the Research Institute at the Hospital for Sick Children as well as a professor of pediatrics at the University of Toronto, Canada.

otolaryngologist (ear, nose and throat doctor) or a speech-language pathologist to manage your child's voice changes. There is treatment available to improve vocal cord function and voice quality. Other causes of vocal cord paralysis can be observed in children with cancer, particularly after treatment for a brain tumor or a tumor of the neck. Observation and speech therapy are the standard treatment. In some cases, surgical treatment or vocal cord injections may be used to restore or improve voice function.

Nausea and vomiting are common side effects of chemotherapy agents. Prolonged periods of frequent vomiting may expose the vocal cords to irritating stomach acids. As a result, children may develop a hoarse voice quality. Encouraging children to rinse the mouth thoroughly with water after vomiting is an effective measure to prevent stomach acids from irritating the vocal cords. If vomiting is accompanied by violent coughing and hoarse voice quality persists, you should consult your oncologist and speech-language pathologist for further intervention.

Intensive and high-dose chemotherapy may result in mucositis (inflammation of the mouth and throat lining). Children who have mucositis may experience pain during talking or swallowing. Children may stop talking for a short period of time because it is too painful to tolerate. Children may also drool or spit out saliva because it is too painful to swallow.

Chemotherapy may have an impact on hearing. Some chemotherapy drugs, such as cisplatinum or, to a lesser extent, carboplatin, damage part of the inner ear as well as the part of the brain involved in hearing. Typically, hearing is first lost for high-pitched sounds. With prolonged or intensive use of high-dose chemotherapy drugs, the hearing loss may progress to the lower pitches. An audiologist with the oncology team will work with the oncologist to monitor children's hearing levels over the course of treatment. Often the doses of the drugs are adjusted.

Chemotherapy that causes hearing loss indirectly impacts speech and language development. Infants treated with cisplatinum (e.g., infants with hepatoblastoma, neuroblastoma or germ cell tumors) are at risk for losing their ability to hear high-pitched sounds. If children have difficulty hearing high-pitched sounds then they may have difficulty learning how to articulate high-pitched speech sounds (e.g., /s/, /f/). Some sounds that children may have difficulty hearing are important for language development. For example, the /s/ sound is used to mark plural (e.g., dogs, cats) and possession (e.g., daddy's car, mommy's dress) in English. Early speech and language therapy with a certified speech-language pathologist helps children to overcome these difficulties. These services can be found through the hospital, through services provided by school systems or preschool programs for children at risk for learning disabilities.

If children acquire a hearing loss that impacts their ability to hear the sounds necessary for speech and language development then hearing aids or other supportive hearing devices may be recommended. It is extremely important that children who are fitted for hearing devices use them as instructed by a certified audiologist. Failing to do so may result in missed opportunities for children with difficulty hearing to acquire the information needed for age appropriate speech and language development. In addition, children with hearing impairment who do not use their hearing devices properly are at greater risk of missing sound cues, warning of environmental dangers such as oncoming traffic.

How can Radiation Affect Speech, Language and Hearing?

Children receiving radiation treatment to the brain may develop excessive sleepiness called somnolence syndrome. In addition to sleeping excessively (up to 20 hours per day), children with somnolence are easily fatigued. They sometimes also experience headache, irritability, vomiting, and occasionally slurred speech. Speech therapy administered during radiation treatment, or in the period shortly after, should be sensitive to the effects of somnolence. The speech-language pathologist should work in partnership with families to develop a treatment schedule that capitalizes on when their children are most alert during the day. The length and intensity of speech or language therapy should be based on children's age and tolerance for activity.

Motor speech problems have been reported during and following the completion of radiation therapy. If children experience difficulty moving the muscles of their face for talking, and slurred or distorted speech (dysarthria) during the course of radiation treatment, it is likely the result of somnolence. However, children who have cranial radiation are at risk for long-term problems with facial weakness and dysarthria.

Most children with nasopharyngeal carcinoma or parameningeal sarcoma (cancer close to the skull) will undergo radiation to the oral cavity. They may experience changes in the amount and consistency of secretions in their mouth and throat resulting in dryness of the mouth and vocal tract (xerostomia). Artificial saliva is available to moisten the mouth for children with xerostomia.

Radiation can also cause fluid loss. When radiation is given to the neck, the decreased body fluid levels result in shrinking of the vocal cords and changes in the sound of the voice. The pitch of children's voices may change due to the fluid loss from the vocal cord tissue. Radiation can also cause tissue shrinking (atrophy), tissue swelling (edema) or a build-up of unneeded tissue (fibrosis) inside the airway. Changes in the airway are reflected in changes to the sound of children's voices (e.g., they may sound congested). This fluid loss also affects secretions in the ears. Children treated with cranial radiation encompassing the ear canal often develop dry, thick earwax, which can affect their hearing. The regular use of softening agents (e.g., oil or sodium bicarbonate) is recommended to loosen the earwax and help clear the ear canal.

Language difficulties may emerge months or years after radiation treatment to the brain is completed. Receptive and expressive language deficits reflect difficulties learning new language skills. Children may understand directions and use words just as well as they did before radiation. However, they might not learn new language skills at the same rate as other children their age. If children have difficulty following instructions, understanding stories, finding the right word to say or telling stories then they are having difficulty using oral language. A speech-language pathologist uses his or her knowledge of language development to set appropriate goals for children in the context of their ongoing cancer treatment.

Children with cancer benefit from additional language activities beyond the current curriculum during treatment and in the early years after treatment completion. A speech-language pathologist may be available at your hospital or school. The speech-language pathologist should become familiar with the impact of cancer treatment so that he or she can help plan appropriate goals for speech and language development of children with cancer. Language difficulties do not occur in isolation and are often exacerbated by later developing cognitive difficulties related to radiation. As a result, it is beneficial to solidify children's basic language skills early. If children tolerate treatment well, it is appropriate to teach listening, talking, reading and writing skills during alert moments.

How can Families Access Speech, Language, and Hearing Services?

United States

Early intervention programs provide speech, language and hearing services to children aged 5 years old and younger. For children aged 0 to 3 years old, a pediatrician or the Department of Public Health can provide the name of a local early intervention program contact person. For children over 3 years of age, the special education department of your local school will be able to connect you with services.

A common model of service delivery in the United States is for early intervention therapists to visit chronically ill children in the hospital. When the children are discharged, the same therapist can maintain continuity of care by working with the child at home.

For more information about speech, language and hearing services in the United States, contact the American Speech and Hearing Association (*www.asha.org*) at (800) 638-8255.

Canada

Speech, language and hearing services are delivered differently depending on the province or territory that you live in. For more information about speech, language and hearing services in Canada contact the Canadian Association of Speech-Language Pathologists and Audiologists (*www.caslpa.ca*) at (800) 259-8519.

Summary

Speech, language and hearing difficulties may occur during or after children's treatment for cancer. Alerting your oncologist to changes in your child's communication ability is an important first step to addressing potential problems early. Assessment and treatment with a speech-language pathologist and/or audiologist is beneficial for identifying and treating speech, language and hearing difficulties. Early intervention for any speech, language or hearing difficulties is strongly advocated as learning difficulties may increase over time if radiation therapy is a component of your child's therapy.

Key Points

- Changes to speech, language and hearing are dependent on the type of cancer, its location in the body, and the type of treatment received.

- Children with brain tumors are at greater risk for experiencing changes in communication ability.

- Cerebellar mutism is the temporary inability to talk after surgery to remove a cerebellar tumor. Children with cerebellar mutism can communicate non-verbally (e.g., use a hand gesture to signal "yes" or "no").

- Some chemotherapy drugs are associated with hearing loss that interferes with speech and language development.

- Radiation to the brain can affect children's language capacity.

- Early intervention with a speech-language pathologist is appropriate to solidify the speech and language skills of children with cancer before the possible appearance of late learning difficulties.

- Ongoing intervention with an audiologist is appropriate to monitor for changes in children's hearing over the course of chemotherapy or radiation treatment. Depending on their type of hearing loss and its severity, audiologists sometimes fit children with hearing aids or other supportive listening devices to ensure they are able to hear the sounds necessary to develop speech and language skills.

Parent Perspectives

My 6-year-old daughter developed cerebellar mutism immediately after her surgery removing her medulloblastoma tumor. Her world was mostly silent for the next eight months. We tried to use buttons with 'yes' and 'no' on them but to no avail. Her communication began to return in the form of raising her hand about six months post surgery. She would raise it to answer 'yes' to questions. Over the next month this hand raising turned into one-word yes/no answers. Seven months after surgery 3 to 5 word sentences were happening. The words were sometimes half words. The end of one word would drop off and the beginning of the next one would not be pronounced. Her voice was monotone and nasal-sounding and had many pauses between words.

At 10 months after surgery her speech has improved considerably and at times it almost sounds normal. She can now carry on a conversation, although some words are mispronounced. She needs choices when asked a question; open-ended questions often go unanswered. She has just begun to talk to the other children at school when spoken to. At first she would hide her head and not look at them. Now she answers and waves to them. At home and in therapy she's very chatty. She continues to receive five hours of speech therapy at school per week and every day she's sounding more like herself. We had our first of three visits to the neuropsychologist last week.

✢✢✢

My very hyperverbal son was mute for more than twelve weeks after his surgery for medulloblastoma. He had speech therapy immediately, but he was so irritable and uncooperative it was hard to tell if he was benefiting from it. The speech therapist attempted to teach him how to communicate nonverbally, using head nods or pointing to simple picture boards as a way of letting us know if he wanted to eat, go to the bathroom, or just be left alone. I was impressed with the perseverance that the speech therapist had in this very trying situation. He tried a new strategy every session, and kept our hopes up with stories of prior patients he had had with posterior fossa syndrome.

When speech returned, it was a trickle at first. He said, "Bye," whispering first, then saying it out loud. It was so exciting to hear his voice after so long and we were so excited to hear it that we left the room frequently just to hear him say it again. Within a week he said his next words, "One, two, three, four, I declare a thumb war" and within another week he was speaking again. At first it was quite robotic, but within three weeks of his first words he sounded like himself again (as one of my friends said, "you have to remember he had a high squeaky voice before he had cancer"). He continued in speech therapy after speech returned because he had some difficulty with the 's' sound, but the therapist suspected the problem predated his mutism. Now, almost three years after surgery, his speech is entirely normal in tone, quality, and quantity.

✚ ✚ ✚

My daughter received about six months of speech and language therapy before transplant derailed her progress. After her return to school at age 6 ½, she was evaluated and diagnosed with central auditory processing disorder. Our school has been very accommodating and she sees her speech therapist at school alone twice a week, and in group twice a week. She started the Earobics Auditory training system and completed that series last fall. She's made great progress, but my only regret is that we didn't integrate some of her speech therapy and goals while she was on treatment and during transplant. I simply didn't know what to do, and if I had, we could have used some of those boring days as an inpatient to be more consistent with her speech therapy.

✚ ✚ ✚

During the early months of dealing with mutism, we concentrated only on speech. While mute, Caleb's speech therapist made picture boards so he could point to his needs. He practiced sticking out his tongue, and tried to blow. He opened and closed his mouth fish style, and waved bye when the therapist left the room. As always, Dad did wild and crazy things, even while Caleb was in intensive care with a ventriculostomy. Though mute, Caleb could laugh out loud. Laughing, too, was stimulated by Loony Tunes cartoons played on a VCR. It had to be moved right next to his bed in order for his eyes to focus.

Caleb was one of the lucky ones as his period of total mutism only lasted 10 days. We had begged the rehab staff to allow our whole family to spend a night with Caleb in the hotel that is attached to the hospital. They w *really in favor, but our house had always been wild and crazy, an.. wc* *thought Caleb needed the stimulation of a quasi-normal visit. We loaded him in a wheelchair, took some of the gifts and snacks that had been sent along with a urinal, and checked into the Med-Inn. The night went pretty well, with everyone carefully tip-toeing around Caleb. Next morning, I got him up and dressed first, then sat him in the wheelchair out of harm's way while the rest of us bathed and dressed. I thought I heard a weak croak, and at first I couldn't tell where it was coming from. "Can-I-have-some-Cracker-Jack?" I wish I could say speech progressed rapidly from that point, but it took many more weeks, months, and years working on speech basics, breath support, loudness, lowering pitch, getting lips and teeth all working together. As time passed, however, language skills superceded speech as the most important issue facing Caleb. He would be able to get through life if his speech was slightly impeded, but this kid needed to be taught all the milestones of language development and processing that are intuitive for others.*

We spent hours playing games such as Blurt, Uno, checkers, Tri-Bond, Racko, and Guess Who. In fact, Connect Four was the first activity that occupational therapists brought to his bedside in ICU. While masquerading as fun, these games were an attempt to retrain Caleb's brain in such skills as sequencing and inferencing, but also revealed great needs. We were advised to continue speech therapy well beyond the return of acceptable speech quality. This way the therapist could observe Caleb as he approached certain developmental milestones, such as the evolving sense of logic or abstract thinking around age 10 or 11. They were even watching for an evolving sense of humor.

Caleb never met these milestones. To him, 'raining cats and dogs' meant exactly that until we taught him otherwise. He is a concrete thinker, and can't imagine what a story might mean unless told to look beyond the literal. This became much more of an issue this last year during 7th grade. We spent many evenings reading and discussing not just literature, but science and social studies texts as well, as they all assume a grade level sense of logic and the ability to infer and interpret. Our speech therapist says literal interpretation of figurative language is definitely a significant issue as is pragmatics (e.g., properly interpreting social situations). At home we use textbooks on tape, an electronic dictionary, a Scholastic book of idioms, and homemade flashcards of vocabulary words. The school contributed by enlarging materials as needed, shortening assignments and tests, reducing writing requirements, and offering extended time on reports.

✢✢✢

My daughter developed cerebellar mutism after brain tumor surgery. She did not speak for more than 10 weeks. Initially, her returning speech was monotone, slow, nasal and sparse. It took some time to realize the associated language problems although the rate and quality of speech was almost normal in two years. A year after surgery, her neuropsych evaluation revealed that word finding and retelling a story were extremely difficult. When finding words became too difficult or frustrating she would say, "I don't know." She even said she didn't know what a bike was despite having ridden one to the office. In another test, a story was read to her and she was to retell as much of the story as possible. After much cajoling, she finally said the story was about a boy and a boat. However, she correctly answered 14 of 15 multiple-choice questions. Clearly this was not a memory or knowledge problem but rather a glitch in her expressive language.

I could immediately grasp how important this was for school. Open-ended questions had a real possibility of shutting my girl down, thus giving an inaccurate portrayal of her knowledge base. We needed a teacher who would go beyond "I don't know" to find if this was "I don't know how to get my thoughts out" or "I don't know the answer."

The problem could be easily missed because she gets along well with her peers and can be a "chatter box." If one really examines her speech she is best when initiating conversations and has primary control. When telling her own stories there is a richness of detail and expression which is not present when retelling other's stories.

✢✢✢

My son Cole was diagnosed with a left frontal pilocytic astrocytoma at 3 years of age. During surgery Cole suffered from strokes leaving him with a profound right side weakness. Later that same year he had surgery to drain a subdural fluid collection on the brain and re-growth of the tumor. He had three more strokes, this time leaving him with paralysis of the mouth and throat muscles and also left side weakness. He also underwent two years of chemotherapy.

After three years of physical, occupational and speech therapy he is still unable to swallow or speak and has fine motor skill problems in his hands.

He has to wear a bib, because drooling is a problem. He started regular public school this year. He was not scared, but I was. He couldn't communicate with his classmates, except through a little machine and gesturing. I spoke with his teacher and assistant and explained my fears. In turn his teacher spoke with all his classmates, letting them know what Cole's physical disabilities are and that he may need help and also to be patient with him when he is trying to tell them anything. We also decided that Cole needed to learn a new and faster way to communicate. Gesturing is fine at home, but who else would understand?

The solution we came up with was sign language. Because of Cole, his teacher has been taking classes in sign and is teaching him and his classmates as well. These children are amazing with him. We are also learning as a family how to sign and it has made a world of difference. He is able to communicate his needs and wants, without becoming so frustrated. Sometimes the signs are more general, because of finger coordination, but it has opened up new doors of understanding. I was so skeptical of learning sign language at first. I thought he would stop trying to speak. The truth is he may never regain his ability to speak and if he does, this will be a second language. He actual tries harder to make sounds when he is signing. I am not giving up hope for his speech to come back; this is just bridging the gap in the meantime.

✦ ✦ ✦

Nick, a brain tumor survivor for seven years, has progressive hearing loss from the cisplatinum and radiation. When Nick was almost 5 we placed him in a public preschool for deaf and hard of hearing where he started to learn sign language. Nick can understand some basic sign but primarily he reads lips. He views himself as a hearing child because he heard for so long and he has such a great handle on speech. Until this year he went to a school with an interpreter. This year we moved him to our neighborhood school with an aide who knows some sign language. This has been a work in progress but I think we are moving in the right direction. They have a better program for kids who have slight cognitive delays and he gets to be with the neighborhood kids.

Nick has programmable digital aids that drop off all the high and low tones (which he can't hear anyway) in order to put all that power in the moderate tones. We also purchased an FM system for his digital aids last year. The system works with his programmable hearing aids. It goes to and from school everyday with him and we charge it at night. It has a direct audio feed so he can hook directly up to the computer or TV, although he actually prefers captioning on the TV. We are also going to have Center for Independent Living come through our home to give us ideas of things that would make Nick more independent. He can't use the phone because he cannot hear on it. He cannot type quick enough to use a TDD. We are going to teach him how to use the fax machine so he can fax notes to us.

I guess the best advice I can give for kids who have even a moderate hearing loss is to get connected with the deaf and hard of hearing community because there are a lot of adaptive aids available. Even knowing 50 to 100 signs can be a godsend in a noisy public place. Also, sign language works as a reinforcing visual cue that gives kids one more way to process incoming information.

✛ ✛ ✛

My daughter was diagnosed with a choroid plexus tumor at age 9 months. She is now 11 years old. She received speech therapy, occupational therapy (OT), and physical therapy (PT) through the school district twice a week for many years, even though she has always been enrolled in private school. However, when there was a change in the law, we were told she no longer qualified. We now pay privately for these services, and though a huge expense, have found these private contractors to be superior and worth the financial sacrifice. She has shown significant improvement since switching to private therapists.

Chapter 7

Advice to Educators

Kathryn H. Wissler, MS

It is inevitable that during the course of one's teaching career an educator will be responsible for teaching a child who has been diagnosed with cancer or is a childhood cancer survivor. Yet teachers receive little or no training in how to support, guide and advocate for these children in the classroom.

The educator is a key figure in the lives of students who have been diagnosed with cancer. School normalizes their experience and the educator can make a big difference in how well the student adjusts to his or her diagnosis and treatment. What follows is best practice advice for educators when working with a student diagnosed with cancer.

At Diagnosis

School personnel may be among the first people to know about a child's diagnosis of cancer. In fact, they may have noticed symptoms and known of doctor appointments and evaluations taking place prior to diagnosis. Once the diagnosis is made, the school can begin to support the child and family in a variety of ways.

Establish communication

Choose someone from the student's school to act as the liaison with parents and hospital personnel so that medical information is accurate, consistent, and in keeping with the wishes of the family. The student's classroom teacher, guidance counselor or school nurse are good options for this role. The school liaison should feel comfortable speaking with the parents about their child's illness and should realize that this responsibility will extend through the remainder of the school year and perhaps longer depending on the length of treatment. Initial information that needs to be shared includes diagnosis, treatment, side effects, and estimated length of absenteeism from school.

> Kathryn H. Wissler is the educational liaison for the division of pediatric hematology-oncology at Golisano Children's Hospital at Strong in Rochester, NY.

Start support

Begin a campaign of support for the child and family through staff and classmates' cards, letters and visits to the hospital and home. The school liaison can find out if parents are comfortable having visitors and if there are any restrictions at the hospital. Many children diagnosed with cancer are hospitalized for a month or more at diagnosis. Try to keep the communication with schoolmates and teachers ongoing during the time away from school and not just at the initial diagnosis. Schools may want to investigate with the family other supportive measures such as meals for the family or childcare for siblings to assist during these long hospital stays. Siblings attending school in the district may need some extra support during this time. Notify personnel working with them in other schools of the situation and arrange counseling as needed.

Other ideas for support by staff and classmates while the student is absent are:

- Communication via telephone both with child and parents.
- When making hospital and home visits, be sure to call first and bring an activity to do with the student. Examples are reading a book, playing a board game, playing a computer game or watching a video.
- Prepare a tape recording or a video of a class event.
- Use a speakerphone or a video camera in the classroom so the student can speak to the entire class.
- Distribute the child's hospital or home email address to staff and classmates and send instant messages often.

Home/hospital instruction

The child's home school district is responsible for providing home/hospital instruction for students who will be out of school for an extended period of time, even when the child is hospitalized out of the school district area. Most cancer patients miss a lot of school due to hospitalizations, clinic appointments and side effects and are therefore eligible for this instruction. After discussion with hospital personnel, instruction should be instituted as soon as the student can benefit, ideally within one week of diagnosis. The classroom teacher or guidance counselor should be the contact for the tutor assigned. Teachers should give the tutor only essential assignments because tutoring typically occurs only 5 to 10 hours per week depending on the age of the child. It is best for the school to hire someone for this rather than to expect the classroom teachers to do this on their own time. The classroom teacher, in consultation with the tutor, determines grades.

Tutors should have experience working with sick children in intimate settings such as homes and hospital rooms. Tutoring for cancer patients can last from six weeks to more than a year so it is not a small commitment of time. The school liaison should reassure the sick student that school is important and that staff will do everything possible to help the student keep up with school work. Tutoring can help students keep their mind off their treatment. Good tutors provide praise and encouragement, as well as send the message that the student will get better and rejoin his classmates.

Modify class schedules for middle school and high school students

Students in middle school and high school have a much more difficult time fulfilling class requirements while on home or hospital instruction. The amount of work is significantly greater in the upper grades and some subjects (notably sciences and foreign language) require class participation that cannot be easily duplicated in a tutoring situation. Guidance counselors should explore alternative class schedules with the student and her parents. One option is to delay one or more subjects until summer school when the student is feeling better. Some college-bound high school students may opt for an additional year in high school in order to complete all their high school requirements, advance placement coursework, and SAT preparations. These decisions depend on the student's treatment schedule, tolerance for therapy and personal preference.

Prepare for school re-entry

It is never too soon to begin to prepare for the student's return to school. This can be somewhat unpredictable depending on the child's adjustment to therapy as well as the comfort level of the family in having the child return to school. Parents and school personnel should discuss issues for the return as soon as feasible to avoid any barriers due to lack of preparation.

School re-entry visit

Ideally, a member of the hospital team (educational liaison or nurse practitioner) should conduct a school re-entry visit for both the classroom and faculty involved with the student. These visits are usually made after the first few weeks of treatment. There will probably be a need to have two separate presentations, one to the classmates and one to the faculty involved with the student. The classmate visit is designed to discuss the child's diagnosis, treatment and side effects as well as to dispel myths about cancer. It is also meant to prepare classmates for any physical changes in the way the child looks and to talk about ways they can be a friend to their classmate.

The faculty presentation should include all the same information but also give valuable information to staff about what accommodations may need to be in place when the child returns. In addition, it is a time for staff to recognize their own emotional reaction to the student's medical situation and avoid distancing themselves emotionally at a time when the student needs their support. The hospital liaison should provide the staff with printed information containing emergency numbers, resources and general information about late effects of treatment.

School accommodations

Educators should consider accommodations that may be needed prior to a child's return to ensure a smooth re-entry and not delay a return to class. Because these school accommodations take time to plan and involve paperwork, the process to put them in place should begin early. They may include:

- Special transportation
- A one-to-one aide or access to an aide
- Use of an elevator
- Use of a wheelchair
- A modified day

During Treatment

After the school re-entry visit and accommodations for the child's return are in place, the student should return to school. Educators can assist the re-entry best by treating the student as normally as possible while allowing for necessary classroom accommodations as outlined below.

Monitor for missed instruction

Teachers should check to see if the student has missed any valuable instruction due to absenteeism and provide extra help if the student is unfamiliar with key concepts that the class is studying.

Modify assignments

Fatigue is a common problem for students on treatment and can make homework difficult to complete. Reduction of homework assignments, extra time for long-term assignments and extra time for classroom tests are recommended for students who are on treatment.

Waive the 'no hat' rule

Most schools have rules against wearing hats in class. A hat or appropriate head covering should be allowed for cancer patients with scars or hair loss. Be sure to notify all staff (and substitutes) that the student is allowed to wear a hat to ensure the student is not singled out or punished.

Physical education modifications

Students on treatment can usually participate in physical education class but it will take extra effort on the part of the physical education teacher to devise appropriate physical activity for the student. Contact sports are not usually allowed if the student has a low platelet count or a central line. Low stamina and fatigue may make it necessary to adjust requirements in class. Allowing the student to self restrict activities is appropriate. Walking programs and lightweight training (20 lbs or less) are good alternatives to group sports that may involve contact. Many schools require written assignments in lieu of physical education classes, but students on treatment should be encouraged to participate in physical activity as tolerated and not left to merely observe.

Use of the health office

Most children or teens with cancer do not take medication in school so regular visits to the health office are usually not necessary. However, the child should be allowed to go to the health office when feeling ill. The child may rest in the health office if he is feeling tired, although many elementary classrooms have quiet corners in the classroom that are used for resting also. Sometimes children have special toileting needs that are best handled in the health office. The school nurse or aide should have printed information about any catheters or infusion pumps used by the child, as well as phone numbers of staff at the hospital taking care of the student. Central lines rarely malfunction in school, but the nurse should have emergency information in the event of a problem.

Other classroom modifications

Students may need frequent drinks or snacks during the day because of side effects from chemotherapy. Allowing the student with impaired mobility or profound fatigue to leave class early to avoid crowded hallways when changing classes is an appropriate accommodation. Occasionally, the noise level or smell of food in the cafeteria is bothersome to students on chemotherapy. Alternative lunchroom arrangements should be explored if this is the case.

Keep expectations high for the student

Teachers will have to balance the curriculum expectations with the student's need for accommodations due to disease and treatment. It is unfair to reduce essential requirements that will leave the student unprepared for future grades. Teachers may inadvertently minimize the importance of school to the parent and child by reducing expectations in the belief that the child should concentrate on getting better. This is not helpful. The student may interpret lower expectations from the teacher as a belief that school is not important or that he or she will not survive.

Teachers should be assessing the need for additional school services for the student who may be struggling because of an acquired learning problem from his or her treatment. Occupational and physical therapy needs often occur during treatment and can best be delivered at school with an emphasis on fine and gross motor deficits that affect school functioning. Close communication with the family about the child's progress in school is essential. Don't wait until the end of the school year to address concerns about the student's readiness to move on to the next grade. Grade retention due to missed instruction should be avoided for these students; however, it may be necessary for the student to receive summer tutoring to prepare them for the next year.

Counseling

It may be helpful for the student to know that he or she can check in with a counselor at school as needed. Discussions about workload, acceptance by peers, tolerance of therapy and fears about their illness and treatment and loss of abilities may be explored. School may be the best place for counseling as parents are already overwhelmed with treatment schedules, blood tests and doctor appointments and may not wish to add outside counseling to this routine. The school counselor can seek guidance from the hospital social worker who understands the issues confronting a student undergoing cancer treatment.

After Treatment Has Ended

School personnel are usually aware of students on treatment because of the attention given at diagnosis as well as the physical changes in the student. However, treatment may last months or years and during that time the student may change schools within a district and regain her pre-diagnosis appearance. It is not uncommon for new school personnel to be unaware of the student's cancer history. Parents should disclose this information to new staff especially if the diagnosis and treatment put the student at risk for developing learning problems. The new school should also know if treatment and side effects interrupted schooling to the extent that the child may need extra support from the school to catch up.

Testing

All students who received central nervous system treatment (chemotherapy, radiation, or surgery to the brain) should have baseline neuropsychological testing conducted by the school district within a year of their diagnosis or when they turn 6. This is the beginning of the monitoring process by the district for acquired learning disabilities that can result from disease or treatment. Updated testing should take place when parents and school personnel notice any of the following: a change in grades over time; student frustration with school work; problems completing homework within a reasonable amount of time; or poor test performance.

Identifying learning problems

In general, learning problems associated with cancer diagnosis and therapy include problems with short-term memory, processing speed, attention and concentration, grapho-motor difficulties, visual-spatial problems, organization, and planning. Educators should be aware of any red flags in these areas and notify parents when they are affecting the student's work performance. These issues should not be minimized or attributed to other factors such as lack of motivation, interest, or poor effort nor should they be put off in order to spare the family added stress after their ordeal with the child's illness. Steps should be taken to document the learning problem and decide on a plan of intervention through informal or formal means (Section 504 Plan or Committee on Special Education classification).

Do's and Don'ts for Educators

Here are some tips to remember when working with a student who has been diagnosed with cancer.

Don't ask the prognosis of the child: This sends the wrong message to the parent and hospital personnel. It offends parents as it implies that the school will not do as much if the prognosis is poor. The doctors are treating the child for cure and will expect that the school will make available appropriate interventions regardless of the outcome.

Don't minimize the importance of school: Too often the school tells the parent that the important thing is that the child gets well and not to worry about school. This leads to delays in services from the school including tutoring, re-entry, and classroom modification. The fact is that as soon as a child is diagnosed, the school should begin to plan for the child's return. There should not be a "wait and see" mentality.

Don't play the "Whose responsibility is it?" game: Yes, the need for specialized services such as occupational therapy and physical therapy is a result of a medical diagnosis but that doesn't mean that it is not a school responsibility. Gross and fine motor issues with cancer patients can be long standing and will impact their full participation in school activities. Schools should take the lead in providing evaluation and service.

Do find ways to include the student in school activities: Even if a child can not regularly attend school because of treatment effects, teachers can invite the child to come to school for holiday parties, special assemblies, field trips etc. This takes extra planning to meet the child's special needs, but will help to keep a connection with the class when on home/hospital instruction and will greatly enhance that student's feelings about being part of the class.

Do investigate specialized assessments and consultations for students: Educational issues for cancer patients are unique and most school personnel will not have much experience evaluating and planning for their needs. Educators should take advantage of specialized assessments and consultations available to assist with planning for students (neuropsychological, assistive technology and hospital or community liaisons regarding childhood cancer).

Key Points

- A knowledgeable, supportive, and constructive response by the educator to a student's diagnosis and treatment for cancer is vital to the student's success in school.

- The educator must maintain close communication with parents and hospital personnel to best meet the needs of the student during this challenging time.

- Comprehensive planning is necessary and will be rewarded with grateful parents and a well-adjusted student.

Parent Perspectives

My best advice for teachers is to listen with your ears and your hearts. These children have often been terrified both physically and emotionally. They have seen their bodies change, their friends disappear, and their parents cry. Friends they make in the hospital sometimes die. If they develop learning disabilities, they often remember and grieve their losses. Even if they don't remember, they soon notice that they don't learn as quickly as other children. If they were athletes, they desperately miss practice and the camaraderie of the team. When their hair falls out, they are often teased. They have more to cope with than any child should. So, try to learn about the disease. Try to understand that the family is in turmoil and it might boil over at school. Be kind to the siblings. Help repair peer relationships by encouraging compassion and inclusion. Have realistic expectations but provide plenty of encouragement. You can be an angel of mercy for the family or another burden. The choice is yours.

✚ ✚ ✚

One thing Cami's kindergarten teacher did that really helped was to come to the house for a visit when Cami was home from the hospital but too sick to go to school. It helped foster a more intimate connection that helped Cami when she needed support in the classroom.

What I valued most, though, was that Cami's teacher took all her cues from us. She never pretended to know what Cami was going through, never gave unasked-for advice, never second-guessed what we knew was right for Cami. She was just supportive and loving, and that made it easy for Cami to feel comfortable, and for all of us to continue a meaningful dialogue as to how to best negotiate the year.

✚ ✚ ✚

One thing that really made me crazy as my son transitioned back to school, with no hair or eyebrows, was the fact that I had to go in and fight with the principal for him to be allowed to wear a hat! She thought wearing a hat would signal him out and make every one know he was the "cancer kid." Even now, thinking about it makes me crazy! Schools need to listen to parents, and be supportive. The fact that I had to go to the principal with pictures of my son with no hair and beg her too let him wear his hat was very offensive. She did allow it, although she muttered that it was against her better judgment and she knew kids better than me! After a few months my son's friends encouraged him to go hatless, and with the kids acceptance, HE decided when HE was ready to go to school bald.

✦ ✦ ✦

We never had a problem with Brenna wearing a hat or not as far as her school was concerned. Our problem was with making sure that teachers remembered that she HAD to wear a hat when outside to guard against sunburn.

If I could add one piece of advice to parents and administrators on issues like hats, loose clothing etc, it is that there may be an underlying medical reason why the deviation from dress code is necessary or desired, e.g., sunburn on a preschooler's bald skull. A little bit of careful listening and a little bit of gentle inquiry on the part of the teacher or administrator may lead to a reason and strategy that is acceptable to all.

✦ ✦ ✦

Since Danny's treatment started in elementary school, with a relapse in junior high, then the last relapse in high school, I had a variety of experiences with schools and teachers. Here are my thoughts (and some of them are more appropriate for one age over another):

- *The administration should let teachers and classmates know when a child is newly diagnosed, newly relapsed, or hospitalized (the big things). This can be done via school newspaper, announcements from staff, or some other method. The point is, don't let it be handled by the rumor mill, which happens especially in high school. In grade school there is obviously less understanding of how cancer affects a child, so rumors there can be very harmful.*

- *A nurse or social worker should talk to the child's classmates about the disease, explaining what is happening to the child. I will never forget taking Danny to a school Christmas production while he was out of school the first time. Kids stared at him and one asked outright, "Why is your face so fat?" Even in high school, kids thought Danny just "gained weight" over a summer, when the cause was steroids. It would have been relatively easy for someone to explain the medical situation to the teachers and students. The impact to self-image would not be as hard if peers understood why there are changes to appearance.*

- *Everyone at school needs to realize that not all children react the same way to being cancer patients. Some do not want to be identified as a cancer patient. Others are more comfortable with that attention and are willing to play a role, so to speak, of the patient who educates people, who supports other kids with cancer, who participates in organized events like Relay For Life. If the schools want to do something for, or with, or in honor of the child, they should first ask the parents, and then the child, for their opinion. They should not assume, for example, that every child with cancer wants 10 classmates to show up at the hospital or the front door with cards and flowers. Some do; some don't. Both should be respected.*

- *Being offered a choice of home tutors is nice. Danny was allowed to choose his tutor, when more than one teacher offered to tutor. These kids need to maintain control of their life to the greatest extent possible and appropriate, and having some level of control about the people who have access to them is very important to many of them.*

- *Incorporate the child's disease, health and circumstances, where possible, and to the extent appropriate, into the classroom. This can be done, for example, in science. One of the best things that Danny's fourth grade teacher did was to pass out a human body drawing and have kids learn about blood disorders/cancer by talking about Danny. They even drew a picture of a "normal spleen" versus Danny's spleen (which was 4 to 5 times normal size and removed). The kids learned that "Danny's spleen was the size of a football," and that earned him some good storytelling currency at an age that mattered. Only do this after checking with the child and his parents.*

- *If possible, supply the child with a laptop and online communication for getting and sending assignments. More importantly, encourage teachers and students to e-mail the child at home or in the hospital on a fairly regular basis, so he or she can continue to feel connected. This communication should, more often than not, avoid asking too many questions. What child doesn't get tired of being asked, "How are you?" Most importantly, pass on the latest "news" about what is happening at school, in the classroom and among the peer group.*

✦ ✦ ✦

I found that communications between the school and us at home was lacking. Even though I had filled out all the "medical info" forms, sent notes to teachers and school nurse as well as spoke with teachers directly, there were too many times when incidents occurred that I wasn't notified about directly. I know many within the school are overworked but it was so hard for me to understand why they couldn't communicate things to me after all the notification I'd given them. Examples are: injuries on the playground, chicken pox/strep throat outbreaks, etc.

✦ ✦ ✦

My daughter's preschool was very concerned and organized about the chicken pox reporting. They noted on each child's folder whether he or she had already contracted chicken pox. They told each parent individually about the dangers to Katy, and then frequently reminded everyone in the monthly newsletters. The parents were absolutely great, and we always had time to keep her out of school until there were no new cases. With the help of these parents, teachers, our neighbors, and friends, Katy dodged exposure for almost three years. She caught chicken pox seven months after treatment ended and had a perfectly normal case.

✦ ✦ ✦

What Daniel's teachers did, but not enough in my opinion, was treat him special and make sure the class did too. They made a big card when he got out of hospital, but didn't deliver it to him until he had been home for about four weeks. They didn't encourage the kids to keep in touch with him. We had a nurse go in at the beginning but that didn't make a huge difference after a month or two. We were brand new to the school at that point so I didn't even know many of the kids' last names nor their phone numbers.

Kids were really mean to Daniel, calling him 'baldie,' etc. The school took a zero tolerance policy towards it and came down really hard on the culprits, but I think they could have done some preventive work such as inundating the kids with kindness lessons. Daniel didn't feel like all the other kids until this year (three years after diagnosis and one year off treatment) and I suspect it could have been different. One thing the school did do, which I am grateful for and could not have tolerated otherwise, is to follow our lead on everything—homework, class placement, desk placement, etc.

✦ ✦ ✦

My 14-year-old daughter has the typical profile of a child whose brain was irradiated at a young age to treat leukemia. She retained most of her high verbal abilities and she looks normal. She has developed her long-term memory to compensate for her slow processing abilities. So, she seems, on the surface, to be quite capable. But, she has a 30-point spread between her verbal and nonverbal abilities. Practically speaking, this means that she cannot process novel information at all. So, if she is in a new situation, she often feels paralyzed, because she doesn't know what to do. Some of her middle school teachers don't understand and this scares me to death.

They went on a field trip this year to a neighboring city to see a dance performance. My daughter knows that she has to stay with an adult at all times. The chaperones told the kids that they could explore some and meet at a certain place in an hour. My daughter (thank goodness) stuck with one of the chaperones, even though this embarrassed her. Well, when the buses left, several kids were inadvertently left behind. They called the school, and someone went back to pick them up. I asked my daughter what she would have done if she had been left behind, and she said, "Walk home." And she didn't have a clue where she was. She also does not generalize well—meaning after we talk about this over and over, if a similar but not identical situation arises, she can't apply what she learned from the prior situation. She now carries a cell phone when she is off campus, but this hidden disability makes her so very vulnerable.

✦ ✦ ✦

At the beginning of the year, Brian's teacher, who was an RN prior to teaching grade school, sent out a paper notifying the parents of the other children that there was a child with a compromised immune system in class. She required that they sign a paper acknowledging the rules: no sick children allowed in school and permission to teach personal hygiene. If the parent's refused to sign, their child was moved to another classroom. The teacher wanted Brian to be safe, especially during flu season. She had a lesson in the class for all the kids to learn how to wash their hands. She also taught the importance of covering your mouth when you cough and washing your hands after you blow your nose. She had some neat little pictures of germs and taught the class in a way that the kids were careful but not paranoid about germs. She was wonderful!

✦ ✦ ✦

In my 12 years doing our school re-entry program there have been a couple of things teachers have done that are very helpful.

- *At all levels when a homework packet is prepared for the child still home after a diagnosis of cancer, the teacher puts a star, or some other mark, on the worksheets that MUST be done to meet the class requirements. Then the student can do those assignments first and only do the other ones if he or she feels up to it. This allows the students to do everything the class is doing or only the bare essentials—whatever feels best to the student.*

- *I always request that teachers be sure to let substitute teachers know about the child with cancer in the class. There have been some unpleasant incidents regarding wearing a hat or scarf in class, needing to have extra bathroom privileges, etc.*

- *At the middle school and high school level it helps for the team of teachers to know to let the student with cancer out of class a few minutes before the bell rings to avoid the hall crush of students and allow extra time to get to the locker or just to get to the next class. Also, often a teacher will find a "buddy" to go along with the student and help carry books (of course only if the student agrees that he or she needs and wants this).*

✦ ✦ ✦

Molly began her new school (7th grade) in January. In February, they scheduled a 3-day history trip to Boston and Salem. Her blood counts were low, so she was unable to do chemo, but the upside was the hospital said she could go on the trip. My husband was adamantly against her going while in treatment; I was unsure. The hospital said it was most important to live as normal a life as possible and that having things to look forward to was as much a part of therapy as chemo.

We were still not sure, so the hospital recommended that one of us go but not be an official chaperone. I called the school principal and she thought that was a terrific idea. She said everyone was hoping we'd let Molly go and they'd stay in close contact. She gave us the name of the hotel they were staying at and we booked a room on another floor. Each evening Molly stopped by to fill us in on her day and each morning she stopped by before breakfast. For an evening outing (bowling) her two cousins (28 and 34) went as chaperones—too cool—so that again it wasn't us hovering over her.

It was a 3-day trip and she made it through two exhausting days before she said she couldn't do anymore. So the third morning we had breakfast with the group and just headed home. It was PERFECT...she felt a real sense of belonging and independence and we felt good about being nearby! And we felt a real sense that the school was totally on her side.

✝ ✝ ✝

I think it's really hard for our teens to find kids they can really identify with or who can identify with them, because their life/experience is pretty unique. My son struggles with this, too—he has friends, but not really the soul mate type connections that mean a lot at this age. That, mixed in with not really having the energy to keep up with all the extras and some varying levels of depression from feeling crummy for so long, added to normal teen/high school issues is overwhelming at times.

The efforts made by certain very special and rare teachers have really helped him. One teacher especially this year has been so human—in the first place, he acknowledges that cancer exists in Justin's life. The summer after Justin's diagnosis, one teacher called and asked if he would like to meet her niece who had had cancer. This girl was hope in person: a beautiful, vibrant, healthy-looking college student, who told him all about her experience (and encouraged him to use it to his advantage whenever possible, like when you wanted tickets to a certain concert.) The math teacher also gave the students class time to write him get well cards and then she mailed them to him; he treasured those cards because they were personal and came from the kids. It's the personal stuff like this that has kept him going.

What has not been good for him is avoidance of the subject of cancer. Teachers need to know that they should not be afraid to call home or bring up the subject of the illness once in a while—silence and isolation are painful. It is not unprofessional for them to show personal interest or concern. Our cancer kids don't want pity or special allowances; they just need some sort of acknowledgement about their experiences and struggles.

✦ ✦ ✦

Recently my son needed to do a write-up as if he were his teacher making comments on his report card. Here are his comments:

> *Dear Andrew: I think you are doing well in a lot of topics such as science, math, social studies and reading. One thing that you need to work on is slowing down and being more organized. If you just slowed down with your handwriting, it would be neat, and if you were more organized, then you would always know where everything is and never be searching for things and staying in for part of recess. Overall I think you are excelling in fourth grade. Keep up the good work (picture of a smiling face)."*

My son understands his deficits, and as you can see strives each day to work on them. Organization is a huge issue as are processing, multi-tasking and handwriting. What I see more prominently, however, in his self-evaluation, is determination and a great attitude. Chemo and radiation did not wreak havoc on these attributes and could not dilute them.

While it pains me to think of his struggles in school, I will take his winning attitude over a perfectly neat desk and straight As any day. I just wish I could sneak into his classroom and put everything in order for him. Not because he is my boy, but he is a great kid, and he never complains, just digs deeper. Man, it makes me want to give him the moon and the stars.

Yes, our survivors pay a big price, but each step of their difficult journey is paved with true grit as well as greatness.

✦ ✦ ✦

I think that oftentimes the school is caught in between the understandably anxious parents who are worried about their neutropenic, physically and psychologically vulnerable children, and the oncologists, who are saying that the return to school is very important in the child's long-term outcome. The teacher can help by approaching the family often about what they need and want. Remember that what the parents said in January may have changed by April, and expect these changes. Keep the lines of communication wide open—these families are feeling lonely and isolated and unable to communicate well. It may be hard to do, and you may be rebuffed at times, but call often.

It is important to integrate the cancer child into the classroom and the peer group as much as is possible. Be imaginative about this integration; you will be creating irreplaceable memories not only for the cancer child, but for their classmates, who are struggling with worry and anxiety about their classmate.

My son's school read 'Sadako and the Thousand Paper Cranes,' a story about a girl who contracted leukemia after Hiroshima. She began folding cranes in the hope that she would get 1,000 of them done and be granted her wish. She died 380 cranes short of her goal, but thereafter, cranes have been a sign of peace and hope. The teacher allowed the kids to talk about their fears and concerns, including those related to death, then the students folded 1,000 paper cranes for Ethan. They used paper with favorite colors, poems, music, stories, or just handwritten wishes for him. We took them home and hung them on strings on the ceiling over his bed. They are remarkably beautiful and still stand as a symbol of how much his classmates cared about him while he was in treatment.

The school needs to have a zero tolerance for teasing. Be hypervigilant about this. Encourage incorporating the child with cancer in games— change the game to make it possible. Realize that cancer treatment is time limited, but the effects linger long after the child has hair again. The cancer child and their families are living a "new normal" and the long-term effects of chemotherapy and radiation will be evolving over the 5 to 10 years following the child's treatment. The school can be proactive and part of the solution, or they can be obstructive and part of the continuing heartbreak of childhood cancer. We have so many very positive experiences that have happened and continue to happen through school, and I wish that for every child who struggles with cancer.

Chapter 8

Cognitive Late Effects

Raymond K. Mulhern, PhD
Shawna L. Palmer, PhD

Cognitive late effects, defined by problems with thinking, learning, and remembering, have become an important area of concern, especially for children treated for the two most frequent types of childhood cancer: acute lymphoblastic leukemia (ALL) and brain tumors. Many children treated for cancer may have temporary problems with their academic achievement during and following their treatment because of school absences. However, children who have chronic problems with their academic achievement may be experiencing cognitive late effects from their cancer and its treatment. Formal cognitive testing will usually be needed to make a clear diagnosis. Although estimates vary according to the child's diagnosis and age, aggressiveness of therapy, and length of follow-up, cognitive problems among children treated for ALL and brain tumors are much higher than among healthy children. These cognitive late effects have been associated with brain damage caused by cancer and its treatment, most commonly, radiation therapy and some types of chemotherapy.

Sources of Cognitive Late Effects

Acute lymphoblastic leukemia (ALL)

ALL accounts for one-fourth of all childhood cancers and 78% of all cases of childhood leukemia. In the United States, approximately 3000 children are diagnosed with ALL each year, although the causes of the disease are unknown. In addition to the chemotherapy needed to eliminate leukemia cells in the blood and bone marrow, special therapy is necessary to destroy leukemia cells present in the brain and spine. Traditionally, this therapy has included cranial radiation therapy (CRT) and chemotherapy delivered into the spinal canal, usually methotrexate (MTX) or MTX combined with other drugs. However, because of the known risks for cognitive

Dr. Mulhern is a pediatric psychologist and chief of behavioral medicine at St. Jude Children's Research Hospital in Memphis, TN.

problems resulting from CRT, treatment is now usually restricted to chemotherapy.

An overwhelming majority of research studies have found significant associations between CRT and cognitive late effects, with the strongest evidence coming from studies which repeatedly evaluate the cognitive abilities of survivors over time and then compare the results to those from healthy children or children treated for cancer with different approaches. Most often in these studies, cognitive problems are revealed by testing the child's intelligence, resulting in an intelligence quotient (IQ), combined with other tests of academic achievement and cognitive abilities.

For children who do experience cognitive problems, it is not unusual for the onset of the problems to be quite subtle but progressive so that it may not be until 2 to 4 years following completion of therapy before the difficulties become obvious. Some research studies show that lower dose CRT may be less harmful that higher dose CRT, especially among very young children who appear to be more sensitive to CRT effects on cognitive abilities. The term "Gr or Gray" is used to measure the amount of irradiation. Lower doses of CRT would include a range less than 18 Gr.

In treatment approaches that reduce or eliminate CRT, often the chemotherapy must be more intensive to be effective. Some types of chemotherapy can cause cognitive problems as well. Methotrexate (MTX) is most often identified as a cause, although the seriousness of the problems can be quite variable, depending upon the timing, dose, sequence of drugs, and supportive care. Unfortunately, since many of the chemotherapy alternatives to CRT are new and because cognitive late effects take years to appear, there is insufficient scientific information to be able to predict which of these alternatives are more or less harmful to the child. Other types of chemotherapy, such as corticosteroids (e.g. prednisone), and especially dexamethasone, may also increase the risk for cognitive late effects but these effects are not as well documented.

Brain tumors

Brain tumors in children are considerably more complex than ALL because there are many different biological types which can occur in any of many different structures of the brain. Like ALL, the causes of most childhood brain tumors are unknown.

Brain tumors are the second most frequent type of cancer diagnosed in childhood, with

Dr. Palmer is a psychologist and neuroscientist in behavioral medicine at St. Jude Children's Research Hospital in Memphis, TN.

treatment typically including surgery, CRT and chemotherapy. CRT doses and other treatments to the brain are typically much stronger than those used in the treatment for ALL. Because of this, serious cognitive late effects are more common among children treated for brain tumors. Other problems, such as hormone deficiencies, growth retardation, secondary cancers, as well as hearing loss from treatment with cisplatin chemotherapy, are also recognized in the brain tumor literature as late effects of treatment. Some of these, such as uncorrected hormone deficiencies, can intensify cognitive problems. However, radiation therapists are increasingly using computerized techniques where individual CRT beams are altered to conform to the shape of the tumor, sparing a greater amount of the normal surrounding brain. It is the hope that such techniques will result in fewer late effects.

In the treatment of childhood brain tumors, CRT has consistently been linked to cognitive problems. Unfortunately, 40 to 100% of long-term brain tumor survivors have some form of cognitive late effects, with impaired IQ found in nearly 90% of patients previously treated for medulloblastoma, a common brain tumor of childhood. When compared to brain tumor patients who do not receive CRT, those patients who receive CRT consistently score lower on IQ testing. The effects of CRT may cause a continuing pattern of IQ and academic decline over time. These declines in IQ over time appear more severe for those who receive greater doses of CRT.

Other factors that may cause cognitive problems in brain tumor survivors include seizures and hydrocephalus. Seizures have not been adequately studied in children with brain tumors. Seizures are often successfully treated with anticonvulsant medications. However, these medications may themselves be linked to behavioral and learning problems. Blockage of the flow of cerebrospinal fluid can cause increased pressure in the brain and enlargement of the ventricles, termed hydrocephalus. Hydrocephalus must be treated with a surgical procedure to relieve the pressure ("shunting") because chronic pressure can cause multiple problems with cognitive development and loss of vision.

Symptoms of Cognitive Late Effects

Cognitive late effects as traditionally measured by tests of academic achievement and IQ are well documented in the research literature. These problems can eventually produce limitations in age-appropriate activities of daily living such as school performance, employment, independent living, and quality of life among children surviving cancer. The reduction of cognitive late effects is now an important endpoint in evaluating the success of childhood cancer treatments where treatment to the brain is required.

Initially, some physicians attributed learning problems in school to the nonspecific effects of chronic illness, school absenteeism, or adjustment problems. However, many studies have objectively shown that cognitive problems are real. A recent study has strongly demonstrated that declining IQ, the single most commonly occurring symptom among affected children, is not due to a loss of previously acquired information. Instead, the IQ loss was because former patients acquired new information at a rate that was only 30% of the rate of their healthy age peers. This finding emphasizes the importance of understanding the barriers to new learning, which result in cognitive late effects.

Recently, research studies have tried to uncover the changes in basic or "core" cognitive processes that cause declines in IQ and achievement. Many of these core symptoms are termed "executive functions" by psychologists. Executive functions include the ability to pay attention to the task at hand despite distractions, to shift attention when needed, and to plan and organize behavior. Executive functions are thought to be closely related to the healthy development of the frontal and pre-frontal areas of the brain. Other core cognitive processes may be more widely distributed in the brain. These include mental processing speed, efficient learning and retrieval of new information, and using previously learned information to help with new learning. The most recent research studies of cognitive late effects emphasize these core processes because they provide more information about the basis for cognitive late effects and how they may be treated.

Very bright children can sometimes overcome the core symptoms and continue to perform normally, at least for a while. Eventually, however, most children with these core symptoms will have increasing difficulty in school. For example, some of the first behaviors that may be noticed include completing in-class assignments and homework at a slower pace. Although children may look like they are paying attention in the classroom, they may not be mentally keeping up with the pace of instruction. Over time, the child may fall farther and farther behind.

Some children who are aware of these developing problems may also develop problems with their self-esteem and social interactions with their classmates. Recent research suggests some children surviving cancer with late cognitive problems may also have difficulty with identifying emotions as expressed by facial expressions. However, the connection of this problem with social difficulties is not yet established.

Brain Changes that Cause Cognitive Late Effects

Brain imaging has shown changes following both chemotherapy and CRT. Early studies with computed tomography (CT) scans showed several abnormalities such as brain shrinkage, blood vessel damage, damage to the white matter (which will be discussed in more detail later), and enlarged ventricles. The root causes for these abnormalities and how they relate to cognitive problems are only now being understood. It is generally accepted that damage to the small blood vessels of the brain from CRT and chemotherapy begins the chain of events. These changes have a negative effect on white matter of the brain which is composed of glial cells. Glial cells serve a supportive role by providing structure and insulation for brain nerve cells ("neurons") which dramatically improves the efficiency of brain functioning. The process of glial cells growing and wrapping around the neurons of the brain is called myelination, and normally continues from birth into the third decade of life. Magnetic resonance imaging (MRI) scans of the brain are very sensitive to white matter changes. New technologies have been developed that can actually measure changes in white matter development.

Some very recent research studies suggest that CRT may both slow the normal development of white matter and injure existing white matter. White matter injury seen on MRI is termed "leukoencephalopathy." Currently it is thought that these two effects could be responsible for at least some of the cognitive late effects seen in childhood cancer survivors. Chemotherapy, especially high dose MTX, and CRT are associated with white matter injury.

Other Factors That Affect Cognitive Late Effects

Gender

When gender has been reported to have significant effects on cognitive late effects, females are at greater risk. For example, one study compared children surviving ALL who had been treated with intrathecal MTX, standard dose MTX or high dose MTX with or without CRT. Females receiving high dose MTX with CRT were more impaired than males receiving the same combination therapy and more impaired than other females receiving conventional MTX with CRT. The reasons for these gender differences are not yet clear but some speculate that it could be related to hormonal influences.

Age at treatment

A younger age at treatment is often found to be a critical risk factor for cognitive late effects. For example, it is well-known that children who are younger when treated for medulloblastoma experience more cognitive late effects than those who are older, even though both groups of children receive that same type of treatment. One recent study has shown that the rate of learning of new information is dramatically reduced compared to older children even years after treatment has been completed.

It has been suggested that brain development can explain why younger children are more likely to have cognitive late effects. The immature, developing brain in young children appears to be more fragile. There is some evidence that white matter development in the brain of very young children may be especially likely to be damaged.

What Can Be Done To Avoid or Minimize Cognitive Late Effects?

The best way of avoiding cognitive late effects of cancer therapy would be to prevent childhood cancer which, unfortunately, is not yet possible. The next best way to prevent cognitive problems would be to develop new methods of treatment that are less likely to damage the brain. This has become a high priority for the National Cancer Institute, the Children's Oncology Group, and individual institutions that are developing new treatments. However, in the absence of risk-free treatments, there are some clues as to how cognitive late effects could be minimized.

Many research studies have recognized considerable differences in cognitive performance even among patients who were diagnosed at the same age, are the same gender and who received the same treatment for the same type of cancer. One possible explanation is that the home, school, and community environments of some children allow them to compensate for core deficits and thus improve their performance and achievement in school. For example, among healthy children, ethnicity and parental education can account for a significant proportion of the IQ score. Similarly, among children previously treated for ALL and medulloblastoma, studies have demonstrated that higher socioeconomic status is associated with higher IQ.

One implication of these findings is that the child's environment may be able to modify the intellectual development of children treated for cancer, even among children with similar core deficits. Can children who experience enriched environments following treatment overcome their deficits more easily? One could speculate that the child who had interactions with teachers who were taught about the child's specific area of deficit, and who were skilled in assisting the child to practice these weak areas of function, would be more successful in learning to overcome and compensate for their deficits. In addition, having better informed parents with access to extracurricular resources to supplement their child's education may improve the outcome. This is an important area that requires more scientific study.

Treating Cognitive Late Effects

Although research on the patterns and risks for cognitive late effects among survivors of childhood cancer has been progressing for the past three decades, the development of proven interventions for these problems has not been as rapid. Broadly speaking, interventions can be divided into two approaches: those intended to avoid or reduce the neuropsychological toxicity of therapy directed toward the brain, and those intended to minimize or rehabilitate deficits that cannot be avoided.

Prior to any plans for intervention, a formal plan of cognitive testing should be set forth for each child based upon known or suspected risk for cognitive late effects. This assumes that a qualified psychologist has been identified as a consultant to the institution. The number and timing of the tests should depend upon the risks. For example, a school-aged child with cancer should be evaluated at least every six months during treatment and then yearly for the next three to five years. The increased frequency of surveillance in young children is in part related to the fact that some important skills have yet to emerge, making the absence of deficits early after treatment deceptive. Such assessment plans should not wait until the child is having significant problems, because early assessments often allow for educational interventions that may prevent problems.

If cognitive late effects are unavoidable, one may attempt to minimize the impact by direct intervention with cognitive rehabilitation or medications, and/or through more indirect approaches involving manipulations of the child's environment. Some of these approaches are discussed in other chapters of this book by Drs. Armstrong, Butler, and Copeland. Cognitive rehabilitation is a term used to describe interventions intended to restore lost cognitive functions or to teach the child skills to compensate for cognitive losses that cannot be restored. Although some evidence for efficacy is available from the child closed head injury literature,

Dr. Butler's program is the only one at present in the United States that is attempting to validate a standardized, 20-session program of cognitive rehabilitation for survivors of ALL and brain tumors in a seven institution consortium funded by the National Cancer Institute.

The use of medications, especially the use of stimulants such as methylphenidate (Ritalin), has recently received interest. Impressive gains in activity level and quality of life have been shown in one study of adult glioma patients treated with methylphenidate. Another study of childhood cancer survivors with learning problems compared the effects of methylphenidate to a placebo (sugar pill) when the children were not told if it was the medication or placebo. Children who took the real medication showed significant improvement on behavioral testing in the laboratory of some of the core symptoms of cognitive late effects mentioned earlier. Whether these improvements will extend to learning in school is currently under investigation.

Finally, one should not forget the potential positive impact of improved communication and education of the child's parents and teachers. Routine communication between the cancer treatment center and the child's school should be the standard of care, especially in cases in which subtle neurological (e.g., hearing loss in the speech frequencies, visual field cuts) or cognitive deficits (e.g., problems with attention, memory, or processing speed) can obviously impair the child's ability to function in a normal classroom environment. Because all of the problems listed above are unobservable to teachers, there may be a tendency to misinterpret the child's behavior in the absence of knowledge of the deficits. Children are often labeled as having attitude problems, or as being daydreamers or unmotivated to learn when, in fact, the child had real disabilities that were unknown to the teacher. Although parents can have an important role in facilitating communication between the cancer center and the school, a telephone call or visit from a cancer center teacher or social worker can have a profound impact on the adaptation of the classroom environment to meet the child's needs.

Conclusions

This chapter has attempted to highlight the most important issues relevant to cognitive late effects in childhood cancer, including the types and causes of symptoms of these late effects in children with ALL and brain tumors, and ways in which these symptoms may be reduced or treated. Obviously, more research in this area is needed, especially with regard to the development of effective interventions to treat cognitive late effects. On a practical level, parents of children at risk for cognitive late effects should understand that neuropsychological evaluation of their children should be included as a standard of care at their child's cancer center. Sometimes, referrals to psychologists for testing is made more difficult because such testing may not be covered by insurance. Assistance from the child's treating physician to declare the testing medically necessary may be required in these circumstances. Ultimately, the combination of these efforts are directed at improving the quality of life of children treated for cancer and returning them, as closely as possible, to the developmental trajectory that they had before cancer.

Acknowledgements

Preparation of this manuscript was supported in part by the American Lebanese Syrian Associated Charities and grants CA 21765 and CA 20180 from the National Cancer Institute.

Key Points

- Cognitive late effects are defined by problems with thinking, learning and remembering.

- Cognitive problems are more common in survivors of childhood cancer, especially ALL and brain tumors, than among healthy children.

- Cognitive late effects are a result of the effects of cancer and cancer treatment on the brain.

- Very young children and those receiving aggressive treatment to the brain, especially with CRT, are more likely to have cognitive late effects.

- The best approach to cognitive late effects is the development of less harmful cancer therapy.

- Treatment of cognitive late effects is only beginning to be developed; more research is needed in this area.

Parent Perspectives

My daughter underwent a bone marrow transplant using an unrelated donor in 1999. She is now four years post BMT, and still lagging behind her peers both academically and socially. Aside from her medical late effects, she has difficulty with memory, spatial concepts, organization and a mild expressive speech delay. Our school system has struggled to understand her issues and provide support services, although it's not out of lack of concern for her, just a lack of experience in educating childhood cancer survivors. We've really had to be proactive in advocating for her, requesting periodic reviews of her IEP and making appropriate accommodations.

✦ ✦ ✦

"It is more like pockets of learning disabilities than a global decrease in intelligence, although the overall IQ can go down over the next several years." I remember the doctor and social worker saying this when trying to console me after I consented to whole brain radiation to treat my 5 year old's cancerous brain tumor. This type of radiation commonly causes kids to have problems with processing speed, working memory, sequencing, and visual perception. Kids tend not to lose what they already have learned but have trouble getting new stuff in. For my girl who could not read, write, or do time or money this meant academics would likely be very hard. In addition, she had significant tumor-induced hydrocephalus, which can produce its own set of learning disabilities.

Reading has been a struggle. Some of her problems appear similar to dyslexia as she often makes many of her letters backwards and reads words backwards. She spelled log G,O,L and in fact, frequently writes from right to left. She can recognize the word elephant but has trouble with the flashcard ON and A. She will look at a word such as CAR and say DOG. We have been using the Wilson method and this seems to help if she takes her time. Sequencing numbers has not been easy either. She can figure out 5+1=6 but this is by counting from one to five and then one more to make six. She cannot start at five and immediately know the next number is 6. One of the biggest challenges at home and in the classroom is her processing speed. Even when she knows exactly what to do, it takes her three to four times as long as her peers to actually do the work. I worry about her participation in class as other kids may have already answered the question before she can get her hand up in the air.

This sounds so overwhelming and depressing, however, she does has strengths. She has a wonderfully inquisitive mind, excellent understanding and recall of verbally presented material, a sense of humor and the ability to follow multi-part directions. She is persistent, independent, and social. She does best with creative, flexible experiences in education combined with some repetition drills (that work best if made into games). With support and encouragement she will succeed.

✦ ✦ ✦

I work hard to prepare teachers for my daughter—a survivor of leukemia who had cranial radiation at age 4. She is verbally very bright, but has many functional disabilities. For instance, she is literal. Everything is black and white. She cannot shift activities easily, is slow to do her work (completes about a fourth of what other students do in the same time frame) and cannot function in novel situations. She just can't think of options and choose one. So, life has to be very predictable and structured, and the teachers need to be understanding and help her stay on task.

One day, she handed in her math homework that included a table with information. She didn't know it was called "table"—that's something with four legs that you eat from. The teacher told her she had to stay in from recess to draw a new "table" on "loose leaf" (which I call "lined paper"). She was totally baffled. Loose leaf is something floating in the air. How can you put a table on it? And which table since the room was full of tables? So, she sat in lunch detention with the behavior problem kids, and she just sat there, the whole time. The teacher thought it was defiance; I call it confusion and terror. So, they pulled her out in the hall and started lecturing her about defiance (which she doesn't understand either since it is a non-concrete concept), and she broke down in sobs. They called the counselor, who called me and told me my daughter had "emotional problems." They just don't get it.

✦ ✦ ✦

My daughter had a BMT when she was two years old. It included total body radiation, which has caused some cognitive problems. One day during a conversation with my 8-year-old, I mentioned that someone's baby was now a year old. She gave me a curious look and asked, "How old is it?" I repeated, "It's a year old." "A year old? How old is that?" she asked again. I again repeated "a year old." She became very frustrated and said, "I don't know what that is!" I was flustered, I couldn't figure out what she was having trouble with, I mean what's so hard about "the baby is a year old"? Because I was aware she had difficulties in this area, something told me to break it down. So I stated that the baby was born on October 8 and that on November 8 the baby was one month old, then the months pass until October 8 comes again and the baby is one year old. She brightened up and said, "OH, the baby is ONE year old." Changing the words "a year old" to "one year old" made all the difference. The point is, she's my child and I love her so of course I'm willing to take the time to analyze the situation and work it through. I wonder how often she hits these roadblocks in school and doesn't understand what is being said?

✦ ✦ ✦

Jon finished treatment for high risk ALL in 1999 when he was 13. He received triple intrathecals during treatment but no radiation. He is now almost 16 and we are working on getting his driver's license. This is my worry: Jon shows lapses of attention. For instance when you are speaking to him he looks at you and then apparently "wakes up" and asks you to repeat what was just said or happening. That's not a big deal—what is a big deal however is driving with lapses of attention. A few days ago he made a left turn in front of an oncoming car (he says he didn't see it). He also has difficulty with organizational skills, memory, and fatigue.

✦ ✦ ✦

Many of our irradiated kids have trouble learning to read. It helps to know if it is reading aloud that is the problem or reading comprehension. Sometimes it's just visual/spatial difficulties—they can't go from the end of one line on the right side of the page to the beginning of the next line down on the left side of the page. Using a ruler under the lines and then moving it down one line can solve that problem.

Reading aloud is sometimes a challenge for survivors because their ability to juggle several things at once has sometimes been damaged. When you read aloud, you have to use your eyes, brain, hands, and mouth at the same time. For kids with executive functions problems, they just can't keep all that meshed. But, many kids can read silently and understand.

We had some educational testing done when my daughter was in 2nd grade. Her reading aloud was kindergarten level, but her comprehension was 4th grade. I told her we should celebrate the good news (and it was good news, because a lot of irradiated kids have comprehension problems). She said "Why? It shows I can't read out loud and that's what we need to do in class." I said that the life skill was understanding what the words meant, not being able to read them aloud. And she understood just fine! I said that we could make a new rule with the school (I meant the IEP here) that she would never have to read aloud again. She got a big smile and we went out to lunch to celebrate.

✦✦✦

My son's short-term memory is so terrible that it's scaring me. Just last night after getting him into bed and giving him a kiss and hug he called me back into the room certain I had forgotten to kiss and hug him. He was serious and only 30 seconds had passed! The bell at school rang at the end of the day today and he "forgot" that the bell had rung and kept working in the computer lab until a teacher found him 15 minutes after the bell. I could go on and on.

✦✦✦

Our daughter (age 11) has some long-term effects from her treatment for stage IV neuroblastoma nine years ago. Her treatment included high-dose chemotherapy, radiation to the brain, and bone marrow transplantation. Her learning ability (in particular, comprehension and short-term memory) has been affected. The special ed department at the school told us she was entitled to extra help because of her "other health-impaired" status. This is a label given to children who have undergone specialized treatments that have been proven to result in learning problems. She is in a normal classroom setting, but a special education teacher comes into the room several times daily to give extra help to the kids who need it. Examples of services are: helping with problem solving (especially math), giving her extra time to do work, as well as allowing her to repeat tests that she didn't perform well on. We have found this to be a great help in her education. She is now making As and Bs as well as exhibiting a more positive attitude toward school in general.

✦✦✦

My daughter received 1800 rads of cranial radiation and intrathecal methotrexate when she was 17 months old. She is now 9 years old and in third grade. She has many learning challenges, including slower processing speed, attentional difficulties, as well as difficulty with short-term memory and multi-step processing. She benefits from additional help in school. In the past she has needed additional drilling in phonics, math fact repetition, and refocusing on multi-step directions as well as additional time to complete testing. It is challenging for her to maintain her focus throughout the day.

After much observation, I am convinced that these kids have a quirky organizational system. My husband and I both realize that school is a struggle for her. We have sought help through the special education system, and our daughter is now classified as traumatically brain injured. Her self-esteem is high, she is a very bright, verbal child with a lot of strengths. We are working diligently with all of her teachers and all of the resources available to ensure that she gets the best education possible.

✦✦✦

My son was on a high-dose methotrexate protocol from age 3 to 6. He entered preschool while on therapy, and we enrolled him in a private kindergarten because of the small class size. He transitioned to public school in second grade with no problems. He is now 18, an A student who excels in math. He has had no after-effects from his years of treatment.

✦✦✦

My daughter, who had a bone marrow transplant, continues to struggle with spelling. She does extremely well in her spelling book, and practices her spelling words by writing them each five times every night before her test on Friday. On Friday morning, she can (and does) orally spell all of her spelling words correctly. However, when she gets to school and sits down at her desk at 8:15 to take the test, she inevitably fails. We have struggled with this all year, and have asked her what the problem is. She reports that the spelling words "just fall out of her head" and try as she might, she cannot remember how to spell them, even though by most standards, she has prepared as best she can. She's very frustrated by this, and so is her teacher. (I have mixed feelings—my theory is that spell check was invented for just this reason!)

✦✦✦

Mary Margaret (age 10) was diagnosed at 4 years of age with neurofibromatosis, and later on with a related optic glioma. Mary Margaret has won the citizenship award at school every year, including kindergarten. I've been especially impressed with her this year. There's a boy in her class who is being mainstreamed after being in an alternative class for several years. He was a challenge for the teachers and for the other students, because of his temper, outbursts, and repetitive behavior. None of the kids were friends with him and would tease him terribly; they'd throw sand on him on the playground, stuff like that. Mary Margaret would make them stop, saying "Stop picking on him. How would you feel if you were him and people were doing this to you?" She told me once that this boy was sitting by himself at lunch, because no one would sit with him, and she went and sat with him, even though her girlfriends were saving her a seat. She could miss 100 math awards and I'd be more proud to hear stories like that and see her get recognized for THAT kind of behavior. Being nice is way more important than being good at math, that's our family motto.

✝ ✝ ✝

Pre-diagnosis, at 12 ½ years old, our daughter was the highest achiever in her grade. Within a week after surgery to remove a golf ball sized tumor from her cerebellum, she advised me that her mind did not work as quickly as it had before. She then received cranio-spinal radiation: 5,500 Gy to the tumor bed and about 2,350 Gy to the rest of the brain and spine.

She is not able to be in large groups of people as she seems to get brain overload. That is, she cannot process all that is going on around her and seems unable to separate one conversation from the babble of the group. She gets a headache, like a migraine, when this occurs. She can recover and be fine if she can get a "time out" and go to a quiet room to decompress for an hour or so. Over time we have seen her becoming more and more isolated from her peers, as she has tremendous difficulty communicating. She simply cannot keep up with a normal conversation, it goes too fast for her to process the information and contribute. When she does have something to say she has trouble finding words and appears to lose the train of thought before she can formulate the sentence completely. Many discussions with her are short, incomplete phrases and require 100% attention to try and fathom what she is trying to get across. Sometimes she will make a comment on a topic well after the conversation has moved onto another topic, which is rather difficult amongst peers.

She even asked why she should even bother studying because, even if she knows the material when she studies, she does not know it for a test. The information is simply gone. We obtained extra time for her on tests and permission for some to use open book tests. We had tests written that had less repetition on the questions so she could complete in less time. To complete a normal 1 hour test was taking her 2 to 4 hours and she may still not be completing the questions, as she just became exhausted and had to stop.

She has a short-term memory lapse, which means that she can study and know all the material for a question now and be asked the same question in a minute and have no idea about the topic or remember that that was what she covered a minute prior.

This is also true with directions.

"Please do a certain task."

"OK will do."

"Did you do it?"

"Do what?"

While this could also be a typical conversation with quite a few teens who are not troubled by a brain tumor, it really appears that she simply forgets, and is not being willful.

✦✦✦

Because of my daughter's short-term memory loss, she was worried about learning two combination locks when starting middle school. Her special education teacher had her take her locks home the week before school so she wouldn't have that worry on the first day. She had plenty of time to practice with them and was more relaxed about it. She also walks through her whole schedule at every new school before school begins. (Her biggest worries center around not being late to class.) Her anxiety shows up the strongest during any type of change, and in our town they go to a new school every two years until high school. We will do the same thing this year as she starts high school.

✦✦✦

In the early 1970s, at age 3, I had 2400 rads of cranial radiation. I always had to struggle and work harder in school than anyone else to get good grades. When I took the LSATs to get into law school, I was very disappointed in my performance. I went back to the hospital where I was treated and was stunned to discover that my learning difficulties were caused by my treatment for leukemia. I had my first educational assessment and it showed strong aptitudes in vocabulary, comprehension, and verbal reasoning. But I had poor short-term sequential memory and processing speeds. I hired an educational consultant, worked on my areas of weakness, and applied to take the LSATs under untimed conditions. My scores were much improved, and I will graduate from law school this year.

Chapter 9

Physical Effects of Treatment

Debra L. Friedman, MD

Cancer and its treatment may cause numerous physical consequences that affect children's education. Some of these effects diminish after treatment ends; others continue or manifest themselves later. Parents and educators need to be aware of these potential impacts and develop strategies to minimize their effects. Parents can help the child cope with these limitations, but within the school environment it becomes the job of the educators to understand how to help the child achieve and to make his learning experience as rich and normal as possible.

For many survivors of childhood cancer, the physical effects are mild. Others are profoundly affected and have permanent physical disabilities. Some of these disabilities are easy to spot—a lost limb, for example. Not all physical disabilities are so obvious, however, and many of the hidden ones are also debilitating.

Numerous variables can affect the risk of developing long-term problems. The risk of physical effects closely relate to the treatment approach and doses used. The child's age at diagnosis is a big predictor of physical complications. Because children are still growing and developing, their bodies are much more susceptible to certain kinds of damage than adults.

Intensity of treatment and length of treatment can also adversely affect school performance, as can cognitive, social or psychological problems, all of which are covered in other chapters in this book.

In this chapter, we will discuss physical effects that are likely to arise from treatment of the most common childhood cancers. We will describe the range of effects by physical system, explain what causes them, and show how these effects may impact learning and a child's ability to function in school.

> Dr. Friedman is an assistant professor of pediatrics at the University of Washington and directs the cancer survivorship program at Children's Hospital in Seattle, WA.

Nervous System Effects

The term "nervous system" includes both the central nervous system (the brain and spinal cord) and the peripheral nervous system (all of the nerves and systems that transmit sensory information between the brain and the rest of the body). The two most common childhood cancers—acute lymphoblastic leukemia and brain tumors—are both associated with permanent damage to the central nervous system. Brain tumor survivors, in particular, often develop a host of physical issues as a result of their disease and its treatment. Other cancers and treatments can also cause physical changes to the nervous system.

Radiation to the brain can cause problems with learning. The higher the dose of radiation, the more areas of brain exposed and younger age at time of treatment all increase risk. Surgery for brain tumors can sometimes also result in learning problems. More subtle learning problems can result from chemotherapy given intrathecally (into the spinal fluid). These neurocognitive effects are discussed in detail in Chapters 2 and 8 in this book.

Hydrocephalus

Hydrocephalus ("water on the brain") is a blockage of the flow of cerebrospinal fluid resulting in increased fluid and increased pressure on the brain. Children with brain tumors may develop hydrocephalus because of a tumor, swelling (edema) of brain tissue, blood clots, or scarring.

Acutely, a hydrocephalic child will require a surgical procedure to relieve the pressure. Some children will continue to require medical intervention to drain excess fluid. A permanent, surgically inserted mechanical device called a shunt may be placed in the brain to drain excess fluid. Several things can go wrong with a shunt. Signs of shunt failure include headache, nausea, vomiting, clumsiness or gait changes, weakness, fatigue, fever, vision problems, irritability, and personality changes. These signs and symptoms may develop at school.

Teachers must be notified that a child has a shunt and should know generally how it works and what can go wrong with it. If a shunt shows signs of failure, the parents should be notified immediately because complete shunt blockages can be life-threatening emergencies. Doctors of children with shunts should inform the school in writing about what activities, including physical education and sports, are safe.

Leukoencephalopathy

High doses of methotrexate combined with radiation therapy can cause problems with the white matter of the brain; this is called leukoencephalopathy. Children with leukoencephalopathy have significant difficulties in school. Some of the problems that can develop are impaired short-term memory, difficulty with organization, inability to follow multi-part directions, and many others. These children need thorough neuropsychological testing to identify strengths and weaknesses and to help develop an educational plan that best addresses the child's needs.

Seizures

Seizures are temporary electrical disturbances in the brain. Generalized seizures affect the whole body and can be frightening to witness. Partial seizures are more subtle, and can go unnoticed or appear to be something else entirely, such as a behavioral outburst. Seizures can result from brain surgery, cranial radiation, or from certain drugs (methotrexate or vincristine). Usually the seizures occur during therapy, and may persist once therapy has been completed.

Sometimes seizures can be controlled by medication. Unfortunately, these anticonvulsant drugs can make a child feel sleepy or confused. In other cases, medication cannot eliminate the seizures. Parents should inform teachers of the kind of seizures their child experiences, how they usually manifest, and if there are any events that are likely to cause them. Most seizures end uneventfully after a minute or so, although after-ward the child may feel tired and disoriented for a while. Teachers should inform parents if they think that the child has had a seizure.

Strokes

Some children have strokes during therapy, and the effects may persist after treatment ends. Some children may have a stroke off therapy if they were treated with high doses of radiation to the brain or with very high doses of methotrexate. Depending on the location and severity of the stroke, these children may suffer permanent physical or mental impairment. The effects on learning depend on the location and severity of the stroke.

Peripheral nerve dysfunction

Millions of individual nerves govern how the body perceives and reacts to stimuli. Some childhood cancer survivors suffer damage to these nerves. If the nerves of the head and neck are involved, potential problems are crossed eyes and other vision problems, hearing loss, vocal cord paralysis, and facial paralysis or tics. Damage to the nerves of the torso and extremities causes coordination and fine motor problems. This can result in clumsiness, problems holding a pen or pencil, and poor handwriting. Sometimes writing is so difficult that children cannot finish tests on time and may need special services such as a computer keyboard and untimed tests. The most common chemotherapy drug that causes this is vincristine, but related drugs like vinblastine and vinorelbine can cause similar problems. Physical and occupational therapy can sometimes help and should be provided.

Children who must struggle to hold and control a pencil are obvious to educators. Others who seem normal to teachers may have coordination problems that interfere with their ability to perform certain tasks (e.g., copy from blackboard, button coats, put books in book bag). They may use so much energy concentrating on the mechanics of the tasks that they cannot pay attention to what they are supposed to be learning. If the teacher notices that a normal-seeming child is constantly missing deadlines or is easily frustrated, he should talk with the child's parents.

Hearing

Hearing loss is a common late effect of survivors of cancers of childhood cancers who received high doses of radiation therapy to the head or received chemotherapy agents called cisplatin or carboplatin. It often starts as a high frequency hearing loss but then can progress into hearing loss that can affect language reception and expression even after treatment is complete. The risk is worse with higher doses of radiotherapy, cisplatin, or carboplatin, or with their combined use. Risk is also higher in children who were younger at the time of treatment. Children at risk should have hearing exams at least annually.

Children with hearing loss are disadvantaged in mainstream classrooms without significant accommodations. Cancer-related hearing loss results from damage to the nerves that perceive and interpret sound; therefore, traditional technologies, such as hearing aids, often do not work. Cochlear implants have helped some children. However, the greatest hope for relief lies in emerging digital technology. Accommodations in school include use of an FM trainer device (mechanism that delivers the teachers words directly to the student's ear), speech and language therapy, sign language, and classroom aides. If a child at risk for hearing loss has normal hearing at the start of the school year, teachers should be alert to performance or behavior changes that might signal a decline in auditory function.

Vision

Several cancers can result in vision problems, either from tumor invasion or from treatment. Survivors of retinoblastoma, a tumor of the eye, can develop a number of complications that can result in decreased vision. They may have had an enucleation, which means the eye with cancer was removed and a prosthetic (false) eye is used. Sometimes if they have had the disease in both eyes, one eye is removed and the other is treated with radiation therapy. Radiation therapy can sometimes also cause poor vision. Survivors who had either enucleation (removal of the eye with cancer) or radiation therapy often have a small eye socket.

Survivors of orbital rhabdomyosarcoma who receive radiation to the eye are at risk for dry eye, cataracts, and small eyes. They can also develop problems with the retina, cornea, and optic nerve that can affect vision.

Children who have had a stem cell or bone marrow transplant and received total body irradiation (TBI), or children who have had cranial radiation for leukemia can also develop cataracts. Less commonly, prednisone or dexamethasone may cause cataracts.

While cataracts are not entirely preventable, those at risk should wear sunglasses with ultraviolet protection when in the sunlight (including recess). Cataracts can make it difficult for students to read from a blackboard due to the poor contrast of the white chalk against the dark board. Placement of the student's desk at the front of the class or close proximity to the board can assist with this reduced visual ability.

Some brain surgeries can cause double vision, crossed eyes, focusing problems, or areas of blindness within the visual field. Sometimes there is nothing wrong with a child's eyes, but he or she is effectively blind because damage to the optic nerve or brain cortex makes it impossible for the brain to interpret the images he or she sees. Children with facial nerve paralysis may not be able to blink, thus putting them at risk for additional eye injury.

Children who cannot see must obtain information in other ways. Successful teachers often use more auditory or experiential teaching techniques. For the children who have impaired vision or tracking abilities, reading, writing, and other precision work may be a nearly impossible struggle. Most of them will require accommodations, such as books with large type or Braille, readers, and voice recognition computer programs.

Heart

Childhood cancer survivors who received anthracyclines (doxorubicin, daunorubicin, idarubicin, epirubicin, mitoxantrone) or radiation therapy to the chest are at risk for long-term cardiac toxicity (heart problems) that can include problems with the way the heart muscle pumps (cardiomyopathy) or the way the heart beats (arrhythmia). However, it is very rare that the effects are so profound that they interfere with education. The risks to the heart are related to the amount of chemotherapy or radiation therapy, how it was given and at what age.

While no particular accommodations may be needed in the classroom, survivors at risk for heart conditions must be identified so the teacher can watch for signs of trouble such as dizziness, chest pain, or weakness. The doctors of these children must specify in writing any physical limitations, including physical education and sports.

Lungs

Some survivors have an increased risk of pneumonia, sinus or bronchial infection, pleurisy (inflammation of the lining of the lung), or pulmonary fibrosis (scarring of the lungs). Lung damage can result from chest radiation, complications from bone marrow transplant, or after receiving chemotherapy agents called busulfan, bleomycin, or nitrosureas such as carmustine (BCNU) and lomustine (CCNU).

Brain tumor survivors may suffer severe sleep apnea, a condition that causes them to stop breathing during sleep, often hundreds of times per night. At best, this leaves them chronically tired. Most of these children must be hooked up to machines during the night, to monitor their oxygen levels and help them to breathe. In the worst cases, the children must have an artificial airway inserted in their trachea (tracheostomy) and breathe with the help of a ventilator. This interferes with their ability to talk.

If lung damage is mild, there may be no significant impact on education beyond frequent absences due to illness or poor performance in sports and other physical activities. More severe damage may mean that the child needs to breathe pure oxygen occasionally or use a nebulizer daily, to administer breathing medication directly to the lungs. Teachers should report any chest pain, coughing or shortness of breath to the parents. Chronic sleep deprivation makes concentration difficult and lowers a child's frustration tolerance. Children with tracheostomies may have to physically cover the hole in their neck to speak or they may have to use one of several technological speaking aids. The teacher will have to educate the class to this situation and ensure that the child's efforts to communicate are not overlooked.

Kidney and Bladder

High-dose radiation and certain chemotherapy drugs (cisplatin, carboplatin, and ifosfamide) may cause kidney damage that generally does not interfere with education. In rare cases, these late effects are so severe as to require dialysis or kidney transplant.

Survivors of kidney cancer ("Wilms tumor") usually have only one kidney. The remaining kidney works normally, but it must be protected from severe injury. High doses of radiation therapy, usually given for sarcomas in the abdomen can occasionally result in problems with urinary function and control.

In most cases, kidney and bladder late effects do not have a significant impact on learning. However, malfunctioning kidneys can cause disturbances in the delicate balance of salts and minerals that the body needs to function. If a child becomes particularly irritable, weak, or complains of cramps or chest pains, he may require medical attention.

Bladder control problems cause social embarrassment at any age. Children with this problem should have a change of clothes available and they need ready access to a private place to handle toileting.

The Intestines

Radiation and certain drugs can cause chronic diarrhea or constipation and can affect bowel control. Children who are on treatment may be significantly underweight and require the use of a feeding tube or they may become very overweight due to treatment with steroid drugs. Rarely, children require radiation treatment that damages their salivary glands. These children must have water with them at all times.

A child who is worried about having a bowel accident cannot concentrate on schoolwork. Students in this situation must be able to take discreet bathroom breaks whenever they need them. They should also have a change of clothes available. Intestinal distress can cause severe abdominal pains, which can sometimes be helped by lying down with a heating pad or by brisk walking. These children may also make uncontrollable digestive noise and care must be taken to minimize any embarrassment and disruption that might result.

The teacher should meet with the parents of a child who requires gastric or nasogastric feeding to learn how the system works and what to watch for. Younger children may require an attendant to manage the feeding system for them.

Despite their overweight appearance, children on high doses of steroids are very hungry much of the time and need frequent healthy snacks. They are already irritable from the steroids and hunger just makes it worse.

Spleen and Immune System

Some cancer treatment can damage the spleen or require its removal. Children without a functional spleen are at increased risk of life-threatening infection. Children who do not have a functional spleen need to get special vaccines and need to see a doctor whenever they have a fever. Some children and teens take daily antibiotics to protect them from infection.

Cancer, chemotherapy and radiation therapy can all weaken the immune system. This is most severe during therapy and it usually gets better with time after therapy ends. However, in the first year off therapy, children's immune systems may still be weakened and they may be more prone to illness. For children who have had a stem cell or bone marrow transplant, the effect is more pronounced. While on treatment, children do not receive vaccinations.

Children with weakened immune systems may miss quite a bit of school. Sometimes they must be kept home to protect them from diseases like chicken pox, which can threaten their lives. Parents should explain the situation and any special requirements to the teacher. It is often helpful to have the parents of the sick child send a letter to all of the other parents asking them to report any possible exposures to infectious disease. Appendix A includes a sample letter to send to the parents of classmates. Teachers can also help protect the child with cancer from infection by teaching good hygiene to all of the students in the classroom.

The Glands

Many organs and glands make up the endocrine system, which ensures that necessary hormones are secreted at the right time and in the proper quantities to keep the body working. Some functions that are governed by this system are growth, aging, food metabolism, regulation of fluid levels, and sexuality. Radiation and some chemotherapy drugs can damage the glands or the hypothalamus, a part of the brain that works with the hormone-producing glands. This damage may not become evident until many years after treatment is completed.

An underactive thyroid can cause a child to be listless, cold, overweight, or constipated. An overactive thyroid does the reverse: children may be nervous and jittery; they may have hot flashes or sweat profusely; they are often underweight and have pounding hearts; they often have diarrhea. Damage to the adrenal glands may cause high or low blood pressure, metabolic problems, or hormone imbalances that affect puberty or cause infertility. Children may enter puberty too early, too late, or not at all.

The pituitary gland and the hypothalamus work together to control the functioning of all the other endocrine glands. Damage to either of these can result in any of the situations listed above. Some of these conditions may be partially controlled by medication, but the child needs close monitoring. The pituitary also controls the production and release of growth hormones. If this process is compromised, children may not grow normally or they may be frail. Growth hormone deficiency often requires complicated medical intervention that includes daily injections of growth hormones, medically induced delays in puberty to encourage vertical growth, and other treatments. Children with damaged pituitaries may also develop metabolic problems, such as the inability to metabolize protein, fats, or sugars.

Survivors of acute lymphoblastic leukemia can develop the "metabolic syndrome." This is most common in those children treated with cranial radiation. This includes fatigue, obesity, high lipid levels in the blood stream, high insulin levels in the blood stream and sometimes pituitary problems.

Whether hormones are "raging" or absent, the child with endocrine problems is constantly buffeted by urgings from his body that are hard to ignore. A child who is nervous, edgy, and distractible or lethargic and dull is tough to teach and can try the patience of the best teachers. Parents must help the teacher learn to understand the cause of these behaviors so she can develop strategies to help the child learn.

Children who do not grow or whose bodies look different are subject to teasing by the other children. Some children need a huge amount of sleep and may occasionally have to sleep, in to restore their energy level. An obese child with high cholesterol and high blood pressure is at risk for stroke and heart attacks, just as an adult would be.

Bones

Some cancers cannot be cured without amputation of a limb or extensive surgery to "salvage" a cancerous limb. Many children can participate in various sports despite these physical limitations, while others are plagued with weakness or pain. Often physical and occupational therapy is helpful.

Radiation therapy in growing children can result in under-development of soft tissue, cartilage and bones. This can cause children to have asymmetry of parts of their body, which may result in feeling self-conscious about their appearance and can also affect their ability to participate in activities in school.

Low bone mineral density from steroids (prednisone and dexamethasone) or radiation to the brain can occur in childhood cancer survivors, especially in children treated for acute lymphoblastic leukemia and children who had bone marrow transplants. Children with very low bone mineral density are at risk of fracture. Survivors of pediatric leukemia who received radiation therapy to the brain may become obese.

Many of these conditions will not directly impact education, but they may significantly affect the child's social experiences in school. Children can be cruel to those who are different and cancer survivors may already feel self-conscious about their appearance.

Parents of a child with osteoporosis or other skeletal late effects should notify the school. In most cases, physical activity is encouraged in these children because weight bearing exercise helps to build bone mass. If any adjustments to types of physical exercise are necessary, the doctor should write a note explaining this to the school.

Obesity

While some childhood cancer survivors are undersized and frail, obesity is a more common result of treatment, particularly after cranial radiation or high dose steroids. The problem is further complicated because many of these children also have high blood pressure, too much insulin, and an excess of fatty substances in the blood. In addition, some survivors seem repelled by healthy foods while craving foods that are high in fat, salt, and sugar. The diets of these children must be carefully monitored.

Very obese children are very tired children. It is hard for tired children to keep up with their classmates. They may also be embarrassed and lacking in self-esteem. No one they encounter will assume that they are fat because they had cancer. The teacher can assist by helping the class to understand that outward differences do not equate to character traits and by encouraging healthy snacks and good eating habits in all of the children.

Hair Loss

Many children lose their hair while on treatment. When it comes back, it may be a different color, thicker or thinner, or curly where it used to be straight. On some treatments, the child loses her hair and grows it back, only to lose it again every few weeks or months in ensuing phases of treatment. If the hair follicles are damaged by high dose radiation, survivors may be partially or completely bald permanently.

Clearly, hair loss by itself is not an educational issue. Self-esteem is however, and survivors must be protected from ridicule or shame about their appearance. Bald children should be allowed to wear hats or scarves while at school if they wish. Special programs that teach inclusion and acceptance of disabilities should be developed and presented to the students. A policy of zero tolerance for cruelty should be adopted.

Fatigue

Fatigue is addressed as a separate issue because it is the constant companion of some childhood cancer survivors. The child, who has been living with it daily, may not even recognize that she is tired, but she still suffers its effects. For survivors of acute lymphoblastic leukemia, especially those treated with cranial radiation, the fatigue may be part of the metabolic syndrome. Other times, there is no clear physical cause. The important thing is to make sure that the child receives a full evaluation for fatigue symptoms to make sure that there is no physical cause that can be treated. Many times the cause of the fatigue cannot be identified, but it is nonetheless a real phenomenon and must be taken seriously.

Exhaustion hampers concentration, enhances confusion, interferes with coordination, and can make the child irritable and easily frustrated. If the child is chronically fatigued, it is necessary for educators to be open to adjustments, such as rest periods or extra time to complete assignments. Sometimes these children miss school or come in late simply because they are too tired to function effectively. If the teacher begins to see signs of fatigue in a survivor who was previously doing fine, he should notify the parents so the child can be evaluated.

Summary

The end of treatment is to be celebrated for a childhood cancer patient, but it is not the end of the cancer experience. In fact, many effects do not appear until long after treatment has ended. One of the challenges for the parents of survivors is to find the correct balance between moving forward after cancer and remaining vigilant about its lasting effects. The child too, must learn to pay attention to signs of trouble without obsessively dwelling on his health.

Parents of survivors must take primary responsibility for managing the health and education of their children, but that task is made much easier if educators and resource staff are willing to educate themselves about the real and lasting problems these children face. Working together, parents and teachers can create an environment in which children who have survived cancer and its treatment can succeed.

Key Points

Effect or body system	Treatment
Stroke, seizures, other CNS	Radiation, methotrexate, surgery
Nerves outside the brain	Vincristine, vinblastine, vinorelbine
Vision	Radiation, steroids, surgery
Hearing	Radiation, cisplatin, carboplatin
Heart	Radiation, anthracyclines
Lung	Radiation, bleomycin, busulfan, nitrosureas
Kidney	Radiation, cisplatin, carboplatin, ifosfamide
Bladder	Radiation, cyclophosphamide, ifosfamide
Intestines	Radiation
Spleen	Surgery, radiation
Immune system	Radiation, chemotherapy
Thyroid and neuroendocrine	Radiation
Bone and body composition	Radiation, surgery, steroids
Fatigue	Unknown

Parent Perspectives

My daughter's physical late effects from chemo and radiation include mild renal insufficiency, bilateral cataracts, growth failure, and attention deficit disorder. Although this list may sound daunting, compared to her days on treatment most of these issues are easily addressed and the symptoms quite manageable. Her renal problems don't require any treatment, and we expect they will resolve on their own. She will have cataract surgery in the fall, and gives herself a nightly injection of human growth hormone to promote normal growth. Her ADD is well controlled with stimulant medication, so barring any new developments, she's on her way to a pretty "normal" life!

✦✦✦

Ethan has significant right-sided weakness (residual from his right-sided paralysis) and is still pretty clumsy (a combination of the location of his brain tumor and vincristine—and maybe heredity—I am pretty clumsy, too). It has been upsetting to him that he is different from the other kids and it makes it harder for him to feel comfortable making friends (his teachers all agree that other kids like him and make an effort with him). The school has essentially assigned a guardian angel to him each recess to make sure that nothing untoward happens without being "in your face" about it. I do not think Ethan knows it is happening.

The teachers report that the kids are very careful with him and include him in games. I have witnessed a soccer game, where a child trying to steal the ball from him did not rush Ethan the way she would other kids, but was not letting him by either—very kind and very inclusive behavior. He did not feel good at the game, but he felt that he could play, which is not the reality without the accommodations the kids were making. When there is an activity that might be hard for Ethan (like "Wheel Day" when kids were roller skating and skateboarding, two things he is not able to do at this point), there was an adult assigned to "make it work" for him. He came home from a day on wheels in the park smiling from ear to ear, so I think they were successful.

✦✦✦

My son Matt's vocal cords were paralyzed post surgery and he needed a tracheotomy. I remember when he was on a ventilator at night for central apnea, the night nurse (we had 24 hour in-house nursing for about eight months) told us one morning that he talked in his sleep. I think I cried. Anyway, at about six months or so, we put a valve-like device on the trach for gradually increasing amounts of time and he started to say a few words. He was two and a half at the time. To make a long story short, it's seven years since his surgery, the trach has been gone over five years, after continuous speech therapy, Matt is pretty much understood by most people we meet. And for those who have seen the longer haul, it's pretty much a miracle.

✦ ✦ ✦

My daughter had 1800 cGy of cranial radiation the week she turned 4. She has several physical late effects. Low growth hormone and an early, rapid puberty left her quite short. She was one of those kids who had an incredible problem with vincristine. Now, ten years later, and after years of physical and occupational therapy, she is still weaker and more uncoordinated than her peers. But, she has tremendously improved since treatment ended! We tried many activities—therapeutic riding, gymnastics, T ball, etc. She finally found one she liked—ice skating. Doing that several times a week really made a tremendous difference, and it made her feel more "normal" which going to physical therapy does not. The physical late effect that most impacts her life is severe chronic fatigue. She is in middle school, and it takes all of her energy to get through the day. She usually comes home and falls asleep immediately for several hours. She gets up to eat dinner and do some homework, then is back in bed by nine and sleeps eight more hours. On weekends, she sleeps 16 hours most days. We are currently looking at clinical trials that give supplemental growth hormone to post pubertal kids to see if this will improve her strength and lessen her fatigue. It's a tough way to live.

✦ ✦ ✦

What comes to mind with physical effects to me is something you can see, like a loss of an extremity or blindness, but many brain tumors kids have invisible effects. My girl had to switch handedness due to initial paralysis of her right arm. Although her strength has improved she does not have the control or stamina to write with the right hand. She has continued left fine motor control problems and dysmetria (shakiness of the arms). Projects—such as art projects or writing activities—are very hard. Other kids can whip through the steps, but Lisa has to be very deliberate in all her actions. It can be very fatiguing.

We need to watch her self-esteem since she usually finishes last. However, she looks completely normal. Another little hidden thing is that she has a VP shunt because of tumor-related hydrocephalus. We ask the teachers to make sure that balls aren't thrown at her head during recess, and to notify us if she gets symptoms of mechanical failure. We recently ended up in the ER for a shunt blockage and were suddenly in the intensive care unit, planning surgery for the next morning. Not only did she miss several days of school but her previous deficits seemed to all come back. I was shocked at how off-balance she was after surgery. Psychologically it is hard too. It is a reminder that your life again can be disrupted or changed forever in an instant.

✛ ✛ ✛

At one point just prior to the seizures being diagnosed, the neuropsychologist theorized that Rose's increasing problem of "not feeling like myself," and of "not feeling real" was attributable to the bilateral frontal lobe damage which controls personality, and that she might be experiencing "disassociation." There were other symptoms also, such as things going "white," shaking legs, reflux of stomach acid, a glazed expression ("I feel like I'm staring"), and an inability to invoke a response from Rose at that moment. Rose would just clutch onto me in fear until the symptoms passed. The description of these symptoms prompted the neuropsychologist to suggest seeing a neurologist. Concurrently, Rose was referred to the psychologist who quickly determined that dissociation was not the issue. Shortly thereafter, the EEG results were loud and clear. Rose had abnormal electrical activity in the brain—whether seizures or "methotrexate spells" has yet to be resolved. The seizures/spells have not stopped even with anticonvulsant medication.

✛ ✛ ✛

Joseph had twelve cycles of vincristine/actinomycin D/Cytoxan chemotherapy and 5000 cGy of hyperfractionated orbital radiation (twice daily for six weeks). With this treatment regimen, almost all of his above-the-neck side effects will be due to the radiation, not the chemotherapy drugs.

Many of the side effects of radiation on the body are, of course, delayed for months or even years.

Like most children who are a couple of years out of treatment, Joseph's scans and doctor visits are now more related to dealing with the long-term effects of the rhabdomyosarcoma cure rather than the disease itself. He has a big cataract on his right eye from the radiation, and his vision in both eyes is rapidly getting worse. He still needs eye drops every two hours all day because his tear ducts were damaged by the radiation, and he has terrible problems with light sensitivity. He will suffer "bony hypoplasia" which means that the bony structures which absorbed radiation (in this case, his right temple and in and around the right orbit) will not grow any more, so his face will look increasingly asymmetrical as he grows up. The doctors are optimistic that it won't be too noticeable since he was turning five when treatments were done.

✦ ✦ ✦

My son was diagnosed with ALL at age 17, at the end of his junior year of high school. During the second half of his 3-year-plus treatment, he experienced a lot of fatigue. It was often hard for him to drag himself to classes. He had a lot of trouble completing busy-work style homework that had to be written out in longhand. I remember being frustrated that he could understand the concepts of his courses, a fact proven by his scores on exams, but his course grades were pulled down because he was too tired to do the homework.

Nevertheless, he was able to complete college in 4 years. He collected his engineering degree and within six months he had a job in his field—a challenging job that he enjoys.

✦ ✦ ✦

One of the persistent and difficult side effects of treatment is hearing loss. Hearing is vital to learning, of course. This is especially the case with younger children who have yet to learn, differentiate and speak complex phonetics. This is one of the subtle late effects after cancer treatment, yet is often downplayed, overlooked or ignored in view of more "pressing" issues such as survival.

In the case of a child with cancer, educators are bound by law to provide assistance to the hearing-impaired child. With our daughter, two types of assistance provided were:

- *An FM hearing device, a box-like apparatus that sits on the child's desk, and is tuned to the frequency the teacher communicates through, via a small microphone he or she wears on their clothing. The student wears a small headset, or earphones, and thus the voice of the teacher is amplified.*

- *An audio specialist. This person visits with the child on an intermittent basis to help with speech pronunciation, teach sign language if necessary, and help the child discern the difference between similar high-frequency sounds. For example, high frequency sounds such as "F" and "S" sound very much alike to the hearing-impaired child, and the teacher can help the student discern the difference and even learn to lip read.*

To obtain the necessary help from the school, several points should be considered:

- *Provide the school with the results of all hearing tests.*

- *Insist on quality equipment. Some schools may provide simple hearing aids that were donated to the school or school district. Although they amplify noise, they do not have the capacity to amplify high-frequency sounds or reduce ambient noise. They may be large for the child's ear(s) and are unsightly. Ensure that a quality FM device be employed. Ask the hearing-impaired teacher to research the latest equipment available. It is expensive, so stress that the devices are the property of school district and may also be shared with other children.*

- *Ask the teacher to employ common-sense help. The child should be seated in the first row of the classroom, nearest the teacher. Request that the teacher stand near the child when addressing the classroom.*

- *Investigate the latest digital hearing aids, which identify and amplify high-frequency sounds. These must be acquired privately and are expensive (as much as $5,000); check with your insurance carrier to see to what extent they are covered. If the cost is prohibitive, ask your social worker if any charitable organizations assist with this type of problem.*

Chapter 10

Psychological Late Effects

Anne Kazak, PhD
Mary T. Rourke, PhD

Childhood cancer patients and their parents often look forward to the time when treatment ends and life can return to "normal." What can come as a surprise to survivors and their families is that cancer does not end when treatment ends. Instead, families learn that cancer survivorship has its own set of medical and psychological issues. The goal of this chapter is to summarize what is known about the psychological late effects of cancer—or the long-term influences of the cancer on the feelings, thoughts, behaviors, and relationships of survivors and their family members—and to present some guidelines for managing these effects.

Transition to End of Treatment

Much of what we know about the period just after treatment ends comes from clinical experience with families. Many families are surprised to find that the end of treatment does not necessarily bring the sense of relief that they had expected, but rather brings a new sense of worry. Children, teenagers, and their parents may worry about the illness returning, especially since they no longer have blood work or scans performed as frequently or don't see their medical team as regularly. They may worry about whether alternate treatments would be available if the cancer recurred. All of these concerns can be magnified for families as their contact with their medical team become less frequent.

Even when these more focused, specific worries are not evident, the transition off treatment, like any major transition in a family's life, is likely to bring a general level of stress. Most families of survivors quickly

> Dr. Kazak is professor and director of psychology research in the department of pediatrics at the University of Pennsylvania School of Medicine, and director of the department of psychology at The Children's Hospital of Philadelphia, PA.

find that "getting back to normal" doesn't make sense. Many things in a family's life change between the time of diagnosis and the end of treatment. The cancer survivor may be in a different grade at school and is certainly older with a different set of developmental needs. The parents' work situations may have changed, and the family's activities are likely to be different than they were before the child had cancer. For all families—cancer or not—routines change and evolve over time.

When treatment ends, families must find a "new normal" routine, one that fits with the family's needs at this specific period of time. This process has different challenges for parents and for children. Parents often focus on reconnecting to the community (school, church, peers, work, etc.), while also paying close attention to their child's health and other needs. Most children and adolescents are eager to get back to the routine business of being a child. They simply want to be like their peers, and not have to adjust their activities because of illness- or treatment-related issues.

Psychological Late Effects

Just as certain medical treatments can have a long-term effect on the body, certain life experiences can have a long-term effect on the way survivors and their family members feel, think, act and interact with others. We refer to these effects as psychological late effects. Like medical late effects, they may not even begin to emerge for many years after treatment ends. Childhood cancer is a powerful experience for the diagnosed child, as well as for those closely involved with him or her. Because of this, psychological late effects can occur in the childhood cancer survivor, in the survivor's parents, brothers and sisters, and possibly in other close family members or friends.

Psychological late effects do not tend to take the form of general depression or anxiety. Survivors appear to be functioning well overall and do not appear to be more depressed or anxious or to have more behavioral issues than other children their age. Instead, there are two focused areas in which survivors and their family members tend to develop psychological effects related to cancer and treatment: posttraumatic stress and social competence.

Posttraumatic stress

Posttraumatic stress is a term that describes reactions that people have after they experience a trauma. It is easy to see why childhood cancer can be traumatic. At diagnosis, parents are told explicitly that their

Dr. Rourke is a psychologist in the Division of Oncology at The Children's Hospital of Philadelphia in Philadelphia, PA.

child may die. Survivors and their siblings may also hear this information, or may interpret the life threat from their parents' urgency, the survivor's physical reactions to treatment, and the abrupt changes in their family routine. Cancer treatment can be experienced as a horrifying, scary, painful series of events for everyone involved. Families develop relationships with other children going through treatment for cancer. If one of these children relapses or dies, it is a serious loss and can be especially frightening.

Posttraumatic stress reactions to these traumatic events can begin soon after the initial diagnosis, or many years later. There are three kinds of posttraumatic stress symptoms:

- **Persistent re-experiencing of the traumatic event:** At some point in their lives, most parents and survivors will re-experience traumatic or scary parts of the cancer or treatment. They may have distressing images or thoughts of the treatment just "pop into" their heads, especially when they see, hear, or smell something that reminds them of their treatment. Sometimes one of those reminders may even make a survivor or parent feel right back in the middle of the cancer/treatment situation. They might have bad dreams, or might get very upset when something reminds them of the cancer. For many people, going to oncology follow-up visits is a strong reminder of the treatment experience and can trigger these kinds of symptoms in the days or weeks preceding the appointment.

- **Increased anxiety:** Many survivors and family members will have a high level of anxiety. They might have bouts of irritability, feel jumpy or on guard, or have trouble sleeping or concentrating. Survivors and their parents often feel overly concerned about the survivor's health, watching too carefully for small changes that could signal the cancer's return. A simple cough and cold, for example, could convince some parents or survivors that the cancer is back.

- **Isolation:** Some survivors and family members may react to cancer by avoiding people or places that remind them of the cancer, or by feeling numb. Avoidance is somewhat less common in survivors and their family members, but still occurs in some people. Survivors, siblings, or parents may try hard not to think or talk about the cancer experience, or to stay away from things or people that might remind them of the cancer experience. They may feel distant or cut-off from others, that their feelings have been muted, or they may not have expectations for a full life. Some survivors, for example, refuse to watch medical shows on TV or won't talk about the cancer experience with their family.

Posttraumatic stress vs. posttraumatic stress disorder

Most people will have some symptoms of posttraumatic stress in the years after having (or having a child or sibling who had) childhood cancer. Some people will develop several symptoms in all three of the categories described previously. If this happens, and if the symptoms significantly interfere with their normal activities, they can be diagnosed with Posttraumatic Stress Disorder (PTSD).

Child and teenage survivors of cancer do not appear to have high rates of PTSD, but they do tend to have at least some significant posttraumatic stress symptoms. While parents and teachers might not see survivors frequently becoming very upset, the symptoms still can get in the way of normal development. For example, an adolescent who is very upset when reminded of her treatment experience may do everything she can to avoid talking or thinking about her cancer. She might hide scars or signs of her treatment from friends, which could force her to avoid activities that would reveal her "secret." She may not put on shorts, swimsuits, or certain dresses, or may feel uncomfortable socializing with friends or dating, even though she would like to do these things. Otherwise routine activities, like changing for gym class, can become an extremely stressful, or even painful, experience.

Because younger survivors may report no other significant areas of difficulty, it may be difficult to know that they are experiencing posttraumatic stress. Teachers and parents should therefore be alert for signs that things are amiss. A child or adolescent might become so distracted by a high level of worry or vigilance about his health that his ability to focus on other things suffers. At school, for example, children or adolescents might have difficulty concentrating on schoolwork or completing homework, resulting in lower or inconsistent grades. Teachers or parents might notice children withdrawing from social activities or from important friendships.

Young adulthood can be a particularly difficult time for survivors. Young adult survivors may comprehend, for the first time, the things that they lost or missed because of their cancer experience. They may experience new medical late-effects of treatment, which can be unsettling or even scary. Certain medical consequences clash directly with common goals of young adulthood. For example, infertility can interfere with intimate relationships and family planning, and cognitive or physical limitations may prevent the establishment of independence. These new losses can be magnified as these survivors watch peers and siblings make transitions that they are not able to make. Probably because of these issues, most young adult survivors will experience some aspects of posttraumatic stress, and young adult survivors are more likely than adolescent survivors to develop PTSD.

Parents and siblings of survivors may show even more posttraumatic stress than do adolescent survivors. As research has begun to look at fathers' as well as mothers' reactions, we are learning that in nearly all families, one or both parents can be expected to have some signs of posttraumatic stress. Further, rates of full-blown PTSD are elevated among both mothers and fathers. This is true even though the parents may be doing well overall in other areas. Research that focuses on mothers' reactions and does not consider effects on fathers and other caregivers/guardians can underestimate the prevalence of long-term psychological effects within a survivor's family.

There is little research on sibling reactions, but the research that does exist suggests that many teenage siblings have at least mild to moderate symptoms of posttraumatic stress in the years after their sibling completes treatment. Siblings might have persistent worries about their brother or sister's health, and sometimes they become upset when reminded of the cancer experience. Like the adolescent survivors, teen siblings may be functioning well overall, and the posttraumatic stress may not be apparent at first glance.

Causes of posttraumatic stress

We do not know why some people develop more posttraumatic stress than others. It makes sense to expect that those survivors who endured more difficult treatments, or whose diagnoses had worse prognoses would be more likely than other survivors to develop PTSD or some symptoms of posttraumatic stress. This does not seem to be the case. More objective things like treatment intensity, diagnosis, and age at time of treatment do not appear to be related to posttraumatic stress for most survivors and their family members. Instead, what people believe about their illness, treatment, and current medical status is related to posttraumatic stress. Survivors (and their parents) who believe that their treatments were more intense, and those who believe their life is still in danger—regardless of what the medical team says—tend to have more posttraumatic stress symptoms.

There are some exceptions to this rule. Some research suggests that the presence of more serious medical late effects of treatment could be related to posttraumatic stress in young adult survivors of childhood cancer. In addition, while there is no specific research on posttraumatic stress and cognitive impairment, research in other fields suggests that survivors who have cognitive impairment as a result of their disease or treatment could have higher levels of distress than others.

Social Development

Developing social relationships is a primary developmental task of childhood and adolescence. Experiences with friends and classmates help children build an understanding of who they are, as well as a sense of self-esteem and competence. Because cancer and treatment at least partially remove children from the normal everyday activities in which most children build these relationships, it seems likely that social development is an area at risk for difficulties.

Overall, survivors of childhood cancer are rated as more socially isolated and have fewer best friends than do other children. In some studies, classmates continue to see survivors as being "sick." Children whose physical appearance and athletic ability were affected by their treatment may be at higher risk for social difficulties

There seem to be few immediate consequences of these social differences. Despite being identified as more socially isolated and having fewer best friends, childhood cancer survivors are as well liked as their classmates. Teachers also rate survivors as less aggressive than other children and, in some studies, as more sociable. Further, survivors themselves do not report feeling lonely or depressed. The potential for longer-term problems associated with these differences exists, however, and has not yet been well researched. Being less involved with peers may affect self-image and self-esteem, and may not give survivors the social practice they will need as young adults. These kinds of difficulties are likely to emerge slowly over time, and might not be evident until several years after treatment ends. While there is little research on social issues in older survivors of childhood cancer, there are some indications that the marriage rates are lower than average in some cancer survivors.

Special situations

Because injury to the central nervous system can result in specific social skill deficits, there may be some social issues that apply to two specific groups of children: those treated for brain tumors, and those who have cognitive or learning issues resulting from their treatment.

Brain tumor survivors frequently have significant cognitive changes after their treatments. Depending on the site of the tumor and the specific treatment received, these survivors may have a harder time with the mechanics of interacting with others. Specifically, survivors with central nervous system injury might have difficulty:

- Balancing their own needs with the needs or desires of other children
- Understanding social situations in the ways that other kids understand

them

- Inhibiting impulses
- Generating, evaluating, and selecting appropriate responses in social situations

In addition, depending again on the degree of cognitive impairment, they may have different abilities than their peers, adding more complexity to social situations.

A second group at risk is those non-brain tumor survivors who received cranial radiation and/or chemotherapy to the brain as part of their cancer treatment. Specifically, some children treated for leukemia received high doses of intrathecal chemotherapy and cranial radiation, which have been linked to learning difficulties during survivorship. Children who received cranial radiation for other tumors (e.g., retinoblastoma, tumors to the head) or as part of the treatment for bone marrow transplant may also be at risk for later cognitive difficulties.

Other chapters in this book address the academic and learning issues that these children face after cancer and treatment. Treatment-related cognitive difficulties can also affect social development in at least two ways. First, children with learning needs may feel different from their peers, and can develop a negative sense of their own ability. These issues can lead a child to socially isolate him or herself, and may lead other children to view the child as different. Second, there are some forms of learning disability that have social skills components. Children with nonverbal learning disabilities, for example, often have difficulty perceiving the complexity of social interactions. They can have difficulty understanding play or conversational rules, such as how to enter a group of other children, how close to stand to others when talking or playing, and how often to make eye contact. Identifying and understanding the nature of these issues for affected children is key to minimizing their impact on children's social success in the classroom. Children with learning disabilities who have these kinds of social deficits should have a section in their IEPs addressing ways in which schools can accommodate these difficulties.

Social effects on the survivor's family

There is very little research on the social consequences of childhood cancer for members of a survivor's family. Some research suggests that parents may feel lonely or isolated after treatment ends. During the survivorship period, parents may have continued concerns about their child's health, while the number of people available to hear and respond to those concerns decreases substantially. Medical teams are seen less frequently, while friends and family members—excited by the victory of survival—may not understand a parent's concerns about relapse and the possibility of late effects. Being aware that these feelings can emerge, and finding new ways to talk to supportive people in their lives about the stage of cancer survivorship, can help parents feel more connected and less isolated.

It's Not all Bad News: Competence and Strength

Focusing on psychological difficulties during survivorship can lead us to overlook the fact that most childhood cancer survivors and their families are functioning as well as other children and families. Even those survivors or family members who have some posttraumatic stress and/or social difficulties are likely to be doing well in many areas of their lives.

Further, even those people who can cite specific medical or psychological hardships that resulted from their own or their child's cancer experience are likely to believe that they grew stronger from that experience. There is little formal research on this topic, but many psychologists working with survivors have anecdotal reports that parents and survivors grow to appreciate at least some parts of the cancer experience. Parents and survivors frequently explain that childhood cancer taught them to put things in perspective in ways that other people do not do, that they are not as materialistic and are more empathetic. Survivors frequently feel that they are more mature than others their age, and that they value their family relationships more. Family members and survivors may feel proud of their ability to manage—and survive—a challenge like childhood cancer and survivorship. Drawing on these strengths and the positive aspects of the cancer experience can help survivors and their family members weather any challenges they might face.

Managing Psychological Late Effects

Most psychological late effects, for survivors and their family members, are normal reactions to the very unusual life event of childhood cancer. Understanding that reactions are normal, and therefore likely to occur at some time in nearly everyone, is the first step in managing the reaction and putting cancer in its place. It is also important to keep two things in mind:

- Reactions to childhood cancer are likely to emerge unpredictably, and to wax and wane over time as a survivor's or family member's life circumstances change. Knowing that reactions may come and go, and change over time, can help survivors and their family members recognize when they might be happening.

- Reactions to childhood cancer are common not just in survivors, but also in parents, siblings, and maybe even other family members. Because the experience of cancer as a trauma is different for everyone, the specific reactions will vary for everyone. Reactions may even emerge at different times. It can be frustrating for parents to understand, for example, that even though they have a pronounced worry about their child, the child may not be worried. It is helpful to be aware that different reactions in different family members are expected.

Strategies used to manage any major life event are appropriate to manage the kinds of difficulties most people face after childhood cancer. Specifically, the following guidelines will help most people manage reactions they experience:

- Connect with others to reduce isolation. Parents and survivors generally have a web of extended family members, neighbors, friends and/or community supports. Reaching out and re-engaging with parts of this network, or finding new points of connection with a larger community, can help survivors and families feel a general sense of support as they establish new routines. It may be harder to connect with existing supports around reactions to the cancer, particularly after the cancer is "gone." Simply talking about survivorship as another step in the journey can help families stay connected to each other and to others in their lives. Discussions do not necessarily have to be long or focused on the hardships, but can and should include talking about the ways in which cancer has enriched a family.

- Be curious. Family members, teachers, friends and many others in a survivor's life may find it difficult to know where to begin. Once treatment ends, family members may no longer know how to talk to each other about cancer or survivorship issues. Many will assume that the survivor, parent, or sibling may not want to talk about the cancer or survivorship, or they may not know what to ask or talk about. Simply asking questions can give important people in a survivor's life the information they need to best support the survivor and his/her family, and can help the survivor or family member not be isolated in the survivorship period.

- Be respectful. Part of being appropriately curious is being respectful of the answers that people give and of the limits that survivors or their parents set. For example, when a child expresses sadness, a natural tendency for an adult caregiver (parent, teacher, friend) is to try to fix the situation by explaining all the reasons why the survivor should be happy. This strategy can backfire, as it can feel like a listener is not understanding the emotion expressed. It is important to simply accept the feelings that survivors (and parents and siblings) express, and to let them know that you understand what they are trying to tell you. At the same time, if survivors and family members communicate that they do not want to talk about a particular topic, it is wise to respect that limit.

- Don't assume disaster. It is easy to assume that survivors or their parents must be hurting and need to express that. Most survivors and family members experience a mix of positive and negative effects that varies over time. There are likely to be times in every survivor's (or family member's) life when things are difficult. There will also be many times when the very same individuals are experiencing no distress at all, or when they do not have a need to express it to anyone who asks. If a survivor, parent, or sibling says they are fine, unless strong evidence indicates otherwise, it is probably the case that they are fine. Even when a survivor or family member does indicate some difficulty, overall they are likely to be doing well, and the presence of sadness or distress—while it does merit attention—does not usually signal disaster.

- Remember the importance of ongoing family-school collaboration. During survivorship, the focus on moving on can lead families, survivors, and teachers to neglect a consideration of how cancer or survivorship issues may continue to influence the survivor. Teachers often have specific questions about medical, learning, or emotional issues, but may be reluctant to bring up the cancer with the survivor or parents. Parents may not realize that teachers may see things—both strengths and areas of need— that are only evident in the school environment. It is very important that parents and teachers (and the survivor, when appropriate) clearly and openly discuss relevant issues and questions at the start of a school year and whenever any social or academic change occurs. Some questions that teachers commonly raise, even many years after a child's cancer is successfully treated, include:

  – Should the survivor be expected to be fatigued during the school day, and how do the parents want to handle that situation?

  – Should the parent-school team continue any cancer-related accommodations that were put in place when a child was on treatment?

  – Are there any health issues about which the teacher or school nurse should be particularly vigilant?

  – Are there certain cognitive or social risks that a teacher should watch for?

- Is the child particularly sensitive about any ongoing physical, emotional, or cognitive changes associated with the cancer treatment?

- How would the parents like the teacher to communicate any questions or concerns that might arise?

When appropriate, school-related issues should be addressed in an IEP.

- Keep an eye out for extreme difficulties, and seek help as necessary. While most survivors and parents will manage the fluctuating psychological effects of cancer over their lifetimes, there may be times when symptoms significantly interfere with development. Signs that cancer and/or survivorship are getting in the way for children and adolescents are the same signs that may appear when other issues cause psychological distress. Parents and teachers will know that children need more help if they begin to fall behind their peers developmentally, begin doing poorly in school, have significant difficulty with their classmates, or become very sad or worried. Other signs that children or adolescents may be having more difficulty include increasing physical complaints (e.g., headache, stomach ache, fatigue) that have no medical cause, frequent school absence or refusal to attend school, and behavior problems. When parents or teachers are concerned that these issues are getting in the way, referral to a counselor or therapist can be helpful.

Interventions

When symptoms become an issue for childhood cancer survivors and their families, it is important that interventions target the specific symptoms that are derailing the child/teenager and/or the family. Research on the effectiveness of specific interventions for specific problems is in its infancy; programs with different emphases are being developed around the country.

Reducing posttraumatic stress

Cognitive-behavioral therapy, available from many licensed or certified mental health providers, is a recommended approach for posttraumatic stress symptoms. This kind of therapy teaches people to identify thoughts that cause distress, and to develop new ways of thinking that will alleviate worry and posttraumatic stress. In addition, research is now investigating group interventions that address cancer-related posttraumatic stress within a family context. These family interventions teach the tools of cognitive behavior therapy, while also helping families build a shared understanding of the cancer/survivorship experience. Helping families build a coherent family story that reflects every family member's perspective is considered to be an important element in helping to put cancer in its place.

Promoting adaptive social development

When social skills deficits interfere with development, social skills training may help. Social skills training programs for children with cognitive deficits, and particularly for those treated for brain tumors, are being developed and offered at some major pediatric centers across the country. These group programs usually teach specific social skills in a group format, allowing children to see and practice the skills they are being taught. Consulting with pediatric hospitals or brain tumor organizations can help parents identify whether programs are available in their area.

Some social skills training programs may also be helpful for children who experience the more subtle social difficulties that accompany specific learning disabilities. In addition, some researchers have begun to publish intervention guidelines for children with nonverbal learning disabilities. Because the learning issues that many childhood cancer survivors face are consistent with the symptoms of nonverbal learning disability, these intervention guidelines, which can be applied by parents and teachers, may be helpful. School psychologists and other mental health and school personnel can best help families and teachers target the most appropriate interventions for a particular child.

Preventive Interventions

Are there things that families can do earlier in the treatment process to prevent posttraumatic stress, or to set their family on a survivorship path that includes a minimal number of roadblocks? Although no research is available at this time to answer this question, it seems intuitive that there are things that families can do preventively. Families are likely to find it helpful to talk to each other about their experience at different stages in the treatment and survivorship process, and to gain as many tools as possible to manage any worry, concern, or sadness that they might experience. If concerns arise, survivors and family members can participate in support groups run by the hospital or local cancer organizations, or they can participate in individual or family counseling. Researchers are beginning to investigate preventive interventions, and are working toward providing care to families early in the treatment process that will minimize the risk of any long-term psychological effects.

Key Points

- Psychological late effects are long term emotional and behavioral reactions to childhood cancer, treatment, and survivorship, and commonly include symptoms of posttraumatic stress and/or social difficulties.

- Most survivors and their family members have at least some minor psychological late effects; some survivors, parents, and siblings develop more severe psychological late effects.

- Psychological late effects emerge unpredictably over time, and may change as a survivor's or his/her family's life circumstances change.

- Different psychological late effects can occur in survivors, their parents, their siblings, and maybe even other family members.

- More research is needed to understand positive psychological effects of the cancer/survivorship experience.

- Most psychological late effects can be effectively managed using strategies appropriate after any major life change. More serious or distressing reactions can benefit from counseling.

Parent Perspectives

We have worked with the school to identify ways to make Ethan more socially connected with other kids. Last week his class presented a project that they had been working on for about a month called "The History of Me." Each child drew a time line of his or her life and highlighted the important events, then built a story around these events and eventually pulled together an oral presentation of their life story, complete with a life-sized drawing of themselves that they could refer to during the presentation. Ethan's had a very prominent port scar and an accurate rendition of his very long, very curly, very lush hair which he has refused to cut.

It was a spine-tingling tearjerker to hear Ethan present his cancer experience with his unique 8-year-old, 20/20 hindsight view of the whole ordeal, but it was also pretty amazing how many other kids had trauma and illness in their lives—divorce being the most frequent. To hear 8 to10 year olds talk about their feelings about those experiences was pretty powerful. I think it made Ethan feel less alone in his struggles, and was a healing experience for a lot of the kids. The videotape is priceless, and the kids went back and watched it as a class and talked about it further. As a psychiatrist, I give this exercise two thumbs up. As a parent, it was beautiful and unbelievably sad to watch. I should have packed a hanky.

✦ ✦ ✦

My daughter was treated in the mid 1990s at a large children's hospital that didn't use sedation for painful procedures. So, from ages 3 to 6, she had adults hold her down for 17 spinal taps, several bone marrow aspirations, and hundreds of needle sticks. She developed severe posttraumatic stress disorder that has taken years of therapy (and thousands of dollars because most of the "medical" treatment is covered by insurance but they only cover 10 visits/year for "mental health" problems.) She basically disappeared inside herself for a long time. She developed an elaborate fantasy world and stayed there. She also became very hypersensitive to sounds and touch. She cowered when she had to go to the hospital and needle pokes terrified her. You'd think she grew up in a war torn county and was shrinking down to escape incoming bombs. It was heartbreaking. But, we are making progress, slowly but surely, with medication and talk therapy.

✦✦✦

Not only survivors get PTSD. I did too. The driveway to the children's hospital where my child was treated was lined with beautiful flowering cherry trees. After the years of treatment were over, whenever I saw a flowering cherry tree, I got nauseated and a couple of times actually threw up. When we had to go to the follow-up clinic, I asked if we would be separate from the kids on treatment. I was told yes, but when we arrived, the waiting room was full of kids on treatment. When the first one started to cry about getting an "owie," I burst into tears and couldn't stop.

✦✦✦

My son was very well liked before, during, and after treatment, but he never felt like he fit in after his initial diagnosis. Kids weren't "pretending" to like him, but I think he felt as if they were nice to him because they felt sorry for him. He tended to lose sight of the fact that they all liked him before. Saying this, I feel that is why he made some of the friendship choices that he did (most of them detrimental). He felt comfortable with the kids who were outcasts because he felt like he was on an even playing field. He could have easily kept on with his "jock" and "popular" friends, but his self-esteem and image were badly damaged. And for what it's worth...there really is no school intervention that can "make" a kid feel like they fit in.

✦✦✦

Last night I read an article by Ken Moses (http://www.pediatricservices.com/ prof/prof-15.html) and have to say it really spoke to me. In fact for the first time since the world of childhood cancer came crashing into my life four years ago, I felt connected to the range of emotions I experience on a daily basis verses the emotions I'm told I should feel by people who just don't get it.

In the aftermath of Michael's aggressive cancer treatment and unrelated bone marrow transplant, and with one new diagnosis after another seemingly coming his way every year, I grieve for the loss of my healthy child. I grieve for my lost expectations of supportive family and friends who tripped over each other during the crisis trying to be supportive, only to watch this support all but dissolve away during the long slow crawl to recovery. I sometimes feel a mixture of grief and hope for the plans Michael has for his future knowing that to achieve some of those goals will take a miracle...and I rejoice in every little achievement that sees him accomplishing something that may seem ordinary to others but is momentous to him. But I keep those feelings inside, to avoid the rolled eyes, the sideways glances, the change of subject, the messages either spoken or inferred of, "Get over it," "It's not as bad as that," "Get a job," "Get anti-anxiety medication," and the most common: "Michael survived, you should be happy with that."

Recently, Michael's joint problems have made it necessary for him to stay off his feet as much as possible. He can't ride his bike or walk any great distance—even to and from school—due to pain. This is tough to accept for a teenager tired of being left behind. Michael already missed eight weeks of school this winter, due to illnesses. I felt deeply saddened at this most recent setback, but everyone seems to feel I shouldn't feel sad, so I actually felt guilty for feeling depressed, then angry at myself for feeling guilty! (conflicted....who me?)

What this article did was confirm that these conflicting emotions are actually normal, in a society that censures "negative emotion." Just the acknowledgement that other parents feel conflicting emotions made me feel less alone. It left me with the realization that society needs some serious educating about childhood cancer survivorship and the aftermath left in it's wake, including the fact that parents are also survivors in every sense of the word. Perhaps then more people will "get it."

✝ ✝ ✝

The main problems for Cami after treatment have been social/emotional. Some days these absorb all her attention while she's at school. There have been mornings she hasn't wanted to get on the bus. She's coping fine academically and is good at hiding her feelings, so the teacher was clueless. There is a real temptation to look at all this as normal 2nd grade "stuff," but I know my kid and I've pushed for them to help her. There are no peer counseling groups nearby—none at all in a non-hospital setting—and the last thing I want for Cami is to have her have to go to yet another doctor. But because we have a solid 504 (see Chapter 14) in place, we've been able to call on the school psychologist for help, and she has been wonderful. She used to work on an oncology ward, which makes it a lot easier on us! She's done some small group stuff with Cami, who feels very different though she now looks "normal," and some one-on-one work. It really seems to help. It makes a difference that Cami has also been open about her stress level, so she can let it out (cry) at home. We talk about it and do role playing, but the counselor and I have agreed that she needs basic tools for social self-protection—getting what she'd like without being a wimp or a bully herself, until she catches up developmentally.

✦ ✦ ✦

Gabriel has had a lot of depression since treatment ended but I can see he is slowly getting better. One thing that has happened is at nine months off treatment I think he finally believes he will be a survivor. His fear of relapse is much more in the background and he is starting to dream about his future. He is also showing more interest in helping other kids/teens going through treatment. A 13-year-old hospital friend of his, Katie, just recently died of cancer. At first when he learned she was not going to beat her disease, he told me he didn't think he could see her any more, it was just too scary. Then something shifted and he said he wanted to see her.

One of Katie's last wishes was to have her hair dyed purple. So I drove him to her house with all the stuff he needed to do her hair. She was so sick and in terrible pain but absolutely determined to have purple hair. It took at least a half hour to just get Katie settled in her wheel chair. Then her mom and I left the two of them alone. A few minutes later I peeked in on them and there was Gabriel massaging the dye into Katie's hair with such tenderness, talking softly. Katie sat with her eyes closed looking content. Two weeks later she died with her purple hair.

This whole experience off treatment has been lonely for me because there really isn't the on-going support I had while Gabriel was on treatment. It is as much an unknown territory as being on treatment was.

✦ ✦ ✦

My daughter is almost hyper-social when in situations where she can deal with much younger children, or much older children/adults. Adults find her to be extremely charming, and the words I hear most often are "totally adorable" and "soooo sweet." She will happily chat with any adult about her illness/BMT experience like a pro. She charmed one of our adult tablemates at a wedding we attended recently (she was the flower girl). One of them was a surgeon who was so taken by her I thought he might swipe her and take her home. (She and he talked "medical shop" about central lines vs. PICCs).

But, put this kid is a room with kids her own age and she is lost in a sea of missed social cues. She just can't seem to read situations and figure out how to act. She also cries very readily, partly out of frustration, compounded by the fact that most kids know that they can get her to cry. I am so sad for her some days! The other day, she told me that someone pulled her hair in the recess line and she didn't know who did it, but that "they all laughed and no one would tell." Teachers do not take this type of bullying seriously, insisting that she needs to "learn to deal with it." To some extent, I agree...but every day I have to stifle the urge to go to school with her and find the mean kids and teach them a lesson. I do feel like she makes improvements each year, and I pray that she will continue to learn coping mechanisms and will find her place in this world with her self esteem intact.

✦ ✦ ✦

We found that it really helped to find an excellent, experienced, warm, fun, play therapist and get her on your team. We described her as a "feelings doctor." I told my kids that they had been through a really hard time (the siblings have just as hard a time as the child with cancer), and that some of the cancer stuff was scary and painful while some things were fun like the gifts. When complicated and frightening things happen to people (children and adults) they have lots of big feelings and imaginings about them. They could be really angry at the doctors for hurting them, but glad that the medicines made the cancer go away. They could be scared that they (or their brother or sister) might have to go back to the hospital. They might be worried and relieved, frustrated, sad, and furious all at once. It is hard to make sense of all these big feelings without some help, so a good child therapist makes a remarkable difference in how children feel and function.

✦ ✦ ✦

I believe that it only gets more complicated as kids with disabilities age, so getting help early prevents more problems later. With a good team in place (psychotherapist, neuropsychologist, educator) children can turn out to be fabulous, competent and compassionate adults. My daughter is. She'll always have struggles—the radiation left us with that legacy. But who doesn't have struggles? With help, these kids can make sense of what happened, what it means, and how to maximize their strengths while using strategies to compensate for their weaknesses.It's exhausting to advocate for our kids for years. We are also dealing with our own grief at the price our kids paid for survival. But, the results of getting the help you need outweigh all the time and energy.

Chapter 11

Survivorship Programs

Barbara Anne Hieb, CRNP
Susan K. Ogle, CRNP
Wendy L. Hobbie, CRNP

Over the past thirty years, new advances in the treatment of childhood cancer have led to dramatic increases in the number of children cured of their disease. Unfortunately, the treatments that cure children may also cause physical, cognitive, psychological, and social effects that may not become apparent for several months to years after the completion of treatment.

Comprehensive evaluations of late effects are best performed in an established survivorship program where a plan can be formalized for life-long follow-up care. This chapter first defines comprehensive survivorship programs and then focuses on the role of these programs in the early detection and intervention for cognitive late effects in long-term survivors of childhood cancer.

Essential Components of a Comprehensive Follow-up Clinic

Survivorship clinics are most often located at major pediatric cancer centers. Although the size and location of programs vary, successful programs have several necessary components, including:

- A dedicated medical team, including a medical director, nurse practitioner, clinical psychologist, school liaison and social worker.

- A group of sub-specialty health care providers (e.g., endocrinologist, cardiologist) who are interested and experienced in caring for survivors of childhood cancer.

- Financial and philosophical support from the cancer center.

Barbara Anne Hieb is a nurse practitioner in the cancer survivorship program at The Children's Hospital of Philadelphia, PA.

Effective survivorship programs focus on three critical areas: clinical care, education, and research.

Clinical care

Health care providers evaluate survivors for physical, psychosocial, and educational effects using risk profiles based on the child's previous disease type and treatment protocol. The risk profiles guide surveillance testing and allow for early therapeutic intervention. Clinical health care providers give developmentally appropriate care to survivors of all ages.

Survivors may have difficulty when applying for life and/or health insurance. For example, some survivors are unable to obtain an insurance policy or they are charged increased premiums for medical coverage. Survivorship programs often write letters to insurance companies detailing the survivor's past medical history and stressing the importance of ongoing follow-up care for the identification of potential late effects. Survivorship programs often recommend that a survivor seek employment at a large company with several options for health care coverage plans, where past medical information is rarely elicited. In addition, survivors should answer only those questions specifically asked on the questionnaires. If the question asks whether he/she has cancer, the survivor who is in remission should say no. If the question asks whether he/she has a history of cancer, the survivor should say yes. Two excellent resources include:

- *Childhood Cancer Survivors: A Practical Guide to Your Future* by Nancy Keene, Wendy Hobbie and Kathy Ruccione
- *A Cancer Survivors Almanac: Charting Your Journey* by Barbara Hoffman

Education

Health care providers in survivorship programs educate and provide guidance for survivors and their families regarding the potential late effects of the disease and treatment. For example, parents of survivors who received cranial radiation at a young age will be educated about the risk of cognitive difficulties that may arise years after radiation is given. The need for neuropsychological testing is explained and ways to identify emerging problems are discussed.

Survivorship programs also emphasize health promotion and maintenance. Healthcare providers discuss the importance of maximizing good health practices,while minimizing risk-taking behaviors that may impact the long-term physical and/or psychological late effects of therapy. For example, survivors at risk for heart problems

Susan K. Ogle is the nurse manager of the outpatient oncology department and nurse practitioner in the cancer survivorship program at The Children's Hospital of Philadelphia, PA.

will learn about the role that healthy eating habits, not smoking, and regular exercise play in keeping their heart healthy.

Another essential component of educating survivors is providing them with a detailed, written summary of their disease, treatment and follow-up guidelines. Every survivor of childhood cancer should have such a summary, in order to provide a detailed medical history to all subsequent health care providers. A summary form is available online at *http://www.patientcenters.com/survivors*. Click on "Cancer Patient's Treatment Record."

Research

Learning more about late effects and how to best identify and treat them is an essential part of comprehensive follow up programs. The research goals of comprehensive follow-up programs include:

- Investigate new areas of potential late effects.
- Utilize current data to help guide clinical practice in caring for survivors.
- Validate the current recommended surveillance guidelines and their effectiveness in the early identification of late effects.
- Identify the impact of the aging process on the organ system(s) already affected by previous disease and treatment.
- Provide outcome information to alter future treatment protocols to reduce potential late effects, while maintaining current survival rates.

Assessing Cognitive Effects and Educational Needs

Survivorship programs develop a risk profile for each survivor, based on disease and treatment, which is then used to determine the likelihood of developing neurocognitive deficits. Many survivors of childhood cancer have no educational difficulties, while others develop learning problems that can range from subtle to severe.

Several factors (treatment and non-treatment related) influence a child's cognitive functioning. A thorough neurocognitive evaluation takes into consideration all physical, psychological, and social treatment-related factors as well as non-treatment related factors.

> Wendy L. Hobbie is the coordinator of the cancer survivorship program and advanced practice oncology nurses at The Children's Hospital of Philadelphia, PA.

Physical factors that can cause cognitive late

effects include any therapy directly affecting the central nervous system, including radiation or chemotherapy used for children with brain tumors, some types of leukemia, and some forms of lymphoma. Those children who have relapsed or been diagnosed with a second cancer and have received intensive or prolonged therapy may also be at increased risk. Other physical disabilities that may also increase the risk of learning problems include loss of vision or hearing.

Social factors that can increase the risk of problems in school include prolonged hospitalizations and frequent school absences. Temporary or permanent fatigue also may affect schooling and social relationships. Psychological factors such as anxiety, post-traumatic stress, and distractibility or difficulty concentrating can also affect cognitive functioning.

Non-treatment related factors that can affect academic functioning include:

- Developmental delays prior to treatment.
- Academic performance prior to therapy.
- Prior need for special education services, for example, resource room, individualized educational program (IEP), or self-contained classroom.
- Behavioral characteristics, including high energy levels or attention deficit disorder.

Referring for Neurocognitive or Psychoeducational Testing

After the results of the initial evaluation have been evaluated, any survivor at risk for cognitive late effects should be referred for formal neurocognitive testing. As there is wide variability among tests and interpretations, a psychologist familiar with late effects of childhood cancer should be consulted to determine which tests are most appropriate for individual survivors based on their risk profiles. There are two broad categories of neurocognitive testing: neuropsychological and psychoeducational testing.

Neuropsychological testing is a comprehensive method to evaluate cognitive functioning. It includes detailed and specialized testing of cognitive functioning to identify strengths and weaknesses (if any). These tests need to be administered by a trained neuropsychologist who has experience working with survivors of childhood cancer. See Chapter 5, *Neuropsychological Testing*, for detailed information.

Schools sometimes give survivors educational and/or psychological tests to evaluate basic intellectual, academic, and cognitive functioning. Special education teachers, guidance counselors, or school psychologists administer these tests. Parents can give permission to have just educational tests done, or both psychological and educational tests done. Or, they can provide the neuropsychological test results to the school in lieu of school administered tests.

Once an evaluation is performed by either method described above, a complete summary of the results with clear recommendations should be given to the parents. School personnel and parents then use the information to develop appropriate accommodations to help the child succeed academically.

Serial evaluations are often necessary to monitor cognitive function over time, as changes may be progressive. A psychologist who is familiar with the late effects of childhood cancer should determine how often the child should be tested.

Providing Anticipatory Guidance

Survivors and their parents need accurate information to become effective advocates for an appropriate education. Survivorship programs can assist survivors and their families to re-establish connections and facilitate reintegration into the school system. Communicating with educators in the child's school system is essential. An Individual Education Plan (IEP) meeting may be necessary to address needs and ensure appropriate resources. School guidance counselors, school or survivorship team psychologists, and the education liaison often help families navigate through the education system.

The survivorship team also assists families with the information obtained from neurocognitive testing. The survivorship team can help the survivor and family set realistic life goals based on the results of the comprehensive evaluation and formal educational testing. During periods of transition, the team must prepare the family for future planning based on recent neurocognitive information. Transition from high school to college, vocational training school, or the work force is a critical decision-making time for all adolescents. However, these choices can be more complicated for survivors with cognitive deficits.

If college is a realistic option for survivors with cognitive problems, advice from the high school guidance counselor, school psychologist and survivorship team is necessary to evaluate options. Choosing a college or university that provides the most appropriate special education services gives survivors their best chance for success. It may also be necessary to advise a survivor to consider attending a vocational school to develop a specific set of skills for future employment rather than attending college.

Finally, some survivors are neurocognitively disabled by their treatment. The survivorship team can facilitate an assessment of their ability to live independently. If independent living is not feasible, the team can help the survivor and family in identifying alternative living options.

Although many children survive childhood cancer, one of the most significant costs of long-term survival is lasting neurocognitive deficits. Assessment and intervention by individuals who understand these deficits is essential to maximize the survivor's strengths. These types of evaluations are best accomplished through a survivorship program. If such a program is not available at the treating institution, the survivor should request a referral to a survivorship clinic, where he or she may reap the full benefits of such a program. A listing of comprehensive survivorship clinics may also be found on the Internet at *http://www.candlelighters.org/followupclinics.stm*.

Key Points

- Thousands of children with cancer are surviving their disease, and it is imperative that they be followed in a comprehensive survivorship program.

- Survivorship programs include a dedicated medical team including physicians, nurse practitioners, social workers, psychologists, and sub specialists (e.g., enocrinologists, cardiologists) who are interested and experienced in helping survivors of childhood cancer.

- Survivorship programs provide developmentally appropriate clinical care, wellness education, and surveillance and treatment for the late effects of cancer.

- Survivorship programs also help assess the cognitive function of survivors and help families develop an appropriate educational plan.

Parent Perspectives

My son was treated for high-risk ALL at a famous children's hospital, 120 miles from our home, which had top-notch doctors and state-of-the-art equipment. Unfortunately, they did no comprehensive follow up. Yes, they checked for recurrence of disease, but nothing more. My son was at risk for growth failure (developed it), short stature (yep), early puberty (yep), heart damage (nope), hepatitis C (nope), osteoporosis (okay so far), learning disabilities (big time) and many more. I did a lot of research and found that the closest comprehensive clinic was 1000 miles away. We started to fly there every year.

A few years later, we moved to a large city because my son needed more services than our fairly small town could provide. The closest comprehensive follow up clinic to our new location (despite three pediatric oncology facilities within 40 miles) was 160 miles away. So, we drive there once a year and they serve as consultants for the local doctors (pediatrician, orthopedist, endocrinologist, physical therapist, psychologist, etc).

The services we get are irreplaceable. My son gets wellness education and essential info about his disease and treatment. Last year the Journal of the American Medical Association printed research results that showed a shocking number of adult survivors of childhood cancer knew next to nothing about their cancer and treatment. We won't have that problem. Every year, I step back more as he is learning to take over. Every year, he learns more about how to stay well. He knows what he needs to do for follow up, and what he doesn't need to worry about.

The doctor, nurse practitioner, and psychologist are incredibly knowledgeable and I feel that we are in very good hands.

✛ ✛ ✛

One of the best things we did after treatment was to visit a late effects clinic. My daughter was treated for standard risk ALL from the ages of 3 to 6, under a protocol that included triple intrathecals and high dose methotrexate. She was not supposed to be a likely candidate for late effects. During treatment, however, she had a lot of problems that were not "likely."

About a year off-treatment, she suffered two spontaneous leg fractures—another unlikelihood, because she had not had the super-high doses of steroids that many of the kids got. A DEXA scan showed that she had a 4 sigma decrease in bone density, the rough equivalent of a 90-year-old woman. Meanwhile, her grades had begun to plummet in second grade. Where she had always been at the top of her class, now she stopped wanting to read, her writing was illegible, she had trouble concentrating, had temper tantrums, and she had the memory of a butterfly. Neither the educators nor the doctors were much impressed, but it troubled me greatly.

I realized that I no longer felt confident about what I should take seriously. I wanted to guide my daughter back to the most normal life possible, but I did not want to overreact or overlook real perils. Several hospitals near us claimed to have late effects clinics (our own hospital did not), but when I investigated them I could tell that their focus was on gathering empirical data about effects rather than on the health and welfare of the child they were seeing. We chose to go to a comprehensive late effects program, several hours away, on the advice of a friend who said that their focus is on quality of life issues first and data gathering second.

The intake interview was very thorough as were the physical exams. The staff were all terrific with kids. Even though my daughter was only seven, everyone we saw spoke directly to her from the beginning in a respectful and age appropriate way and only turned to me when they were convinced that they needed to. It took all day, but was well worth the time. I came away feeling that finally someone in the medical community cared about how life would be from now on. The report supported that. It stated clearly what they thought we should watch closely, what tests we should do and when, what might come up later and how to know if it did, and what they believed I could safely scratch off my list of concerns.

There was an unlooked for side benefit. Discussing late effects had always been touchy with our oncologists. Although it sometimes seemed that they did not care about what came after the last day of treatment, in fairness, they just felt besieged. Parents were pressuring them to do better follow-up, but as a fairly small practice they could barely keep up with the acute care needs. After reading the report from the program, my oncologist asked what they offered that his practice did not. He also asked why I had picked that clinic and not one of the closer ones. It opened the door to a productive and non-defensive discussion about the different goals of the front line practitioners and the late effects clinics. I have heard that he has since recommended that certain patients be followed up there.

Chapter 12

Cognitive Remediation

Donna R. Copeland, PhD
Robert W. Butler, PhD

Children and adolescents can incur brain injury as a result of accidents, problems in prenatal development, abuse, epilepsy, metabolic disorders, and any number of illnesses and unfortunate circumstances. We now know that those who had cancer in childhood and had central nervous system involvement and treatment are likewise at risk for developing cognitive difficulties as a result. Yet, clinical services are rarely available for any of these children. Only recently has there been a concerted research effort to devise and evaluate remediation programs that have promise of benefiting survivors of childhood cancer and improving their outlook in educational pursuits.

To address this problem, a Cognitive Remediation Program was designed to improve survivors' abilities to attend, remember, and learn. Specifically, the program attempts to counteract the cognitive effects of irradiation or chemotherapy treatment to the central nervous system, which include lapses of attention during school-type tasks, distractibility, and inefficient, slow information processing. Once children have developed these problems, repeated failures at school result in low self-esteem and self-confidence, and isolation from peers.

Because of the global nature of the effects, a holistic, team-centered approach is needed. Parents and teachers should join the child and therapist in developing ways to compensate for acquired losses. With all parties working together, the child can make tremendous strides in overcoming a significant obstacle in life.

Following is a description of the Cognitive Remediation Program, with examples illustrating how it works in practice. The results of a pilot study of the program conducted at Oregon Health & Science University and The University of Texas M. D. Anderson Cancer Center will also be presented. In 2001, a randomized, controlled

> Dr. Copeland is professor of pediatrics (psychology) and chief of the behavioral medicine section at The University of Texas M.D. Anderson Cancer Center in Houston, TX.

clinical trial began at seven major cancer centers in the United States to see if the program is helpful for survivors of leukemia/lymphoma and brain tumors. This study was completed in 2003, and an application for renewal of funding for a revised study containing a parent-training component was submitted to the National Institutes of Health.

The Cognitive Remediation Program involves three kinds of activities: massed practice, learning strategies for increasing attention, and psychological intervention. It consists of at least 20 two-hour weekly sessions with a therapist who tailors the intervention to each student's special needs; for instance, proceeding slowly or rapidly, focusing on math or reading or memory skills, etc. During each session, students practice exercises that improve attention skills and are taught strategies that help maintain focus. Through successful learning experiences, the students' attitudes toward school change, and they begin to feel happier and more self-confident.

> *"Alex" is a seven-year-old survivor of ALL with a significant attentional deficit following treatment when he was two. He had attended a number of special learning programs which were moderately successful. When his parents wanted him to come to Cognitive Remediation, he was angry and tearful. After just one session however, he was smiling, and after the second session, did not want to stop at the end of the two hours.*

The last 15 minutes or so of each training session is spent with the parents, telling them about the strategies the student is learning and coaching them on parenting practices. Emotional and behavioral problems are addressed, and when possible, these are dealt with as part of the program. If a child or parent would benefit from additional psychotherapeutic interventions, a referral is made to another member of the psychosocial/counseling team at the cancer center. Regular dialog also takes place with the school teachers who receive periodic reports of the student's progress in Cognitive Remediation. In exchange, they are asked to comment about changes or continuing problems they observe in the student.

From time to time, a school visit by a member of the cancer center education/neuropsychology team is arranged, to share with the teacher information gleaned from the neuropsychological assessment and training sessions, and to provide recommendations for alterations that would be beneficial to the student.

Dr. Butler is an associate professor in the pediatric hematology/oncology division of Oregon Health and Science University in Portland, OR.

Components of the Cognitive Remediation

Program were derived from three disciplines: Brain injury rehabilitation, educational psychology/special education, and clinical psychology. These components are described in more detail below.

Exercises to Improve Attention and Speed of Processing

Two clinician-researchers in brain injury rehabilitation (McKay Sohlberg and Catherine Mateer) developed a model that regards attention as the capacity for the brain to focus on an object over time and to be flexible in processing the information. This is called cognitive flexibility. The Sohlberg/Mateer model describes four types of attention. They offer a set of exercises to improve each type, which is called Attention Process Training. Types of attentional processes include:

- **Sustained:** the ability to hold a thought or perception continuously across time.
- **Selective:** the ability to focus on one element in a perceptual field while screening out unimportant information.
- **Alternating:** mental flexibility or the ability to move between tasks having different sets of instructions.
- **Divided:** the ability to respond to two or more sets of instructions simultaneously.

For example, to exercise sustained attention, the student may be asked to listen for a few minutes to an audiotaped voice reciting numbers or letters and to press a buzzer when he/she hears a certain number or letter, such as '3' or 'A'. As the student gains competence in the task, it is made more difficult by speeding up the recitation and by making the task itself more difficult. For example, the student may be instructed to press a buzzer in response to hearing the name of a fruit from a list of different kinds of foods. Distractors are added to the exercise to improve skills in selective attention. This may be done by adding background noise on the tape and instructing the student to listen and respond only to the narrator's recitation.

To exercise alternating attention, the student is asked to alternate between two different instructions (such as adding and subtracting numbers), in response to the therapist's instruction to "Change."

To exercise divided attention, the student is asked to perform two different instructions at once. An example is to press the buzzer when a certain number is heard on the audiotape while at the same time circling the names of clothing items from a list of words on paper.

> *"Bruce" was horrified when this task was first introduced. "You mean I have to do two things at once?!" he said as he began to tear up. The therapist calmed him and went over the instructions again, expressing her confidence in his ability to accomplish the task. Much to her surprise and to his delight, he mastered it, even during a conversation the therapist had with a colleague who had knocked on the door during the task. Bruce was so thrilled with his accomplishment, he literally jumped up and down.*

There are many different types of such exercises, and as the student gains competence, they are gradually made more complex and the speed of the presentation is increased. Tasks are first presented at a level in which the student will be successful 50% of the time. When competence is achieved 80% of the time, the next level of difficulty is introduced.

Students almost always find these tasks interesting and engaging, and to avoid boredom, they are alternated with commercial games that are also fun but exercise their attention skills as well. These include board games like Mastermind, card games like UNO and Slamwitch, computer games like Shanghai, and electronic games like Star Wars, Simon, or Bop-it.

Some of the activities are prescribed as homework so that the student is practicing the skills in other settings and at other times outside the program. Homework may also be something that will help the student in planning and organization. For instance, the assignment may be to call a restaurant and make a reservation for the family to dine out one evening.

Strategies

Behavioral strategies derived from educational psychology and special education are used to teach children how to prepare for a task, to maintain focus during a task, and to reinforce good work after a task. To enhance the student's readiness to learn, he/she is taught to organize materials to be used in the task, to sit up straight, and to ask questions about any instructions that are unclear.

> *In the beginning of her training, Dora had difficulty settling down and focusing on the tasks at hand. She and her therapist devised a self-talk method she could use to remind herself to sit up straight and focus. It was "Ready to work!" spoken in an enthusiastic voice.*

During a task, students are taught to read the instructions carefully and to start at the top of a page and work down the page systematically. "Mark your place" is a strategy whereby the student places a small mark or uses a finger to keep track of which line is the focus.

After the task is completed, students are encouraged to check their work and to reward themselves for a job well done. Examples of this might be to say to themselves, "Good job!" and give the therapist a "high five." Or they might pat themselves on the back.

There are an infinite number of strategies possible, and the students are encouraged to create their own. Of utmost importance is a strategy's meaningfulness to the student and its effectiveness in achieving a specific goal.

> *"Robbie" had difficulty paying attention to the teacher at school and his mind had a tendency to wander. He was also a child who was fascinated with cheetahs and liked to talk about them and draw pictures of them. He and his therapist spent some time discussing cheetahs and observed that cheetahs could get lost in the jungle if they did not keep their mind on their goal. Robbie identified with this concept, and used it to remind himself to pay attention at school, otherwise, he might get "lost" and miss some of the information the teacher was giving him.*

Psychological Interventions

Psychological interventions involve helping the parent step back to allow the child more opportunities for independent functioning. Many parents of children with cancer have difficulty with this because their child has required so much extra care. Once the child is off treatment, however, it is often hard to change old habits. The therapist guides the parents in increasing structure at home, revising their expectations of the survivor, making them more consistent with expectations of other children in the home, and being consistent with limit-setting and pre-defined consequences. Family therapy may be necessary at times when additional issues arise.

> *"Walter's" father often complained about his teenage son, and showed no confidence in his ability to assume more responsibility and keep up with his schoolwork. He was very skeptical of Cognitive Remediation, and was rather quiet during the first family meeting. The therapist explained the program to him, and introduced ideas about how he could be getting more out of his son. The father grasped the concepts very quickly; he changed his approach to parenting, and became much less harsh and more encouraging*

of his son's efforts. His son responded favorably and willingly devised consequences for himself when he did not complete his homework.

An optimistic frame of mind is reinforced throughout the training. Students come up with words of encouragement to say to themselves in an internal dialog, such as "I can do it," "I'm going to beat my [previous] record," or "I'm a star."

Students are also taught how to withstand distractions that might occur in a classroom. For instance, the therapist may talk on the phone, tap the student on the shoulder, or make some kind of noise, with the instruction that the student is to ignore the distraction and continue on task.

Therapists reinforce every positive step toward a goal and encourage and train students in organization, judgment, and decision-making. Students are frequently given notebooks with sections containing material for each of their classes, such as homework assignments. The student, therapist, parent, and teacher all work together in training the student to feel a sense of ownership and responsibility for the notebook, to put materials in their proper places, and to remember to carry it between school and home.

Generalization

An important goal of the program is generalization of the skills learned, so the involvement of parents and teachers is critical in the training. This is accomplished by assigning homework for the student to complete at home and/or at school and by frequent consultation with parents and teachers. Parents and teachers are informed about the strategies the student is learning in the program and are asked to remind the student to use them at home and at school. Parents are coached on using structure and routine at home, using attention and ignoring as ways of eliciting desired behaviors, setting reasonable expectations for their child's behavior, and devising appropriate consequences for targeted behaviors.

Parents are encouraged to increase their expectations of the survivor and to foster greater independence of their child. For instance, the parent is asked not to remind the child about homework, but to work with the child and therapist on strategies to help him or her to remember to do it and to bring it in to the sessions.

"Anna" was an immature child whose mother was very indulgent, as Anna was the apple of her eye. Her mother did not realize that because Anna was not expected to take responsibility, she had developed the sense that she "couldn't" do things other children her age could. During the training, Anna began letting her mother know she did not need her help in completing

her homework. "No, thank you," Anna told her mother, "I must do it myself." When Anna came to a session without her homework, the assignment was increased for the next time. This was done in the spirit of a game, and Anna accepted the extra work without complaint, because it was based on a plan she and the therapist had drawn up beforehand.

Pilot Study Results

A pilot study of the Cognitive Remediation Program was conducted from 1996 to 1999 at Oregon Health & Science University and The University of Texas M. D. Anderson Cancer Center to evaluate its effectiveness in improving the attention of survivors of childhood cancer. Participants were 31 cancer survivors with documented attention deficits. Twenty one completed the cognitive remediation program and 10 served as comparison subjects. All were tested on vigilant attention, memory for a series of numbers, and memory for sentences, and arithmetic achievement. Comparison of the two groups' scores showed that the trained group improved significantly in a six-month period of time on all attention measures; whereas the other group did not manifest any significant changes during approximately the same time period. Neither group improved on the arithmetic achievement test, most likely because that measure tends to reflect long-term gains rather than short-term improvement. The success of the program indicated by these results prompted a multi-center randomized controlled study, which began in 2001. Reports of that study will be forthcoming.

Issues in Cognitive Remediation

The efficacy and advisability of stimulant medication is always an issue in a discussion about attention deficit. Indeed, there is some evidence that medication may improve attention and concentration in children whose cancer treatment included chemotherapy or irradiation of the central nervous system. For instance, methylphenidate (Ritalin) has been shown to improve attention abilities in this population. Although this evidence is still preliminary, it appears that a large percentage of these children benefit from the medication treatment, although perhaps at a lower dose than healthy children with ADHD. There is clearly a need for additional research in this area, and it may be that other medications are equally or more effective in improving attentional abilities in childhood cancer survivors. The combination of cognitive remediation with medication is sometimes especially helpful.

"Giraldo" was a 7-year-old survivor of ALL who had received only

chemotherapy for his treatment; he did not receive cranial radiation therapy. Even at the time of diagnosis, he was regarded as a child with an attention deficit. He began Cognitive Remediation, but was having difficulty remaining still enough to attend to the tasks. He said it wasn't him—it was his hands. They just wouldn't stay still. He and the therapist devised a strategy of folding his hands in his lap, but, demonstrating his sincerity and motivation to comply, he felt it necessary to sit on his hands. Nevertheless, impulsivity and hyperactivity were still problems at home and at church, where he would jump up and greet a friend across the room during the service. He was also getting into trouble at school. Giraldo's mother was not in favor of his taking additional medication after his cancer treatment, but when the doctors and therapists whom she trusted recommended giving it a try, she relented. The medication was immediately effective in controlling the hyperactivity, and Giraldo was able to use the Cognitive Remediation training much more effectively. His teacher was delighted with the change in behavior, and Giraldo made the honor roll the next semester.

Although many children who go through the Cognitive Remediation Program will not require medication, it is a valuable aid for some, especially those who have trouble controlling their impulses and hyperactivity.

Another issue that arises with Cognitive Remediation is the expense, in that it requires two-hour sessions every week for at least 20 weeks. Many children can use—and want—even more. Some third-party payers will reimburse parents for this service, but some will not. It is reasonable to regard it as a medical condition that developed as a side effect of cancer treatment; however, some medical insurers insist that mental health insurers cover it.

Maintenance of the gains achieved in the Cognitive Remediation Program is still unproven. There is some evidence that the student continues to use the strategies as long as six months post-intervention, but to answer the question of whether the gains continue after that will require additional research.

Another pertinent question is how soon Cognitive Remediation should be introduced for the child to gain maximum benefit. So far, the intervention has only been offered to survivors who are at least a year off treatment for cancer and have developed an attention deficit. It is not known whether it might be even more effective for patients at the time they are undergoing central nervous system treatment as a means of preventing or buffering its effects.

Acknowledgements:

The program and studies described in this chapter were supported by the National Institutes of Health, the Carol Solov Abbani Foundation, and the Houston Chapter of the Pi Beta Phi Club and Foundation.

KeyPoints

- Survivors whose central nervous system was involved in the cancer or its treatment are at risk for attention deficits, which can be alleviated by cognitive remediation.

- The Cognitive Remediation Program uses cognitive exercises, development of strategies, and psychological support in a three-pronged approach to help students overcome attention problems.

- The program uses a team approach involving the survivor, therapist, parents, and teachers all working together to reinforce the student's continued use of the strategies learned and applying them in home and school settings.

- As a result of their experiences in the Cognitive Remediation Program, many survivors have an improved quality of life, particularly at school.

Parent Perspectives

We recently returned from Rochester, NY, where we are pursuing participation in the cognitive remediation study. It is our hope that our son can benefit from these learning strategies, so that his challenges can be minimized. We hope the message to him is we are vested in his well-being, and we will work hard right along him to help him achieve his pre-diagnosis dreams, as hard as that may now be. Participation in this study is a logistical nightmare but I don't care. My family thinks I'm crazy. I don't care. My son feels supported and encouraged. That's all I care about. Sometimes it's hard to keep adjusting, searching, seeking, advocating and altering the path I thought our lives would take. Over and over I keep repeating the Reebok slogan, "Just Do It." So I do.

✦ ✦ ✦

My daughter participated in the cognitive remediation pilot study. The premise is good, but in reality, twenty 45-minute sessions was not enough to make any permanent changes/improvements. My understanding was that it was a pilot study to see if there was true efficacy, and if so, the program would be expanded. Their techniques were good and on an ongoing (i.e. weekly) basis for several months, I think it would probably really help.

✦ ✦ ✦

I know that this is controversial, but I have seen Ritalin make a miraculous change in a kid's ability to concentrate. There is pretty limited data from the post-radiation, and post-intrathecal chemo kids, but there is a potential reason why it might be effective for them, beyond when a post radiation kid has signs and symptoms of ADD or ADHD (my poor child who survived a brain tumor had ADHD before he had radiation).

Radiation causes white matter volume reduction. ADHD has been associated with white matter volume reduction. Kids with ADHD who were treated with Ritalin as children had less white matter volume reduction than kids with ADHD who were not treated with Ritalin. The Journal of the American Medical Association published an article on this topic. "Developmental Trajectories of Brain Volume Abnormalities in Children and Adolescents" Castellanos et al. JAMA *2002; 288: 1740-1748. You can probably find this journal at your local public library.*

✛ ✛ ✛

My son had Burkitt's lymphoma and a treatment-related stroke that left him with many disabilities. What we were seeing both at home and at school was that he was having an extremely difficult time with organization. I asked the child psychiatrist who has administered the neuropsych tests about using Ritalin, and we enrolled him in a double blind trial after the school year finished.

By double blind I mean the pharmacist gave me a packet of labeled doses (day 1, day 2, etc) but I didn't know which dose contained full strength, half and zero. Then the educational aide was supposed to take notes about my son's behavior based upon a set of questions the doctor provided. Pretty straightforward, but the school did a lousy job. Still, the results showed enough of an effect to merit him going on the meds.

We fiddled with the dose. He is now on 10 mg. sustained release, which he takes with breakfast. I actually have a prescription for twice a day, but he doesn't want to go to the nurse to get his medication mid-day so I am respecting his wishes. He doesn't complain about the morning meds, wears his hearing aids and generally takes care of his glasses and his orthotic, so I figured the kid could have a break on that issue. I've talked to him about whether he understands why he takes it, and in his own way he does understand that it is easier for him to connect with the other kids when he takes his medication.

One thing I noticed tonight (he was having a rough go of it) was that he is actually agitated now when he isn't on his meds. When he's not on his meds, he's literally a bundle of nerves, poor guy. On the meds, he's able to absorb the world and its sudden noises and dark corners with more contemplation and even curiosity.

✛ ✛ ✛

Our daughter Chantell (diagnosed with a medulloblastoma in 1998 when she was 12 ½ years old) gets very frustrated with her short term memory lapses, loses focus very easily, and has trouble completing a task or remembering where she put something a few minutes ago. This is quite frustrating because if she doesn't find something when she is looking for it, and moves to something else she may forget that she was looking for the item and what she was going to do with it. End result—the task she wanted to do is not done.

Initially she took Ritalin, then Adderal, which really helped her with processing speed, attention and focus. She seems to think a bit faster so she appears to be able to complete more thoughts and tasks before short-term memory gets in the way. However, she reacted to those two meds with mood swings that could give the strongest friend or parent whiplash. While taking Adderal, when she had something to say, she would blurt it out, without considering the impact on the party being spoken to, and it came out and sounded like an attack, when frequently it appeared to not be intended as such. Subsequently she has been taking a newer drug StratTera (atomoxetine HCI 40 mg.). I feel that she is less organized than she was on Adderal, but also less tense. We do not feel the same internal fury as we did with Adderal. While a quite subjective measure, this medication feels more benevolent and less character-changing to date than either Ritalin or Adderal.

✦✦✦

My daughter's bilateral retinoblastoma was treated with surgery (both eyes removed), chemotherapy, and radiation. She goes to the public school where she has a half day with a special teacher for the blind and a half day in the regular class with a teacher's aide. She was having some problems in school for a couple of years, but it was hard to tell if it was because she couldn't see or was a late effect from the radiation. So we did neuropsych testing and found the problem areas: language processing and attention. This year we started her on a very low dose of Ritalin to help her focus. Since then, she's improved her reading from a 2.3 grade level to a 4.3 (she's in fourth grade)—two full grades in a year. I just came back from the school, where she received the Most Improved Student award.

✦✦✦

My ex-husband, a clinical psychologist, has insisted that our son Mayer (16 years old and almost three years from diagnosis of a medulloblastoma and whole brain radiation) be on Concerta (a time-release form of Ritalin) full-time. He considers it a reasonable substitute for the energy-producing hormones which radiation might have knocked out, and thinks it may also be mitigating the cognitive effects of radiation, especially attention and short-term memory problems. His enthusiasm for the drug began with a scientific paper correlating IQ loss in kids who've had radiation with the amount of white matter loss as seen on their MRIs. Another paper in JAMA showed that kids with ADHD have less white matter than other kids, except that ADHD kids on stimulants seem to actually have more white matter than ADHD kids who haven't been on stimulants. Concerta does seem to improve Mayer's endurance, alertness, and attention, but I have been wishing to see if now, years later, he might be able to manage without it. We would have to tough out a couple weeks or a month off the drug to have a fair trial, as there are withdrawal issues: when he misses just a day, he gets very tired and indifferent.

✦ ✦ ✦

I wanted to give my girl all the advantages I could since she had the deck stacked against her. She had surgical removal of a brain tumor and whole brain radiation at age 5. It was evident that her processing speed was significantly slower than the average and she had trouble with endurance. I asked our neuro-oncologist if Concerta or Adderal might be appropriate for my girl. Since these also tend to act as appetite suppressants (being amphetamines), he was against this for my daughter. She was well below the 5th percentile for height and weight. He felt it would, at this point, be a detriment to her health and nutritional status.

I then went looking for a cognitive remediation program but found that the study did not really fit for what I thought my daughter needed, as it seemed to focus more on attention issues. Lisa's greatest academic difficulties seem to be in the area of visual perception (letter and number reversal, reading right to left, reading difficulties). Thus, educational strategies and techniques used for dyslexia seemed more appropriate. I read probably a dozen books including information for learning disabilities, dyslexia, and cognitive remediation in special education and traumatic brain injury. Finally I decided the best help for her could be garnered from a special learning differences school that was able to use a variety of techniques for children with varying educational problems. They don't call it cognitive remediation; rather, they say learning differently. Whatever you call it—it is working for us.

Chapter 13

School Options

Loice Swisher, MD

Childhood cancer can derail plans for a child's education. Parents who once only considered a particular school suddenly might have to look at other alternatives. Plans change for many reasons: A child is too sick to attend classes; private schools are unwilling or unable to make necessary accommodations; therapy services are available only through the public school system. Depending on many factors, a family might choose public or private education. In fact, through the course of therapy and beyond, some families use multiple options for schooling.

Public school options include public classroom, hospital or homebound tutoring, and charter school education. Private school options include home schooling, private schools, and religious schools. Because state laws vary, this chapter is a general introduction to school options for children with cancer. Parents can obtain more specific information about the options and regulations in their state by contacting their state's Department of Education.

Public Education Options

Public classroom education

Public schools are often viewed as the best option for many children dealing with cancer and its treatment because public schools are legally mandated to provide a free, appropriate education (see Chapter 14, *Special Education: The Law*). In addition to a variety of therapy services, public schools are required to provide instruction in the least restrictive environment. In order to do this, schools have devised several options to aid children.

A child may be placed in:

- A regular (general education) class without additional support.
- A regular (general education) class with modifications, adaptations and

> Dr. Swisher, MD is an advocate and mother of a 9-year-old girl who had a medulloblastoma brain tumor.

additional support.

- A special education classroom.

- A special education classroom with additional support.

If the school cannot provide an appropriate education then it must pay for private special education day school or residential placement.

Public schools are required by the Individual with Disabilities Education Act (IDEA) to devise a plan for transitioning to life after high school. Some students will be able to continue on a normal academic course, while other students may need more assistance. School districts have a department for vocational evaluation that may offer specific programs. Such programs include regular vocational education, special education vocational programs, community work-study programs, and centers for independent living. Transition planning starts between the ages of 14 and 16.

Some school districts and organizations are developing video-based distance learning that enable children to participate with their class from home. Currently, the quality and expense of the equipment varies and few school districts or teachers have experience with such a set-up. However, some children are using video conferencing systems to remain part of the class while recuperating at home.

Home or hospital tutoring

The public school system provides home or hospital tutoring for children with physician-documented illnesses that prevent attending regular classes for more than a few weeks. The major drawback is that the tutoring is usually only three to five hours a week. Since schoolteachers serve as tutors, these hours may be in the late afternoon or early evening. If staying on grade level is an important goal, parents may need to do supplementary teaching and encourage independent study. In these cases, the tutor can help provide material to cover and suggestions on how to go about it. Students might also have an assigned classroom where they can participate in special events (e.g., holiday parties or school assemblies) or attend school when able. See Chapter 4, *School Re-entry,* for more information on this topic.

Classroom-based charter school

Charter schools are independent, self-managed, tax-supported public schools that are given autonomy in exchange for performance accountability. Local leaders apply to a school district for a time-limited "charter" to start a school with a special mission. Since these are public schools, the Individuals with Disabilities Education Act (IDEA) applies and qualified disabled students are accommodated.

Charter schools are relatively new. Minnesota passed the first charter school law in 1991. In 2002, there were approximately 2,700 charter schools operating in 36 states, Washington D.C. and Puerto Rico. Some schools have completed their first charter term successfully and have been renewed. Other charter schools have been closed due to lack of achievement, poor financial management, discipline problems, or ineffective administration. In some cases these failures forced children to repeat grades.

Charter schools may be attractive to parents of kids with cancer because charter schools tend to be smaller in size, usually encourage innovative teaching techniques, and have staff invested in the children and school's success. Since they are public schools, students are entitled to evaluation for IEPs and 504 plans, which may not be available to private and homeschooled students. As with many developing ideas, charter schools have had many bumps in the road. Parents need to fully investigate the fiscal management, the teachers' credentials, and the school's track record with special education students as well as achievement of students in general.

Non classroom-based charter schools (cyber school or on-line schools)

In 2002, twelve states were providing the latest twist in education—cyber charter schools. Cyber schools rely on the Internet for transmission of curricula, assignments, and communication with teachers while the child learns at home. The actual time on the computer varies greatly. In some classes, the child will download an assignment that requires reading a book and writing a report. At other times, actual classes may be viewed over the computer. The cyber school is responsible for providing equipment and supplies—including a computer and Internet access. In contrast to home schooling, the responsibility of curricula development, subject expertise, and record keeping is shifted from the parents to the cyber school. However, parents are the primary supervisors and provide day-to-day monitoring of schoolwork.

In many states, cyber schools enrollment is available to any child residing in the state. In addition to children with cancer, parents of full time athletes or entertainers, former home schoolers, pregnant teens, and children with chronic illnesses may view this as a viable option. Because non-classroom based charter schools are publicly funded, students are entitled to a free, appropriate public education. As with home schooling, the child can work at his or her own pace, take breaks as needed and take extra time for repetition. Unfortunately, cyber schools may not have developed mechanisms for providing services such as occupational, physical and speech therapy. Cyber school students can receive a regular high school diploma.

Parents may encounter hurdles from the local school district if they choose this alternative. The National Education Association position statement on their website opposes these schools as "an abuse of the charter school concept" (*see http://www.nea.org/charter*). Some school districts have refused to pay and have filed lawsuits against these schools.

Private Options

Parents have many options for educating their children outside of the public school setting. These include home schooling, and attending private or religious schools. Parents can also have their child dual-enrolled. This means that the child can qualify for and receive special education services from the public school while home schooling or attending private schools.

Home schooling

Parents may choose to educate their child at home. Individual instruction and flexibility make this an attractive alternative for some families.

Although the school district monitors the home schooling curriculum, records, and assessment, this is not a public education. Home-schooled children with disabilities do not have Individual Education Plans and the school district has no responsibility for services. Parents are responsible for curriculum design, record-keeping, teaching and assessment. Fortunately, there is a growing base of home schooling resources and parents can purchase already developed curricula. The Appendix D, *Resources*, at the end of the book, lists several home schooling resources. Networking with other home schooling families helps families identify more resources as well as provides social interactions for home schooled children.

Private and religious schools

Private and religious schools do not have to make accommodations or modifications for students with disabilities. Some parents may choose to switch their children from private schools to the public school system to qualify for homebound instruction and therapies. Others find that their child needs more assistance than a certain private school is able to provide. Some parents may send their children to private school because of small class size and more supervision.

Private school children sometimes qualify for assistance from the local school district for some therapies if they are dual enrolled.

Private learning differences schools

Some students (e.g., deaf, blind, brain-injured) have needs greater than some public schools can accommodate. Specialized day or residential private school may be recommended. If the local school district makes this decision then the school district pays for the private school. A public school only has to provide an "appropriate education," not the best education money can buy. If parents choose a private school for their child without the school district's authorization, then the parents are responsible for paying tuition. Local organizations serving dyslexic, attention deficit, and autistic children may be knowledgeable about local private learning-differences schools. The blue pages of the phone book will list local support organizations.

Supplemental Options

Many parents supplement therapies provided in schools with other helpful services. Parents may prefer to choose to send their child to a non-school affiliated tutor, physical therapist, occupational therapist, psychotherapist, or others. With the physician's approval, parents may also consider activities such as swimming, yoga, ice-skating, dance, music classes, therapeutic horseback riding as well as other sports. These extra-curricular activities can provide both fun and peer interaction. Medical insurance may pay for some of these activities; parents pay for others out of pocket.

Making a Decision

There is no one "right way" to educate children with cancer. The options available vary from place to place. To find the best options for a particular child, parents will probably have to search for recommendations. Some potential sources of information include:

- The educational consultant or school liaison at the hospital. Many pediatric hospitals have specialists who may be able to guide parents towards available resources.

- The local school district's special education director. In general, the special education director will focus on the services the school district will be able to provide to the child.

- The local school district's brain injury specialists. This can be an exceptional resource for parents of children with brain tumors.

- The state's Department of Education and corresponding website. There is a surprising amount of information on many of these websites regarding special education, home schooling, charter schools and private schools.

- Advocacy groups for children with special needs. Since childhood cancer is rare, information might be more easily obtained from other groups that have similar needs. Such groups may include those for dyslexia, attention deficit disorder, traumatic brain injury, autism or special needs children.

- Networking with other parents. Sometimes it helps to learn from others' personal experiences. One might be able to find other parents through online support groups or parent-to-parent organizations.

- Local parent magazines. Some regions publish parent magazines of local activities and organizations. Frequently, there are advertisements or listings of independent schools. This is one place to find local learning differences schools.

As children's needs and wants evolve through treatment and beyond, the best option for education might change. Some children go through three or four educational settings to fit their needs over time. You know your child best; with help from professionals and other parents, you will be able to make the best decision for your family.

Key Points

- Public education options include public schools, home or hospital tutoring, classroom-based charter schools, and cyber schools.

- Private school options include home schooling, private or religious schools, and private learning differences schools.

- Parents often combine public, hospital-based and private services to obtain the best therapeutic options for their children. This can take time, creativity, and persistence.

- Many different paths can lead to educational success.

Parent Perspectives

Our son is dually enrolled—both public and private—so that the public school needs to provide services for him. We feel that the small class and school size makes the private school the best classroom option for our son (he was there before diagnosis). They also deal extremely well with social issues—being small is so much more manageable than being huge. The public school provides services that are not available from the private school such as occupational, physical, and speech therapy. These are done after school so he does not get disrupted in his school setting.

✦ ✦ ✦

My 12-year-old daughter is in seventh grade in public school. She had a BMT five years ago for AML. She doesn't have any learning disabilities, but does have a 504 plan. The first week of school, we had a meeting with all of her teachers, the school counselor, the nurse, and the dean. She got a waiver for the ten-day absence policy. Otherwise, if she was absent over ten days she automatically fails her courses. She gets to carry a water bottle at school. She sometimes needs to lie down to breathe (she has scarred lungs). I go pick up her books from her locker so she doesn't have to carry them home. She gets to leave class after everyone else does to avoid the rush and is expected to be late to the next class. I also told the teachers what she is at risk for, so they can keep an eye out for short-term memory problems, difficulty seeing (she's at risk for cataracts), etc. It's worked really well.

I didn't expect much support from the teachers, but they have been wonderful. Her history teacher has offered to bring her homework by the house when she is sick and pick up the completed homework for all of her classes. She hand-carries it to all of my daughter's teachers.

✦ ✦ ✦

We're home schooling the three oldest of our four children. We've been doing it since they were school age but the diagnosis of John (age 8 at the time) with medulloblastoma in 2002 threw everything for a loop. I really had to do a lot of soul searching to figure out what exactly I wanted my kids to learn and how best to teach them. Especially with the threat of a deadly illness, what was important to teach?

We have actually progressed this year much further than I hoped. I decided to cut out everything and start with the very basics. The greatest blessing came from Make-a-Wish. John wished for a Game Cube. This started us on a very regular schedule of first schoolwork, then Game Cube. He would pop up happily in the morning and ask what schoolwork he had to do. I wanted him to learn his multiplication tables and long division this year. He has done that. I've used a variety of resources from the Internet, used book stores and the library. We read a lot together as a family and John likes to plant gardens and work with wood and make crafts. He struggles with reading but we're not too concerned because he loves us to read to him. It would be interesting to know how much of his struggles are from surgery/ radiation/chemo, the tumor, or just being a boy who would rather do math than read. We haven't had any consultations with professionals about his education.

✦ ✦ ✦

Finding a private setting can be a challenge. My suggestions are:

- *Join a parents' support group for parents of special education students.*
- *Ask your hospital educational liaison (if there is one) if she knows of any good private schools that would be a good match for your child.*
- *See if there are any books on private schools in your geographic area.*
- *Call a private school and ask if there are any private school organizations in your area. Speak to the principal or headmaster, briefly explain your child's situation, and ask for referrals or advice.*
- *Call several special ed advocates and ask for referrals to private schools.*
- *Ask your child's special ed teacher if he or she knows of good private schools.*
- *Go to private school open houses and ask lots of questions. Chat with other parents to find what schools they are considering and why.*

- *If your child goes to a psychotherapist, ask if he or she has any advice or recommendations (ours loaned me a book that listed 315 private schools in our metro area with detailed info about each).*
- *Check with local organizations for dyslexic and autistic children. They may have lists of private schools for special needs kids.*

Good luck!

✛ ✛ ✛

Gabriel is in a home school program where he meets with the teacher every two weeks. He likes this program and can work at his own pace. We tried school for a few months and all the teachers were very kind, but Gabriel felt so different from everyone he finally refused to go. I wanted so badly for him to have more of a social life but that was part of the problem. He couldn't go out in the field and play soccer or softball. Even though he was about four months off treatment he still did not have the strength or endurance for any kind of sports. Gabriel told me he felt very different from the kids and really could not relate to them. He was also behind academically and felt very embarrassed about it.

✛ ✛ ✛

Last year we did a year of home schooling after our daughter suffered multiple complications from a brain tumor and subsequent treatment. After we were off treatment, problems required another brain surgery, over a month of IV antibiotics, months of oral antibiotics, and rehab. She was just so fatigued. Home schooling allowed us great flexibility with extended days/extended weeks and time to rest whenever she needed. We didn't miss school for doctors' appointments and could tailor her day to make just about anything a "teachable moment."

We did tons of experience-based learning as she traveled with my parents to New Mexico for the balloon festival, through the Rockies, across the Mississippi, and into the Smoky Mountains. In Williamsburg, she had an audience with Martha Washington and Thomas Jefferson. It was great but I realized we could not keep up with her needs. Her neurocognitive effects including visual perception difficulties made reading nearly impossible for me to teach her. Our neuropsychologist recommended a specific reading program that would work best for her along with repetition and small class size. We were able to find this and more in a small, private Quaker school.

✦ ✦ ✦

It is very important to know your options, as the school system is not always helpful. I happened upon a school recommended from a parent for my other son with cerebral palsy. Our son who had a brain tumor now attends this charter school for children with special medical needs that is funded by the county. Some of the students are residents and others are day students.

There is a nurse in the classroom and several nearby at the assisted living facility it is connected to. I felt this type of school was more appropriate than the school for the hearing impaired because they are better equipped to handle his seizures, tube feedings, medications, and vomiting. They have a recliner in the classroom for him when he is tired, usually after a seizure. In the assisted living facility, kids from the pediatric unit and some of the older folks do intergenerational activities during school hours as well.

My son has a volunteer who works with him in the classroom as a one-on-one aide two to three days a week. He receives speech and language therapy four to five times per week. He receives physical therapy, occupational therapy, adaptive PE and other services. Also, he and I meet with the speech pathologist the last 30 minutes of school each day to learn sign language. That's been difficult for him due to the memory loss issues, but he's learning a little as well as lip reading.

✦ ✦ ✦

My 13-year-old daughter had successful surgery and radiation for a cancerous brain tumor. Although medically fragile during chemotherapy, she said that she needed to go to school. Her former private school did not lift a finger to help. Another local private school said that having her in their school might be "too stressful" for their teachers and other students. When we went to the local public school the atmosphere was warm and receptive. The principal took us on a tour and met privately with my daughter for 45 minutes. At the end of the interview, the principal said my daughter was remarkable and asked if we would like to register immediately or think about it for a few days. I cried. I cried in relief not only for their understanding and willingness to extend themselves but also for recognizing what someone, even in difficulty, can bring to the table of life.

A few days later the principal sent a note with her home phone number just in case we had any questions. The students and faculty were welcoming and kind—inviting her to lunch and becoming friends. The guidance counselor called me to say that she was doing great. When I tried to thank her and the school she said, "We like to think we teach the children to be caring and considerate. Your daughter gives us the chance to prove it."

✦ ✦ ✦

Jon missed about two years of formal schooling due to the BMT. We were blessed with an in-hospital school program (both at his oncology center and his transplant center). We tried to keep up with his teachers at home. The school board in our area provided 5 hours of home tutoring per week for children who are unable to attend regular classes. We decided to go with an hour a day (which was about all he could handle at times). Surprisingly enough, with one-on-one instruction, one hour was sufficient. Of course we were left with homework, which we would do later in the day.

Hooked on Phonics was a great program for my boys. It is now getting passed along from friend to friend. Also, our local bookstore and office supply store always had grade and subject workbooks. My sister home schooled for a few years and was able to order a complete set of curriculum books through her local home schooling support group.

Also, just two cents worth of my thoughts. Be careful when taking on home schooling. There are times when we are wearing many hats. Mom, wife, nurse, advocate... well, you get the picture. Being a teacher on top of that is no small task. Jon and I would have difficulties, since I was telling him what he had to do in yet another venue of his life. It can really become a power struggle. For us, it was necessary, as Jon's immune system was so depleted, but it did provide its challenges. Things I learned were:

- *The local school board will likely have a website for their students and teachers. See if you can hook onto it. It will help you keep a measuring stick of what the other kids are learning at similar ages, and you may get some cool ideas.*

- *Build in some fun for both of you. (Eat the Skittle's at the end of the math lesson, have a craft day, drink hot chocolate with marshmallows while you work).*

- *Take a break and walk away if the situation becomes more about your personalities than the lesson.*

- *Let the child have some control in choosing things like time of day to study, outside or inside study, which subjects they will work on first, etc. but once their decision is made, it is adhered to.*

- *Build 20 to 30 minutes of silent reading time into their day and you sit down and read also. No better teacher than example.*

- *Kids work well for rewards. Their favorite dessert for a good mark. You'll make their bed for cooperation. An extra half hour at bedtime for finishing a book.*

- *Do something to reward yourself. My favorite reward was an inside and out van wash at the car wash. They did a great job, and I sat and had coffee. Do your nails, read a magazine, buy yourself a little treat.*

- *Housework tends to get let go.... IT'S OKAY... now repeat that three times!*

- *If you are not home schooling your other children, build in some one-on-one time with them.*

✝ ✝ ✝

I am a former teacher, turned full time mom, and have three children, ages 8, 6, and 3. My oldest, who is adopted, was diagnosed with Hodgkin's disease a year ago this week. This is my third year of home schooling. Indiana is very home school friendly. We are required to teach an "equivalency" to what would be received in public school. We are to have a 180-day school year, with the days being of our own choosing. We are required to keep attendance. We filed with the state and have our own private school number, but it is not a requirement where I live to do this. Every state has its own regulations and requirements.

Home schooling does not take all day, and we are not bound all day to sit around the kitchen table or anything like that. When a family chooses home based education, it becomes routine, like other facets of family life. Definitely home schooling is not for everyone, and no one should feel pressured into it if clearly uncomfortable with it. However, for others it is vastly rewarding. There have always been questions concerning socialization by some. Home schooling does not have to be viewed as a family completely isolated from others day in and day out. That would be the exception to the rule, as home schooling comes with opportunities to meet others in many, many ways. Here in Southern Indiana, for example, we have a community monthly newsletter packed with information. We have play groups, choir, drama, basketball, science/art/geography fairs, musical recitals, scouts, 4-H clubs, skate nights at a local skating rink, and even a spring formal for teens. In addition, there are nature hikes, specialty tutors, foreign language instructors, and two conventions—one local and one statewide each year. A free statewide magazine, called The Informer, is available as well.

✦ ✦ ✦

I am a single mom who works full time. My daughter needed to go to a public or private school. We started in public school and went through the IEP process. It was very draining to continually advocate for my child, but it made a big difference in the services she got. Usually, how the year went depended not at all on what was written in the IEP, but on who the teacher was. Some were wonderful, some were okay, and one was a nightmare.

My daughter is verbally gifted but very disabled in select areas—processing, visual spatial, non-verbal cues, sequencing, etc. By middle school, she felt very stigmatized by the IEP. If she was pulled out of class, it was very disorienting for her. She really does best in a predictable setting. She also never caught up on whatever she missed, so she frequently felt incompetent.

So, we gave up on public schools. We moved to a metropolitan area with a large number of private schools. We did a lot of research and found a college prep school (middle through high school) that was small and used multi-sensory teaching methods. Even though they do not hire teachers trained in special education methods, merely having 8 to 10 kids in a class addressed most of my daughter's challenges. The homework is always written on the board. Every teacher stops class 5 minutes early and tells the students to copy down the homework, and then the teacher briefly checks each student's assignment book. No stigma. The school is small and easy to navigate—no getting lost now. The lockers don't have locks— so no being late for class because opening the locker takes ten minutes. Also, no embarrassment if the locker combination is forgotten.

The staff works hard on creating and maintaining a close community. Any bullying or teasing is dealt with quickly and respectfully. They work hard on teaching self-advocacy skills, so now my daughter feels comfortable going to teachers with problems, rather than relying on me to rescue her or advocate to resolve problems. These are all important life skills.

We are using her college money to pay for this school. But, I feel that it is an investment in her foundation. Rather than getting further behind, she is forging ahead and developing confidence that she never had before. I also found out after she'd been there a year that the school offers partial scholarships to needy families. We qualified, and now get a financial break.

Chapter 14

Special Education: The Law

Grace Powers Monaco, JD
Gilbert P. Smith, JD

For many children, school is a refuge from the world of hospitals and procedures—a place for fun, friendship, and learning. Because school is the defining structure of every child's daily life, returning to school signals normalcy; indeed, expectations of school attendance impart a clear and reassuring message that there is a future. Some children may dread returning to school because of temporary or permanent changes to their appearance (e.g., hair loss, weight changes) or concerns that they have lost friends due to prolonged absences.

Children with cancer sometimes have physical disabilities that prevent full participation in classroom activities. These physical impairments may alter the way the child looks and also may require time out from the regular classroom work for physical, occupational, and speech therapies. Additionally, school can become a major source of frustration for children who learn differently as a result of the cancer and/or treatment. These learning differences, if handled in an insensitive or uninformed manner, can affect a child's confidence and educational achievements. Some children who survive cancer require specialized education or other accommodations as a result of deficits that develop, but not all children do. This chapter discusses the laws that address the educational needs of children during and after treatment for cancer.

The Laws

There are three laws that provide a child with cancer needed educational services:

- Federal Individuals with Disabilities Education Act (IDEA) (PL 94-142 and PL 99-457 amendments) and

> Grace Powers Monaco, a founding member of Candlelighters Childhood Cancer Foundation, has more than 30 years experience advocating on behalf of cancer patients, survivors, and their families.

the respective state laws that implement this law.

- Federal Rehabilitation Act of 1973 (Rehab Act) (PL 93-112, section 504).

- Americans with Disabilities Act of 1990 (PL 101-336).

Generally, these laws protect the rights of children with cancer who may be left with learning disabilities, attention disorders, high risk of infection, and amputations or other physical limitations that prevent use of the full range of educational programs. These laws, which apply to primary and secondary education, to infant, toddler, and preschool interventions, and to college, university, and vocational education, are premised on education as a right guaranteed to every citizen regardless of physical, mental, or health impairments. Although these laws have the authority of federal mandate, state governments implement them and may interpret the provisions differently. Contact your state Department of Education and state Protection and Advocacy Agency to obtain copies of all publications about special education.

IDEA, the ADA, and the Rehabilitation Act all apply to public schools. Specifically, Title II of the ADA applies to state and local government, and that includes public schools. Children with cancer and other eligible disabilities are entitled to and guaranteed a free and appropriate public education. Special education means specially designed instruction based on the needs of the individual survivor, and includes related services such as transportation, counseling, and physical therapy. Children with disabilities who are enrolled in public schools yet attend private schools (called "dual enrollment") in some cases are entitled to related services provided by the public school.

Individuals with Disabilities Education Act (IDEA)

The cornerstone of all federal special education legislation in the United States is Public Law 94-142, The Education for all Handicapped Children Act. It was reauthorized in 1990 and called IDEA—The Individuals with Disabilities Education Act, and then re-authorized in 1997. In 2003, the U.S. Senate was considering changes in IDEA. Therefore, some of the following information may become out of date if major changes are made in IDEA. In 2003, the major provisions of this legislation were the following:

> Gilbert (Gib) Smith, a long-term survivor of acute lymphocytic leukemia, has been an advocate for childhood cancer patients, survivors and their families for more than 8 years.

- All children, regardless of disability, are entitled to a free and appropriate public education (FAPE) and necessary related services.

- Children will receive fair testing to determine if they need special education services.

- Schools are required to provide a free and appropriate public education through an individually designed instructional program for every eligible child. An amendment to 94-142, called public law 99-457, requires early intervention programs for infants and toddlers at risk.

- Children with disabilities will be educated in the least restrictive environment (LRE), usually with children who are not disabled.

- The decisions of the school system can be challenged by parents, with disputes being resolved by an impartial third party.

- Parents of children with disabilities participate in the planning and decision-making for their child's special education.

The steps in an IEP process are referral, evaluation, eligibility, developing an individual education plan (IEP), annual review, and 3-year assessment.

Areas usually included in the evaluation process are educational, medical, social, psychological, and others. Read Chapter 5, *Neuropsychological Testing*, to learn about the difference between neuropsychological testing and educational testing.

There are 13 eligibility categories for special education under the federal law.

- Autism
- Deaf/blindness
- Deafness
- Emotional disturbance
- Hearing impairment
- Mental retardation
- Multiple disabilities
- Orthopedic impairment
- Other health impairment (OHI)
- Specific learning disability
- Speech or language impairment
- Traumatic brain injury
- Visual impairment

Most children with cancer fall into the "Other Health Impaired" category. Children in private or religious schools have to be assessed by the home school district for consideration for special education services. If special education services are deemed necessary, the child needs to enroll in her local public school. If the parents do not want to move the child from the private school, they attend a meeting to discuss a Private School Service Plan. Also, private schools can, but are not required to implement accommodations or a 504 Plan (see section "The Federal Rehabilitation Act—Section 504" later in this chapter).

The Individual Education Plan

The Individual Education Plan describes the special education program and any other related services specifically designed to meet the individual needs of the child with learning differences. It is developed as a collaboration between parents and educators to determine what the student will be taught and how and when the school will teach it. Students with disabilities need to learn the same things as other students: reading, writing, mathematics, history, and other subjects in preparation for college or vocational training. The difference is that, with an IEP in place, many specialized services, such as small classes, speech therapy, physical therapy, counseling, and instruction by special education teachers, are used.

The IEP has five parts:

1. **A description of the child's present level of educational performance:** Includes present levels of performance (PLOPs) regarding social, behavioral, and physical functioning, academic performance, and learning style, as well as the child's medical history.

2. **Measurable, annual goals, objectives, and benchmarks:** Lists skills and behaviors that your child can be expected to master in a specific period of time. These should not be vague like "John will learn to cooperate," but rather, "John will prepare and present an oral book report with two general education students by May 1." Each goal should answer the following questions: Who? What? How? Where? When? How often? When will the service start and end?

3. **Related services:** There are many specialized services that might be mandated by the IEP that will be provided at no cost to the family. These can include: hearing assessment, speech therapy, social skills training, seizure log, mental health services, occupational therapy, vision/orientation and mobility services, assistive technology assessment, psychological and neuropsychological testing, behavioral plans and functional behavior assessment, recreational services, physical therapy, adaptive physical

education, parent counseling and training, transportation to and from school, and therapy sessions. For each of these services, the IEP should list the frequency, duration, start date, and end date. For example, "Jane will receive physical therapy twice a week, for 60 minutes each, from September until December, when her needs will be reevaluated."

4. **Placement:** Describes the least restrictive setting in which the above goals and objectives can be met. For example, one student would be in the regular classroom all day with an aide present, and another might leave the classroom for part of each day to receive specialized instruction in the resource room or physical therapy. The IEP should state the percent of time the child will be in the regular education program and the frequency and duration of any related services.

5. **Evaluating the IEP:** This portion of the IEP should include a description of how the child's progress towards the annual goals are measured and how the parents will be informed of the child's progress. A meeting of all the members of the child's team is held to review the child's progress toward attaining the short-term and long-term goals and objectives of the IEP. In order to ensure that the IEP is working for the child, parents should make sure their child's IEP is reviewed at least once a year, and more frequently if needed to address parent or teacher concerns. Some states have limits on the number of IEP meetings per year.

Parents should come prepared to IEP meetings. They should bring copies of all current testing and recommendations by specialists (or send ahead of time if possible), which will help support their requests for services. Some examples of successful accommodations relating to education are listed in Appendix C of this book.

It is best for parents to create a positive relationship with the school so that they are able to work together to promote their child's well being. If, for whatever reason, communication deteriorates and the parents feel that their child's IEP is inadequate or not being followed, there are several facts they need to know:

- Parents have a right to examine the child's records.
- Parents have a right to advance notice before any significant actions are taken.
- Changes to the IEP cannot be made without parental consent.
- If parents disagree about the content of the IEP, they can withdraw consent and request (in writing) a meeting to draft a new IEP, or they can

consent only to portions of the IEP with which they agree.

- Parents have the right to have the disagreement settled by mediation or litigation.

Transition Services

Transition planning should begin in the early years of high school, when the student's peers are beginning to gain work skills and amass credits toward high school graduation. Special education students have a right to be prepared for graduation, higher education, and work in ways that fit their needs. For many, extra support is needed to make the transition from high school to adulthood go smoothly. The law requires:

- At age 14, and updated annually, the IEP must contain a statement of transition service needs of the child.
- At age 16 (or younger if necessary), the IEP must contain a statement of all needed services including a statement of interagency responsibilities for providing those services.

The transition plan should address high school graduation, higher education, and work skills and job opportunities. It may also include helping the young adult apply for public assistance, supported housing, and other necessary benefits; learn how to self-manage his medical and mental health care; and gain life skills such as budgeting, banking, driving, and cooking.

Some students will not be able to earn a regular diploma. A special form of graduation called an IEP diploma is also available. This diploma means that he has completed all of the objectives set out in his IEP for graduation.

A General Equivalency Diploma, which is earned by passing an examination, may be an option for some other students. For additional information, see Chapter 17, *High School and Beyond*.

Services for Preschoolers

U.S. federal law mandates early intervention services for disabled infants and toddlers and, in some cases, children at risk of having developmental delays. Infants, toddlers, or preschoolers with cancer may be eligible for these services in order to avoid developmental delays caused by the cancer or treatments. These services are administered either by the school system or the state health department. You can find out which agency to contact by asking the hospital social worker or by calling the special education director for your school district.

Most states divide early intervention services into two categories: a) birth to age 3 and b) age 3 to minimum age for school entry. Contact your state's Department of Education to identify the agency that would evaluate your child. For children under 3, this is often the county's Office of Mental Health and Mental Retardation, the Department of Human Services or the Department of Health. For children over 3, the public school system is responsible. In most states, anyone can refer a child for services with a parent's consent. Self-referrals are accepted.

Screening and evaluation are performed to determine if your child is eligible for services. Each state has its own eligibility criteria, which may include:

- Physical disabilities
- Hearing loss
- Vision loss
- Significant developmental delay (cognitive, physical, communication, social/emotional, or self care)
- A medically diagnosed physical or mental condition in which there is a high likelihood of developmental delay (children with cancer fall under this category)

The following services may be offered by a state's early intervention program:

- Speech and language therapy
- Occupational therapy
- Physical therapy
- Psychological services
- Hearing services
- Vision services
- Assistive technologies (e.g., hearing aid)

Services for preschoolers are provided in a variety of settings. If a child is normally at home, therapy can occur in the home. If a child attends preschool or childcare, then a therapist can work with the child at these locations. In some cases preschoolers are transported to classroom-based programs.

The law requires services not only for the infant or preschooler, but for the family as well. Therefore, an Individualized Family Service Plan (IFSP) is developed.

This plan includes:

- A description of the child's physical, cognitive, language, speech, psychosocial, and other developmental levels.
- Goals and objectives for family and child.
- The description, frequency, and delivery of services needed, such as:
    - Speech, vision, occupational, and physical therapy
    - Health and medical services
    - Family training and counseling
- A caseworker who locates and coordinates all necessary services.
- Steps to support transition to other programs and services.

Transitioning from an IFSP to a preschool IEP should be started at least three months before the child turns 3 years old. Transitioning from a preschool to a school age IEP should begin in January or early February before the beginning of the next school year in order to have an IEP in place before school starts.

The Federal Rehabilitation Act "Section 504"

Children with cancer may also be eligible for services and accommodations under the federal Rehabilitation Act, commonly called "Section 504." Section 504 is a civil rights statute that protects individuals with disabilities from discrimination. Families should request evaluation for a 504 plan when the child does not meet the eligibility requirements for specially designed instruction, but still needs accommodations to perform successfully in school. Section 504 defines a person with a "handicap" as any person who:

- Has a physical or mental impairment which substantially limits one or more major life activities.
- Has a record of having such an impairment.
- Is regarded as having such an impairment.

The "major life activities" addressed by this law include such functions as caring for oneself, performing manual tasks, walking, seeing, hearing, speaking, breathing, learning, and working. All children who have or had cancer have a record of impairment that satisfies the above requirements for services.

Examples of children who require accommodations under the Federal Rehabilitation Act are:

- A child who has difficulty walking and climbing stairs may need additional time to travel between classes or might need access to an elevator.

- A child undergoing chemotherapy or radiation might need some special accommodations to address health needs (e.g., use of separate bathroom, water bottle on desk, time for rest if fatigued, reduced homework during periods of frequent illness, and waiving regular attendance, tardy policies, and procedures).

- A child off therapy with cognitive impairments that do not meet the IDEA requirements might need to have accommodations that eliminate timed tests or provide more time to finish written assignments.

If you think your child might benefit from a 504 plan, call the school district to request all information on procedural safeguards and parental rights regarding Section 504 plans. Next, write a letter to the principal of your child's school stating that your child has a physical impairment that limits one or more life activities and requesting a meeting to evaluate appropriate accommodations. The 504 plan should be a written plan, not a verbal agreement.

The Americans with Disabilities Act

The Americans with Disabilities Act of 1990 (ADA) prohibits discrimination based on actual disability, perceived disability, or history of a disability. Accommodations may include changes required to have equal opportunity to participate in academic and athletic instruction and extra curricular activities at school. The ADA further requires that the disabled cannot be forced to accept an accommodation. In other words, childhood cancer survivors cannot be forced to accept educational plans, such as separate classes, that they do not wish to take. If an appropriate public placement is unavailable, the school system must provide an appropriate private placement to substitute for or supplement the public school's package. The ADA also applies to institutions of higher education.

Any employer with fifteen or more workers is covered by the ADA. Employers can no longer discriminate against the disabled in any phase of employment: hiring, training, job assignment, classification, promotion, transfer, benefits, leave of absence, layoff or termination. On-the-job training can be a powerful resource for the continuing education of childhood cancer survivors.

The ADA requires that:

- Employers may not make medical inquiries of an applicant, unless the applicant has a visible disability, e.g., weakness of arm(s) or leg(s), or the applicant has voluntarily disclosed her cancer history. Such questions must be limited to asking the applicant to describe or demonstrate how she would perform essential job functions. Medical inquiries are allowed after a job offer has been made or during a pre-employment medical exam.

- Employers must provide reasonable accommodations unless it causes undue hardship.

- Employers may not discriminate because of family illness.

- Employers are not required to provide health insurance.

The Equal Employment Opportunity Commission (EEOC) enforces Title 1 (employment) of the ADA. Call (800) 669-3362 for enforcement publications. Other sections are enforced by or have their enforcement coordinated by the U.S. Department of Justice (Civil Rights Division, Public Access Section). The Justice Department's ADA web site is at *http://www.usdoj.gov/crt/ada/publicat.htm*.

If you feel that you have been discriminated against due to your disability or a relative's disability, contact the EEOC promptly. In the U.S., a charge of discrimination generally must be filed within 180 days of the notice of the discriminatory act.

Most important for cancer survivors, the ADA protects someone with a record of impairment. Every cancer survivor has a record of substantial impairment. Consequently, the ADA will apply to them for the rest of their lives. The ADA protects cancer survivors, whether the cancer is cured, controlled, or in remission. However, depending upon how successful a survivor is through the use, for example, of medicines or devices, to counter or moderate an effect of the cancer or the treatment, that survivor may not be considered to have a disability under the ADA that requires intervention or accommodation.

While not all children who go off treatment qualify under the IDEA, it is important to understand that they will all qualify under the ADA and the Rehabilitation Act because they all have a record of having survived cancer.

The Military

Survivors of childhood cancer, who meet the physical requirements of the particular service, may be eligible for a medical waiver to serve in the Armed Forces, reserves, and ROTC and to obtain admission to service academies. The general rule is that the survivor must be completely free of cancer and off therapy for at least five years. The following directives outline eligibility rules and physical standards.

- Department of Defense ("DOD") Directive No. 6130.4, "Criteria and Procedure Requirements for Physical Standards for Appointment, Enlistment, and Induction," December 14, 2000 (section E1.35 outlines eligibility for cancer survivors).

- DOD Directive 6130.3, "Physical Standards for Appointment, Enlistment, or Induction," December 15, 2000.

Scholarships

Some, but not many, scholarships for college are available for survivors of childhood cancer. A list of these is available on the Candlelighters' webpage at *www.candlelighters.org*. Other scholarship programs in your area may be offered through unions, philanthropic organizations, corporations, competitions, religious and service organizations. Kiwanis, Lions, Pipefitters, Knights of Columbus or others.

Finally, check on resources available through your state vocational and rehabilitation agency which may offer opportunities to receive assessment, training and counseling to prepare for work, and if you are working, to get help preparing for better work opportunities. These resources are not just valuable for survivors initially preparing for the world of work, but can be particularly valuable for survivors limited to part-time work. In some situations assistance may be available for state college tuition or vocational training.

Advocacy

Special education doesn't just embrace traditional conventional education opportunities. It embraces education that is "special" for your child. It embraces education that will make your child even more "special" because it will enhance that child's abilities, opportunities, and advantages. It embraces education that caters to the "special" dreams that your child has about the world of being educated and preparing for work. It embraces education that is "special" because it respects and enhances and enables the "core" that is the heart and mind and spirit of your child to have wings and fly into his or her future. "Special" education extends beyond the lower level of schooling and vocational, undergraduate and graduate education to all levels of continuing education that will help fulfill the education or job related goals for your child, not only in childhood and adolescence but also as an independent adult.

If there is a hobby that interests a child then there is a hobbyist society or group or association that caters to that interest. Such entities can be helpful in mentoring, in offering a special preparation program and assistance in getting started in a hobby that could turn into a life of work. Trade union apprenticeship programs, summer jobs and internships, self-education programs via working for yourself—grass cutting, lemonade stand, dog walking, babysitting, junior dog showing— are all fine examples of a hobby/interest evolving into future employment. If a group does not offer a mentoring program, find a willing member to mentor your child, and you may be surprised by the results. Never neglect the truly amazing effects that participating in volunteer programs can offer. What you learn from and who you get to know from these activities help in building a resume that can further enhance later education and employment prospects.

The law is a tool to make this happen. However, the greatest tool is your imagination. Devise a plan outlining where you want to be, seize that plan and make the law work for your family. If the law doesn't work for you, connect with other parents through parent groups, education associations and families reaching out for the fulfillment of their child and CHANGE the law or regulations.

Conclusion

Is it time for a reality television program focused on childhood cancer survivors' handling real world obstacles to education, employment and advancement? If there was ever a condition that forces one to live on the edge—childhood cancer is it. Take inventory: the skills to survive with a sense of self and a sense of humor are in development. Survivor's experiences give them advantages over their peers who have not been truly challenged. They know what is important—life—living— growing—becoming all that it is possible to be. Living well is the best conclusion to the experience of childhood cancer. Use the tools presented in this very special book, legal and otherwise, to dream and strive and survive—live well.

KeyPoints

- A variety of federal laws protect the educational rights of children with cancer or treatment related disabilities. If one law doesn't fit your needs, it is likely that another will. If you are not sure, ask for assistance. Laws enforcing education rights apply to primary and secondary education, to infant, toddler, and preschool interventions, and to college, university, and vocational education.

- Parents have the right to participate in planning and decision-making about their child's education.

- Parents can challenge decisions of the school system, with disputes being resolved by an impartial third party.

- In addition to education laws, other federal statutes such as the Americans with Disabilities Act may provide complementary rights to students, for example, the opportunity to participate in academic and athletic instruction or extra-curricula activities; or to parents discriminated against because of their child's cancer.

- Education doesn't end with formal "four walls schooling." Attempts to deny or prevent opportunity and enhancement of life skills through training in the armed services, or participation in apprenticeship or intern programs may be redressed under other federal laws.

- The law is a tool to achievement and opportunity—make the law work for you.

- Do not be afraid to question, challenge, and pursue your child's interests with all your resources and heart.

Parent Perspectives

Our son was diagnosed with a PNET brain tumor when he was 8 months old. Although I didn't receive any guidance from our doctors, I met another woman whose son was seeing our oncologist. She told me about the early intervention program in California and gave me the phone number for the regional center's intake program for early intervention. I self referred. It took 45 days from the time I called for the evaluation and report. At that time he was still on chemo so we opted for occupational therapy (OT) at home. We later changed to a center-based program and saw dramatic improvements. I can't say enough about this program. There were 16 children and four teachers. Geoffrey basically came out of his shell-shocked state while there; he started to socialize, vocalize, and recover from his tactile defensiveness. This program gave him such a good start and started stimulating his little brain. This is one of the reasons why I think he is doing so well. I can't say enough about getting any services at such a young age when the brain has suffered such trauma.

Some hospitals have social workers who might help you work the system. In our case, we received treatment from several different facilities and were not privileged to have such services available. We have been doing great in spite of that, primarily from talking to other parents. I also get information from the web. There is an excellent website (www.eparent.com) that has information about infant programs by state.

I must emphasize that it is important to ask for services as soon as possible. Some programs have waiting lists. Even if you qualify there may be a delay before your child can get in. Our transition from under 3 to preschool was not as smooth as we would have liked it. Sometimes I feel like we lost time, however he is doing so well now that I don't beat myself up over it.

✦ ✦ ✦

Initially, the school was reluctant to test Gina because they thought she was too young (6 years old). But she had been getting occupational therapy at the hospital for two years, and I wanted the school to take over. I brought in articles from Candlelighters Childhood Cancer Foundation, and spoke to the teacher, principal, nurse, and counselor. She had a dynamite teacher who really listened, and she helped get permission to have Gina tested. Her tests showed her to be very strong in some areas, and very weak in others. Together, we put together an IEP that we have updated every spring.

Originally, she received weekly occupational therapy and daily help from the special education teacher. By fourth grade Gina was doing so well that she no longer needed occupational therapy, and received extra help only occasionally during study hall. She even was recommended for the student council, which was a tremendous boost for her self-confidence. As the years went by, Gina required less and less intervention and she became a model student. Her IEP was only in place if needed. She learned so much from the help she received and it was these accommodations that led her to be a resourceful and accountable student. She has compensated for her disabilities so well that they are no longer an issue! Gina is now a senior in high school. She works at our veterinarian's office and plans to attend college to study for a career in veterinarian medicine or to be a veterinary technician.

Work with your school personnel. They are in unfamiliar territory when it comes to educating a child with cancer. With more and more children now, thankfully surviving cancer, we need to work together to give them the best possible education. It takes time and patience, but it is worth every step!

✦✦✦

Rose was 28 months to 5 yrs old while on treatment (standard risk ALL) which included triple intrathecals and high dose MTX. Her issues showed up even during treatment and have continued—the neurotoxicity/leukoencephalopathy/cognitive deficits and the newly diagnosed seizures (five years off treatment). Thus, her learning disabilities due to neurotoxicity showed up about a year into treatment and were identified further by the school when Rose was in Kindergarten, because she simply could not cut with scissors and displayed a range of other fine motor problems. She could not initiate activities. She could not put her shoes on or her snowsuit, get out her lunch or pack it away, etc. She had an IEP and an educational aide by grade one.

✦✦✦

We have had an excellent experience with the school district throughout preschool and now in kindergarten. We went to them with the first neuropsychological results, which were dismal. They retested him, and suggested a special developmental preschool and occupational therapy. Both helped him enormously. He had an evaluation for special education services done, and now has a full-time aide in kindergarten. He is getting the help he needs.

✦ ✦ ✦

Our son gets help in school from physical and occupational therapists. He gets special education for math and reading, and works with the occupational therapist on the computer and special projects. He also has an adaptive physical education coach twice a week, and does regular phys ed with his class the rest of the time. He uses an auditory trainer—a hearing aid with a receiver that is connected to a piece the teacher wears. It directs the teacher's voice to his ear. He uses a hearing aid in the other ear. His comprehension level is now so much higher. Our IEP has worked very well.

✦ ✦ ✦

During my 2-year-old daughter's treatment for ALL, she experienced severe cognitive regression and failed to continue to develop typically. She was enrolled in the local public integrated program. We had her privately evaluated by a hospital-based neuropsychologist, who recommended, among other things, that she receive speech/language therapy at least 5 days/week as well as a full day, full year, integrated program. The school administration disagreed with the recommendations. They offered her a half-day "patch work" program. They felt the recommended therapies were excessive. Other professionals outside the school agreed with the neuropsychologist's recommendations and they sent the school their letters as well.

After multiple attempts at reasonable negotiation, dragged out IEP meetings, and delayed school recommendations, we finally had to appeal to the Department of Education. We were scheduled for a 3-day hearing and many of the experts involved in her case testified. The decision went in our favor and the school had to reimburse us for all of our expenses, including attorney and expert witness fees, and a private placement that could offer her a full day, full year program with the therapies she needed. It took a lot out of us, especially given that she was on active treatment at the time. Unfortunately, she continues to need intensive services of every sort, and additionally has been diagnosed with intractable seizures. This type of intervention will have to stay with her (and us) for a lifetime.

✛ ✛ ✛

This year (2nd grade) we had time with the school "play therapist" written into our daughter's IEP. One or two recesses a week she would have structured play with this adult and 2 or 3 "typical" kids from the class. It worked out really well. At the younger ages the "typical" kids find it fun and exciting (they see it as special and fun to get pulled from the regular recess). They started with indoor games that our daughter was more comfortable with, and eventually, got out on the playground. They actually role played how to play games, be good winners and losers, etc. By the end of the year we found her confidence much higher during free time and also she made some "real" friendships out of it (meaning she found common ground with some of the girls and have ended up with play dates outside of school time).

✛ ✛ ✛

After my daughter's surgery for a brain tumor; she was mute, blind, and paralyzed in both legs and right arm. I had worried about what we were going to do when the rehab days ran out on our insurance. Then the social worker told me about early intervention (EI) services. We used our medical insurance rehab days until we could transition to a preschool with an IEP in place for speech, physical therapy (PT) and occupational therapy (OT). I also chose to provide her with a variety of other experiences that were based on her therapy needs. Over the next two years she participated in different activities including tap and ballet classes, tumbling classes and swimming classes at the YMCA. She had Spanish classes at the library. My favorite was Kids Music Round where she could sing, dance, march, wave scarves, and shake percussion instruments—all while interacting with other kids.

✛ ✛ ✛

After 12 years in the trenches, I have lots of advice!

- *Getting help before your kid feels incompetent can prevent a lot of problems. I know loads of kids who had IEPs in place early who did great. It gets complicated when kids feel dumb. They start to compensate in all sorts of ways to cover up when they don't understand, and that just sinks them deeper into confusion. If they learn effective strategies to work around the weak areas in ways that are positive, not stigmatizing, they never feel "dumb" in the first place. This is not always the case, but I've seen it happen often enough that I'm a big believer in early intervention. Prevention is better than trying to fix problems.*

• *Get baseline and periodic neurospsych testing from an expert. Good neuropsych testing is WAY better than anything you'll get from the vast majority of schools. Most schools do educational testing, which really measures what kids know, not how they learn. Many leukemia survivors who got 1800 cGy of cranial radiation before age 5 have a classic profile. Good to excellent verbally, low average to really low in many non-verbal areas. When you average this out, you get just that: "average." But that does not at all reflect the child's real capabilities. What is really bad is when the school test results "show" the kid "isn't far enough behind" to qualify for services and then lets the kid sink for years until he/she is academically drowning. It makes no sense. Good neuropsych tests will help you get services in place to prevent the kid from sinking. In fact, many kids with good services in place shine. Why should our kids who simply can't develop good handwriting get Ds or Fs in penmanship when they have a legal right to use a keyboard?*

• *Set up an IEP as soon as neuropsych testing shows any problems, no matter how well your child is doing in school.*

• *Network with other parents in similar circumstances. You can join an online "parents of survivors" group or local support groups for parents of kids with disabilities. Parents who have navigated the system for years can be goldmines of information.*

• *Don't be adversarial with teachers or administrators. Try to form a partnership.*

• *Pick teachers to avoid problems. Preventing problems is far better than trying to fix things when they have gone sour.*

• *Don't go alone to the IEP meetings. Take a spouse, friend, or professional advocate with you.*

• *Take delicious goodies to IEP meetings.*

• *Put an 8 x 10 picture of your child on the table during IEP meetings. This eloquently reminds all of those sitting at the table that the meeting is about a glorious child, not a collection of "disabilities" or "test results."*

✦ ✦ ✦

My 10-year-old son is an ALL survivor with fine motor and processing difficulties. I did some research and everyone seemed to think the AlphaSmart keyboard was the way to go. We got one in the fall and it has worked very well for Dylan. He carries it to and from school and it hooks up quickly to their printer. He has loss of feeling in his fingertips and writing makes his hands tire very quickly. Until getting the AlphaSmart, he wrote little—single or two word sentences if he could get away with it. Now he will write a lot more on stories or book reports. We have a good keyboarding program (Rollertyping) for the PC but we also bought the keyboarding 'applet' specifically for the AlphaSmart. I would recommend that as well.

We stay away from the speed practice—timed anything stresses him out— but he is now beginning to type without looking at the keyboard. He probably practices 10 to 15 minutes a few times a week. I might add that two of his friends who are siblings and have reading disabilities both love it; they write stories on it almost every time they come over, voluntarily. Their mother falls over in shock. I would say the only down side was some of the other boys in the fourth grade class thought it was it unfair and gave him a hard time.

✦ ✦ ✦

I feel like throwing up when our kids are told that they aren't "paying attention" or that they should "hurry up." Often, they are working their hearts out but can only do about 25% of what the non-irradiated kids can do in the same amount of time. So, celebrate that quality is good, but quantity is low. Remember the turtle and the hare? Who won?

Since my daughter started school, I had the teachers tell me how much time was reasonable and expected for homework. Then, I would pick and choose math problems and assignments so that she could do representative ones, but she didn't spend more than the allotted time. Otherwise, it would take her two hours to do what the other kids did in ½ hour. Doing hours and hours of homework kills their spirit and motivation. Doing a reasonable amount of homework well helps them learn and feel competent. Getting this written into the IEP can prevent a lot of heartache.

+ + +

My 6-year-old daughter Lexi is a survivor of medulloblastoma (a type of brain tumor). The problems she is having are difficulty speaking, feeding through a g-tube, right sided weakness (she's right handed), ambulatory with assistance but needs walker/wheelchair, cognitive delays especially in sequencing/math, high pitched hearing loss, and nystagmus on both sides of her eyes.

I think the key to my success so far with this has been the inclusion of all the key players. I requested that all members who had been working with her (therapists and home school teacher) participate in the IEP meeting, as well as all members who would be working with her (from the special ed teacher to the nurse). It was a full house but everyone heard what had to be done first hand. An educational advocate from my Medicaid service coordinators office attended. I also called the assemblyman representing her school district to request his help. Their office helped to put in a good word about having her stay in that school as opposed to going out of the district. I took a recent photo of Lexi and a book of all the work she had done starting with when she first started to communicate. I dated everything she had done to show the quick improvements. The book included pictures she had recently drawn and writing/coloring samples. I also wrote a parent summary of the situation. This had an intro to her, her home life, medical history, social history, what worked for her, what didn't, major concerns, strengths/weaknesses and best ways to communicate.

In addition to this I had a team of a social worker and child life specialist come in to talk to Lexi's class as well as to the teachers. They played a video of a girl with cancer and her thoughts and feelings about being in school. It really helped the teachers to understand how it feels to come back to school from the child's point of view. I wrote my own agenda for the meeting and a sample IEP. I don't think there was anything I wished I had brought with me except perhaps Lexi herself for part of the meeting.

Having to request special education services for Lexi was very difficult to swallow. It meant having to face the fact that she was changed forever. Being prepared for the meeting helped immensely, as did having her current therapists prepared to discuss her progress. I came away from the meeting feeling I had accomplished one small step in the long road to her future success.

Hearing my story impacted the teachers a great deal. The picture was the icing on the cake. None of the teachers or administrators had ever had to help a child with a brain tumor. Many of them were afraid of the unknown. After careful presentation of Lexi's skills and needs, they wanted to dig in and help. They didn't pretend it would be easy, but agreed keeping her in her own school was the best thing for her. Since that meeting the teachers communicate with me regularly. If I have suggestions they try to incorporate them and have tried to come up with creative ways to help her.

✝ ✝ ✝

In 9th grade our 15-year-old daughter was diagnosed with a medulloblastoma brain tumor requiring surgery, craniospinal irradiation and a year of chemotherapy. After surgical resection, Hannah developed cerebellar mutism and posterior fossa syndrome requiring extensive rehabilitation. She was unable to talk, walk, or balance while standing without support. Additionally, she had fine motor problems that interfered with writing and keyboarding.

After leaving the hospital, my daughter went to a rehabilitation facility. When she came home, she got home bound instruction and completed her 9th and 10th grades at home. Right now, she can't keep her balance while standing (without support) and she can't walk. These are the biggest physical issues. She has lost cognitive abilities as well – she has trouble fully comprehending difficult reading passages and certain mathematical problems. Her time to process things is also slow.

Now we are planning to have her start her junior year at the school. The plan is to start slowly (perhaps half time in the high school) and ramp up as appropriate. We had the first IEP meeting with the school district this week. Our daughter, a representative from the rehab facility, and both of us were there. We thought we would have to fight for services, but the district educators were very supportive and themselves had plans and suggestions for all the things we had thought of and more.

The current plan is that Hannah will get home tutoring through the summer to keep her in touch with subjects she has more difficulty with (such as mathematics). Starting in the fall, she is going to be enrolled for a level of credits that she can handle. She will have an aide during her school time as well as one-on-one instruction for certain subjects. When she attends regular class, she will have written notes provided and tape recording of the class as well. Testing will include extra time and help in writing answers. Help will also be provided in standardized testing (e.g. someone to help her mark those little squares and align the answer with the right question.) For reading, they are going to provide large print books. Her nytagmus makes her skip and repeat lines while reading. I'm sure we will discover things and have to make adjustments as we go along. All in all though, we feel fortunate to have such a supportive school district.

✦ ✦ ✦

After my 14-month-old son was diagnosed and we came home, I felt lost. I assumed that my neuro-oncologist was going to tell me what to do for the whole "what do we do when we get home thing" but I got very little information. Our pediatrician (parent of a special needs child) directed us towards appropriate services. Once we were connected, an immediate network of resources and other parents dealing with similar issues opened up. Now my son receives a combination of public and private services. We are fortunate to have an amazing private integrated early intervention program near us. For a very reasonable fee (approximately $100 a month) my child attends a four-hour morning program, five days a week. In addition he also receives public early intervention services on some afternoons. The public program is for 3 and 4 year olds and is based at a local elementary school. There, he gets group and individual physical therapy, occupational therapy, and speech therapy. We use both programs to provide Joshua with a full range of services as well as the opportunity to be in a group setting with both disabled and normally developing children. I think the group setting and being with other kids has made a really positive impact on his development.

Chapter 15

Special Education: Navigating the System

Kathryn Smith, RN, MN

Special education programs within individual school districts can vary substantially and range from a limited amount of additional assistance in a general education classroom to a completely supported, specialized environment. With school budgets being cut, there may be competition between general education and special education for limited resources. The key to being an effective advocate for your child in special education is to learn as much as possible about the process for obtaining special education services, your rights, and how services are delivered, and to approach the school district as a partner in identifying appropriate services for your child.

First Steps

School districts may have slightly different interpretations of the requirements of special education law, and implementation varies, so you should contact the school superintendent, director of special education, or special education advisory committee to obtain a copy of the school system's procedures for special education (called the "Notice of Parents' Rights"). Depending on the district, this document may range from two to several hundred pages. Also write to your state Superintendent of Public Instruction to obtain a copy of the state rules governing special education. To get the address, ask the school principal or a reference librarian, or visit your state Department of Education web site. Regardless of how the state or district interprets the federal regulations, they must comply with the law.

The Individual Education Plan (IEP) process is the backbone of special education services. Therefore, it is important to learn as much as possible about the process and your rights.

Ms. Smith is director of the California Medical Home Project and assistant nursing director at USC University Affiliated Program, Childrens Hospital Los Angeles, CA.

Briefly, the four major rights within the IEP process are:

- **The right to a free and appropriate public education:** A free educational program must be developed to meet your child's unique needs. Services must be provided to allow the child to benefit from his education, such as speech therapy, physical therapy, special equipment, transportation and others. If a school district cannot provide the needed services, they must contract with community agencies or non-public schools to provide the service or placement.

- **Placement in the least restrictive environment:** This means that the child attends classes in a setting as similar as possible to where the child would be placed if he or she did not have any special needs. This may range from a general education classroom with additional supports to a special education classroom, and the placement may change over time depending on the child's needs.

- **Assessment procedures:** These procedures are used to identify your child's strengths and needs, to determine whether or not a child is eligible for special education services, and to serve as the basis for determining which services should be provided. Assessments should be conducted in any area of suspected disability, not solely based on diagnosis.

- **Informed consent:** Informed consent means that the parents get complete and accurate information in order to make good decisions about their child's IEP.

In conjunction with school personnel, you will go through several steps to determine placement, modifications, and services to be provided. The steps in an IEP process are referral, evaluation, eligibility, developing an individual education plan (IEP), annual review, and 3-year assessment.

Parents or teachers can make a referral by writing to the school principal and requesting special education testing. Some school districts will automatically set up an IEP for any child who has had cranial radiation. The parent or physician can send a written request to the principal stating that the child is "health impaired" because of treatment for cancer, listing her problems, and requesting assessments and an IEP meeting. However, a request for an IEP does not require a note from a physician. There is a time line for the referral process, although it varies in different states. The "Notice of Parent's Rights" explains the time requirements for the referral process.

Learning About the Process

It helps to put together a notebook or folder, in which you can keep school papers, notices of meetings, etc. You may also find it helpful to keep a log of phone calls and meetings that you can refer back to should the need arise. Make sure to write down the date, time, name of person with whom you spoke, and the topic of the conversation. As you go to meetings, or meet with various professionals, make notes of the highlights, during or after your meeting. In addition, ask if they have any helpful resource materials, and store them in your notebook or folder. Many parents purchase plastic sleeves from the stationary store that are used for holding business cards. You can ask for the card of anyone you meet and include it in your notebook. Some parents use a notebook with a clear plastic cover on the front and they slip a picture of their child into the pocket. In IEP meetings, it helps to put a face to a name.

Next, take the time to learn about special education processes in general, and within your particular school district. Read as much as you can, talk to other parents, and seek the assistance of professionals whom you trust. When talking to other parents, remember that each family's experience is unique, depending on the individual needs of the child and the interactions between the parents and the child's educators. Become familiar with the terminology that you will hear during the process of seeking services. Appendix B, *Glossary of Educational Terms*, defines many of these. For a very comprehensive list of definitions related to special education, read the book "Special Education Dictionary" listed in the resources section at the end of this book.

The Evaluation

Once the referral is made, an evaluation is necessary to find out if the school district agrees that the child needs additional help and, if so, what type of help would be most beneficial. Usually, a multidisciplinary team—consisting of at least the teacher, school nurse, district psychologist, speech and language therapist, resource specialist, medical advocate (whoever is serving as the hospital liaison with the school), and social worker—meets to administer and evaluate the testing. Areas usually included in the evaluation process are educational, medical, social, psychological, and others, depending on the need. Your written consent is required prior to your child's evaluation, and you have the right to obtain an independent evaluation if you believe that the school's evaluation is biased or flawed in any way.

If a child was assessed by hospital therapists or psychologists, or while in rehabilitation, the district will usually accept those reports and supplement them with additional evaluations if necessary. Duplication of testing should be avoided if possible to minimize the inconvenience for families and to avoid unnecessary costs.

Children with a history of chemotherapy and/or radiation to the brain require thorough neuropsychological testing, which is best administered by psychologists experienced in testing children treated for cancer (see Chapter 5, *Neuropsychological Testing*). Most large children's hospitals have such personnel, but it sometimes takes very assertive parents to get the school system to use these experts.

After the evaluation, a conference is held to discuss the results and reach conclusions about what actions will be necessary in the future. Make sure that in all written correspondence with the school, you clearly request to be notified of all meetings and discussions concerning your child's special education needs so that you may be present if you wish. You know him best, and you and your spouse have the right to be there.

Useful Tips

Other parents who have used special education services and have gone though the IEP process may have some helpful advice for you. You may find the following tips useful.

- Talk to the people important in your child's life (your child's doctor, babysitter, physical therapist) and ask them if they have any thoughts, ideas, or concerns that should be brought up during the IEP.

- Make a list of the concerns that you have, your child's strengths, and any additional services or accommodations you would like provided (see Appendix C, *School Accommodations*). Use this list during the discussion to help keep focused. If this is your first IEP meeting, you may want to practice reviewing this list with someone.

- Some families find lengthy IEP meetings intimidating because a large number of professionals are sitting around the table. The number depends, in part, on how many are involved in your child's care. You may bring whomever you would like with you: a spouse, a friend, an advocate, your child's doctor or nurse. It is up to you. If it is going to be a long day, bring a snack for yourself, a bottle of water, and a lunch if you anticipate being there through lunchtime. If you need an interpreter, the school is required to provide one. It is nice to bring snacks for the team, but this is not essential.

- Bring in an expert who can help to educate school officials about your child's needs. Educational advocates and IEP experts are becoming available. Some of these people work for disability advocacy organizations or disability law firms. Others are freelance practitioners. Some are parents of children with disabilities who have turned their avocation into a vocation. A professional advocate can provide expert services such as researching programs available in your area, connecting you with appropriate resources, helping you write a better IEP, and advocating for your child at IEP meetings and due process hearings.

- Be prepared to take notes, or ask a friend to take notes for you. Don't be afraid to say, "Please wait a moment, I'd like to review my notes about that." You can also audiotape the meeting, but you must give the school 24-hour prior notice.

- Bring any relevant documents that you might need during the IEP such as medical reports, neuropsychological evaluations, or IEPs from previous schools. These will help support your requests for services. Do not let anyone keep your original copies. If a participant in the meeting requests copies, have them copy yours and return them to you before the meeting ends.

- If there are therapies that the school has agreed to provide, make sure they are spelled out in the IEP, including who will provide them and how often.

You may be asked to provide letters describing the medical necessity of requested therapies from your child's physician, current therapists, or teachers.

Monitoring Progress

Monitoring your child's progress toward goals set in the IEP will be the joint responsibility of you and the school. You can't rely totally on the school or the school district to monitor your child's progress or to ensure compliance with the IEP. Keep a copy of the IEP and other important notes at hand, and check them against any communication notebooks, progress reports, report cards, or other information that comes home from the school or that your child tells you about.

Try to attend all official meetings, and also drop by school occasionally to observe how your child is doing. Volunteering at school is also a good way to keep track of your child's activities and progress. Remember though, if you volunteer at school, your job is to carry out the tasks you've been assigned, not assisting your own child.

If the school is not complying with the IEP, start by talking to the teacher and work your way up. Many compliance problems can be addressed at the classroom level. One area that can be especially difficult is monitoring the delivery of therapeutic services. It seems like a relatively simple task, but many parents report that their school district refuses to provide any type of checklist that parents can see to make sure their child is receiving the services listed in the IEP. It helps to include in the IEP a method to report the delivery of therapeutic services.

Another problem area is the administration of medication at school. Some parents have reported refusal to deliver medication at the appointed time, lost pills, and missed or mistaken doses. Most self-contained classrooms have many children who take scheduled medications, and they tend to have processes in place. The worst medication problems seem to occur in full inclusion settings, especially if the student is not capable of monitoring medication delivery himself. You may need to insist on a daily checklist, and increase your own monitoring efforts. You can teach your child to ask for medication in association with another activity, for instance, stopping by the nurse's office on the way back from gym. A child should not be placed in a special day class solely so he or she can receive medication. Medication administration should be available in any type of class.

If your IEP includes academic goals, see if there are measurable ways to monitor progress. Too often parents are told that their child is participating well and learning, and then discover that he has not gained new skills or has actually regressed when an objective measure is used.

If you are unhappy with your child's special education services, or you would like to see changes in your child's program, you can follow certain steps to advocate for your child, make changes, and assure that your rights are protected. These include: discussing the problem with your child's teacher, contacting your child's special education coordinator, contacting the school district's director of pupil services or special education office and finally, putting in a written request for due process.

Due Process

If talking to teachers and administrators does not resolve the problem, due process may be the next step. Due process begins with a hearing—an internal appeals procedure used by school districts to determine whether or not special education procedures have been handled properly.

The due process hearing will determine if the district has followed federal and state-mandated procedures for evaluating a child for special education and setting up a program for that child. Violations range from notifying parents of a meeting over the phone rather in writing, to major issues, such as using untrained or incompetent personnel to evaluate children, or deliberately denying needed services to save money.

Issues that tend to end up in due process include disagreements over evaluations or diagnostic categories, provision of inadequate therapeutic services, placement in inappropriate educational settings, noncompliance with the IEP, lack of extended school year services when appropriate, and poor transition planning.

The following are common elements of the due process procedure:

- Parents must request a due process hearing in writing.
- The hearing must take place in a timely fashion (outlined in the "Notice of Parents' Rights").
- Hearings are presided over by an impartial person who does not work for the district.
- Children have the right to stay in the current placement until after the hearing (this is called the "stay put" rule).
- Parents can attend due process hearings and advocate for their child.
- Parents can hire an educational advocate or lawyer to represent them at the due process hearing. If the parents use a lawyer and they win, they are entitled to have their legal fees paid by the district.

Due process hearings resemble a court hearing before a hearing officer. Both sides will be asked to present evidence and argue their case, and can call on experts or submit documents to support their statements.

504 Plans

Your child may be eligible for some special services under Section 504 of the Rehabilitation Act of 1973. These services and accommodations are written into a document colloquially known as a 504 plan. Children who have IEPs do not need a separate 504 plan, but some may qualify for a 504 plan even if they do not qualify for special education.

Unlike special education eligibility, Section 504 eligibility is not based on having a certain type of disability. Instead, it is based on the following types of impairments.

- Having a physical or mental impairment that substantially limits a major life activity, such as learning (note that, in contrast to IDEA regulations, learning is not the only activity that applies: 504 plans can cover other major life activities, such as breathing, walking, and socialization).

- Having a record of such an impairment, such as a medical diagnosis.
- Being regarded as having such an impairment.

A 504 plan can put many helpful procedures in place, ranging from medication delivery to exemption from timed tests to the provision of a classroom aide. 504 plans are usually not accorded the status of an IEP by teachers and school administrators, but they are legally binding.

Some special education advocates recommend that parents request a 504 evaluation at the same time they start the IEP process. This can mean asking the 504 coordinator to attend your IEP meetings. It may confuse your district, because it isn't a common practice, but it may save time in obtaining some services and accommodations if services are denied under IDEA and the parents have to appeal. If you apply for 504 status and are denied services, you can appeal this decision to your state's Office of Civil Rights (OCR).

Therapy

The goal of rehabilitation is to help children reach their maximum potential, and is based on the individual child's strengths and needs. Commercial insurance, such as through an employer, may pay for a limited period of rehabilitation, but many children with special health care needs require long-term services. Schools provide educationally relevant therapies, such as speech, occupational and physical therapy when needed by the child to assist him in meeting his educational goals. Other agencies in your state, such as the Department of Rehabilitation, the Department of Developmental Services, or the State Title V Program for children with special health care needs may provide additional medically relevant therapies. Therapies provided by the school district will be detailed in the IEP.

The keys to success in navigating the special education system are to be informed, to be prepared, to work as a partner with the school district for your child, and to serve as your child's advocate.

KeyPoints

- The Individual Education Plan process is the backbone of special education services. Learn as much as possible about special education laws, processes and your rights as possible.

- Keep yourself organized. Put together a notebook or other system for organizing documents, keeping track of appointments, saving correspondence and listing your concerns. Make sure that in all your written correspondence with the school you request to be notified of all meetings and discussions regarding your child. Take notes at meetings or during conversations and refer back to them as needed.

- Other parents can provide useful tips. Talk to them and share what they have learned.

- Remember that progress toward IEP goals will be the joint responsibility of you and the school. Be prepared to participate.

- If you are unhappy with your child's special education services or would like to see changes in the program, you can follow certain steps to advocate for your child.

Parent Perspectives

One thing our school counselor told my wife holds very true for every parent. Parents have to be an advocate for their own child. Reliance on the government, on teachers, and on the goodwill of others will get you nowhere.

✛ ✛ ✛

My daughter had a bone marrow transplant at age 2 that included total body radiation. She has had an IEP for several years. Our plan allows Katie to stay in her main class. If at any time she feels she needs help she can leave and go to the "special ed" teacher's room. There the special education teacher will go over the material with her. Sometimes it's one on one, some times a small group. Before receiving daily growth hormone shots, Katie spent the majority of her day with the special ed teacher. Now it's down to a few trips a weeks.

✛ ✛ ✛

Because my son has had such a hard third-grade year, I have really researched the fourth-grade teachers. I sat in and observed three teachers. I sent a letter to the principal, outlining the issues, and requested a specific teacher. The principal called me and was very upset. He said, "You can't just request who you want. What would happen if all the parents did that? You'll have to give me three choices just like everybody else." I said, "My son has had three years of chemotherapy, has a seizure disorder, behavior problems, and learning disabilities. Can you think of a child who has greater need for special consideration?" My husband and I then requested a meeting with him, and at the meeting he finally agreed to honor our teacher request.

I asked for a spring conference with the teacher selected for the next fall and explained what my child was going through, what his learning style was, and what type of classroom situation seemed to work best. Then I brought my son in to meet the teacher several times, and let him explore the classroom where he would be the next year. This helped my son and the future teacher adjust to one another.

✦ ✦ ✦

Dealing with the system is not hard in terms of smarts, but you really have to be persistent and very pleasant. If one can, I recommend sharing this responsibility as it can cause you to burn out fast. My spouse and I take turns doing the good guy/bad guy stuff interacting with the district. At times it can get to the point where you are prone to making rude remarks that do not help, and probably hurt the situation. In addition, having another person to hand off to and later pick it up again is good to keep one fresh. When I feel the pleasantness waning, I hand off to my spouse. In this way, the school district then gets to know both parents are attentive and cannot be split. On the fridge, we keep track of what the issues are that are active, those that are on hold, and those that are yet to be resolved.

✦ ✦ ✦

This year (third grade) has been a nightmare. My son has an IEP that focuses on problems with short-term memory, concentration, writing, and reading comprehension. The teacher, even though she is special ed qualified, has been rigid and used lots of timed tests. She told me in one conference that she thought my son's behavior problems were because he was "spoiled." We asked her at the beginning of the year to please send a note home with my son if he has a seizure, and she has never done it. She even questions him when he tells her that he had a seizure at recess. I began communicating directly with the principal, and I finally received a written notice that he had a seizure. I learned that the IEP is only as valuable as the teacher who is applying it.

✦ ✦ ✦

Every year, even though my daughter has an IEP, I write a one-page document that introduces my daughter and has a bulleted list of strengths and one of challenges. Then I describe the methods that work best for her and ask the teacher to call me at any time for any reason. The tone is warm and the information is upbeat. I always keep it to one page.

When she entered middle school, I asked for and got a meeting with every teacher in the room the day before school started. At the meeting I said, "I know this is a crazy time of year and I so appreciate you meeting with me. This will only take five minutes." They all clapped! Then I handed them the one page paper, went over it quickly, and offered to answer questions. It really helped.

✦✦✦

Early intervention (EI) and elementary school are two different worlds. Early intervention gets the ball rolling, but if services are to continue at the same pace as EI, then a parent may be searching around for what to do. One problem we experienced making the jump from daycare to public school, was that we had no immediate link from one to the other. The IEP was not finished so the teacher just fished around for solutions. I even met with the principal prior to kindergarten and a link up did not happen. Now it is February and we are still trying to get things in place and they are recommending retention. You have got to be your child's advocate. Call, reinforce, follow-up, write, and send copies. They will tell you they are not against you. I believe that, but they are also not for you. I leave every IEP meeting feeling like I've been fighting for services. Our kids' needs are so different from not just the regular students but the special ed students as well.

✦✦✦

When a committee sits down and writes up accommodations, it is a good idea to discuss how the implementation will be monitored. I have seen some situations where the ideas in the IEP are perfect on paper, but the follow-through is questionable. Sometimes, what's happening in the classroom does not match what's on the paper. Parent visits to the class, and other checks and balances, are helpful and can keep things on track. You have to do this without being threatening or demeaning to the staff.

When I worked as a speech/language therapist in the schools, it helped to hear from parents from time to time. Somehow, and I hate to admit it, but a call from a parent now and then helped to keep their child's needs up front in my thoughts and priority list. Besides, their insights and observations were quite valuable. And another observation, "less can be more" when it comes to getting staff to carry out accommodations. They are busy and have a lot to think about, and so are more likely to read and implement shorter documents or bits of info. Sometimes it even helps to just give them a piece at a time, starting with the absolutely most critical things.

✦✦✦

Setting up the IEP is one thing, but as a parent one must ensure its implementation in the most tactful but firm way possible. It is tricky to be a tactful, squeaky wheel. Be sure to choose your battles carefully and be careful not to "bite the hand that feeds you." Also another useful cliche: "You attract more flies with honey than with vinegar."

An ongoing concern for us, for example, is that Rose's IEP calls for constant one-on-one assistance but with all the funding issues going on there's never any guarantee. Fifth grade has been the first year that Rose has received close to one-on-one from her educational assistant (EA) because the school administration put her and another child together to share the EA in the same class. It is working out beautifully. Prior to this she was lucky to have her EA in the same classroom 50 percent of the time. Her deficits are not limited to 50 percent of her school day!

One thing we've done with the school is to determine in June who the next teacher in September will be and then a transition meeting is arranged with the current teacher, the future teacher, the education assistant, the resource teacher and us (the parents). This seems to work well in setting the stage. We provide an overview to the new teacher and the teacher can ask questions. We usually have a "touch base" phone call with the new teacher in the week leading up to the start of school and we make sure that Rose has met the new teacher and has seen the classroom before school starts. We've been fortunate that Rose has kept the same EA for four years, so that eases things as well. The EA meets Rose at the bus as she arrives at school on the first day to help her get situated.

Last but not least, once you have the school trained on all these things, don't change schools!

✦ ✦ ✦

Our son has seizures from a brain tumor, missed school because of surgery, and has a very bumpy neuropsych profile. Right now he has a full time educational aide and after-school tutoring in math, reading and writing paid for by the school. Setting up an IEP with effective short- and long-term goals is important (and something I'm still learning). Finding an educational advocate was good for us. We hired her to help us on some occasions, but not for every IEP meeting. We have a progress report meeting with all his teachers about every two months and an IEP meeting about twice a year—more if needed. I also use the web to get information from nonverbal learning disability sites and the International Dyslexia Association. Just thinking of school makes me want to crawl in a corner, but "Rome wasn't built in a day."

✛ ✛ ✛

Nicole faced NY state regents the first year after diagnosis during the most difficult part of her treatment. She was having high-dose chemo and we knew her low point would be during the week of state exams. Sure enough, we were going for transfusions at least twice a week at that time. When I talked to the school earlier in the month to try to set up some accommodations, they were pretty sure the state would not agree. In frustration, I called the state regents board myself and explained Nicole's circumstances. We explained that we had no idea if she would need accommodations or not. She might be fine, but she also might need to travel two hours one way for an emergency transfusion.

In the end, the state and the school and the hospital all agreed that she would be able to take the test over several days if needed. The test would be locked in a safe, and Nicole and I had to sign a statement agreeing that she would not take advantage of this and that she would not talk to people who had already taken the test. She would also be allowed extended periods of time during one day if needed. She could take the test alone, or she could take the test at the hospital.

Of course she ended up never using any of the accommodations. She did have a horrific nosebleed the morning of her French regents. We knew she needed a transfusion but hoped she could take the test first, which she managed even though she was late.

The day before her 11th grade social studies regents, Nicole went for a transfusion and ended up having an anaphylactic reaction. We didn't get back home until quite late and she slept thru until the morning of the exam due to all of the meds they gave her to counteract the reaction. No studying for this girl. She dragged herself to the test where she listened to a classmate complain about having to be awake so early to take a test. The teacher called her at home to tell her she got the highest mark in the grade...98! This is a good memory. Nicole is now gracing heaven with her sweet soul and sweeter smile.

✛ ✛ ✛

William is 8 years old and his complex partial seizures continue to be well-controlled one year after image-guided surgery to remove his low-grade astrocytoma. Surgery didn't remove the entire tumor, but what an impact seizure control has had on his life!

William is definitely in the group of kids who have neurocognitive and processing issues as a result of having a large brain tumor and treatment. He's been medically stable all this school year, so our big focus has been on academics. His teachers understand that he needs more time for writing, and they've learned how time-consuming transcribing notes from the board can be for him, so they supply him with study guides. Most of his tests this year have been given orally or have been scribed by his special education teacher. He has a great relationship with his after-school tutor. He's tutored two nights a week, though we're hoping to add an extra night next year. His IEP team decided that he should repeat second grade. That was a very tough decision, but we have a feeling an extra year may help. Third grade really stresses reading comprehension and writing skills, and his teachers agree that he's not quite ready for that level of intensity. Along with that, he's just turning 8 at the end of the current school year, while most of his current classmates are already 9. He likes the younger kids. He fits well socially and academically with the next grade coming up.

This summer, the big focus will be on camping, nature hikes, and swimming. His new day camp was a true find: it's at a local college, with counselors who are graduate students training in various fields, including disability sports. William worked really hard this school year. His teachers and tutor worked hard too. It's a continuous process, learning what works to develop skills to help him compensate. There's no one magic recipe for academic success or social acceptance. It takes hard work, keeping at it, and never giving up.

✦ ✦ ✦

My son has leukoencephalopathy from leukemia treatment. He took a learning strategies course for six weeks a few months ago to help prepare him for high school. He really enjoyed the course and the teacher was fantastic with the four boys she was teaching.

This teacher is taking the four boys from the learning strategies course on a 3-day field trip on Monday. Jamie is really looking forward to going. Yesterday morning we had a meeting at the school detailing the trip. After the meeting the teacher pulled Jamie and I aside and told us Jamie should not be going on the trip. Huh? She told me Jamie was given an assignment a month ago to do for her in order to go on the trip. This teacher verbally reminded him about it two weeks ago.

It did not get done. Jamie forgot. She told me she lost sleep the night before about it, knowing Jamie had not handed in the work and should not be going on the trip. Well...to make a long story short the work is done and Jamie is going on the trip.

How the heck does this kind of stuff happen with an IEP in place, excellent resource teachers and a part time teaching assistant? I just don't get it. I have a feeling that some of the school staff doubts Jamie's late effects ("but Mrs. A. the other three boys didn't have a problem remembering to hand in their assignments!"). I wanted to ask her if they had their brain "chemo-fried" and radiated, but I didn't. I wanted to cry.

I called Jamie's resource teacher today and asked her to find out how things went so wrong, so that hopefully we can prevent it from happening in the future.

✦ ✦ ✦

Our son has multiple late effects from his chemotherapy, radiation, and stem cell rescue. He has an FM unit to help him hear his teacher. The school system was great about providing physical therapy, occupational therapy, and speech therapy. They wanted to put him in a special needs school, but I wanted them to continue to mainstream him with support. They said they had no staff, so I put an ad in the newspaper at a university graduate school near his school. We found a 2nd year grad student in special education to help him in the classroom. The school district refused to hire her, so we appealed and had a hearing. We won. The aide is wonderful and helps my son stay on task, understand instructions, and keep organized. I'm an effective, but exhausted, advocate.

✦ ✦ ✦

Early in James's 7th grade school year I recognized that James was still going to need the services of a home bound tutor as the chemo treatments for leukemia were continuing to cause side effects which kept him from attending school full time. I wrote asking the school to convene an IEP meeting and I requested a homebound tutor. (Which I later found out we were guaranteed by state law because James was undergoing chemotherapy treatments).

At the IEP meeting the team did not want to give us a home tutor, they wanted to give James more time in academic classes by pulling him from music, PE and art. They also suggested that he stay home on Fridays to regain his strength. Strength wasn't the issue—nausea, constipation, and treatment appointments were—and they didn't only happen on Fridays!

What really upset me was when the school system's Assistant Special Ed Supervisor suggested that James be given two years to complete 7th grade. Many on the committee agreed. This group did not understand that cancer children feel robbed of being with their school friends, and having a normal school experience. I was sure that if I let this happen, James would feel that the cancer had won. I was furious and stated that this was unacceptable as not everything had been done by the adults in the room to ensure that James receive the 7th grade curriculum and as much of a normal school year experience as possible. This meant that a home bound tutor should be in place, communication should occur between the home bound tutor and classroom teachers, and support should be provided to him when he was able to be in school.

The LD teacher had the most difficulty during the year understanding the measures that needed to take place to help James with organization, his difficulty with visual spatial weaknesses, and his difficulty with written communication. When it was time to write the annual IEP goals, the school gave us less than 10 days notice of the IEP meeting. We requested a copy of the IEP, time to review the IEP and consult an educational advocate. We were also concerned because the home bound teacher gave us a "heads up" that the committee was recommending that James attend Extended School Year in a class with students who had emotional difficulties.

We hired an experienced educational advocate (formerly a school principal), who helped us understand our rights and legal procedures according to the federal law. She also helped me identify the most important academic needs that should be addressed in the IEP. She took over "guiding the ship" through what for me had become rapids of ill advice from the school system. During this time, I attended a workshop by Pete Wright (www.wrightslaw.com). I followed many of his suggestions: organize a notebook with testing, current and past IEPs, communications from teachers, communications with the school, etc. I also identified several articles of the federal regulations which we felt were being interpreted incorrectly by the school. I took my notebook and the Special Education Law publication with me to the meeting.

The IEP we received was a mess. It was riddled with misspellings and inaccuracies, and information left out. It even contained another student's name! With our advocate's guidance, I submitted revisions to the IEP. By employing the advocate, we had someone who knew the legal rights parents and children should be afforded and had experience in writing a sound IEP document to meet the needs of the individual child. She took the emotional piece away by helping us focus on what could and should be done.

✦ ✦ ✦

My son was diagnosed with PNET when he was eight months old. When most parents are informed of available services, they are either too caught up with current situations to fully comprehend the value these services offer, or they are not quite sure that their children need the services. Both are understandable. We all want to believe that developmental issues are only temporary. Sometimes we don't even recognize the developmental issues, because they are so subtle. Seeking evaluations and services is one of the best things a parent can do for a very young child. These young children thrive on repetition and can re-train their brains more easily than older children. Receiving services will greatly improve their quality of life in the long run, and reduce future frustrations for both child and family. I think that getting services for my son early on, was one of the best things that we have done for him. We didn't think that he needed the services, but I can only believe that he would not be doing so well if we had not. He will be attending mainstream kindergarten this fall, on track and the only additional services he requires at this time is speech.

✦ ✦ ✦

My daughter is now a freshman in college. She started special ed when she was an 8 year old with medulloblastoma. I always included her in the meetings. Eventually, by the time she was a junior in high school, she ran the IEP meetings, with me interjecting here and there on medical or educational issues that she couldn't address or didn't feel comfortable addressing. Most teachers were highly appreciative of the information. Now in college, she's on her own but we had all this in place for her. She's now assertive enough to handle issues related to her education as they arise.

Chapter 16

Educational Portfolio

Carol Dean

An education portfolio is a collection of documents in a binder that you take with you to all education-related meetings. The information is updated throughout your child's illness and education. The portfolio a tool to help educators learn about your child and how best to teach him or her.

Families of children with educational challenges need a sturdy binder and subject dividers. Organize the material by topic so that you can readily find the information you need at meetings. You may need to buy a new binder every year if your child's educational documents are voluminous.

Portfolios usually include the following eleven items. However, each child is unique so you should include any additional information that you think is necessary.

Picture of Your Child

A picture puts a face to a diagnosis and test results. It reminds everyone involved in the educational process that they are dealing with a human being—complex and wonderful. "Before" and "After" pictures also work well, as does including any articles written about your child. Put the picture in the plastic sleeve on the front of a three ring binder, or prop a framed picture on the table during the IEP meeting. Some parents make short PowerPoint video presentations of their child at different stages of treatment and recovery.

Tugging at the heartstrings is not a bad thing. If the child has been off treatment for a while, the teachers do not have an accurate idea of what he or she has been through. Anything you can do to make your child multi-dimensional in their minds, rather than the "kid who doesn't follow directions" will help. And nothing is as powerful as a picture. Seeing a skeletal child in a bed with multiple tubes emerging, may increase their empathy for the child's traumatic history, and

> Carol Dean is the mother of an 8-year-old daughter diagnosed in July 1992 with medulloblastoma. Her daughter is now a college student who drives and works part time.

may soften up a tired or hardened educator.

Medical Information

Your portfolio should include information about diagnosis, treatments, and short- and long-term side effects. This can be a letter from the child's oncologist or physician from the survivorship clinic. Some families use the filled out treatment summary form, available at *www.patientcenters.com/survivors* (click on "Cancer Patient Treatment Record"). You can include an article about your child's type of cancer, along with any technical articles on your child's specific late effects. These articles can be obtained from your child's physician or nurse practitioner, or from the technical bibliography for this book available on the Candlelighter's website at *www.candlelighters.org*. Children who have had radiation to the brain are especially prone to learning difficulties. An article describing these issues and how to check for problems related to them is essential. Most teachers have never taught a child who has the potential for these types of problems nor do they know what to look for. You can also keep a copy of this book *Educating the Child with Cancer: A Guide for Parents and Teachers* for your use and provide one to your child's school as a reference. This book is available free for parents and educators. Call Candlelighters' national office at 800-366-CCCF (2223).

Need for Special Services

Ask your child's physicians to write letters describing the medical reasons why special services are necessary. Examples are letters describing the need for physical therapy after surgery or chemotherapies that caused muscle weakness or neuropathies. Children with fine motor late effects should receive services from an occupational therapist. Speech therapy is needed by many survivors and should be provided by the school district. Letters should also describe the child's physical education needs:

- Waiver
- Adaptive physical education
- Regular classes with self-regulation
- Full participation

If teachers need to watch for symptoms during physical education, this should be outlined in the letter. An example is children at risk for heart problems. PE teachers should know the symptoms and have a plan of action should they occur.

Arrangements for School Absences

During and after treatment many children miss a lot of school. Some school districts have absentee and tardy policies that deduct grades for absences. When your child is diagnosed, send a letter to the principal outlining the issues and likelihood of school absences/tardiness. This letter will need to be updated as the medical situation changes and whenever your child goes to a different school (e.g., elementary to middle school; middle school to high school). Make sure your child is not penalized for absences that cannot be prevented.

Neuropsychological Test Results

Children at risk for learning disabilities should have baseline neuropsychological testing and then repeat testing at intervals for several years. Results of these tests are very important, as you will use the recommendations section to help craft an appropriate 504 Plan or IEP for your child. See Chapter 5, *Neuropsychological Testing* and Chapter 14, *Special Education: The Law.*

Put the reports from all neuropsychological reports in your portfolio, with the most recent first. Other test results, such as educational testing and/or vocational rehabilitation testing, should also be included in your portfolio.

Report Cards

Your portfolio should contain all report cards, in numerical order. This can help identify trends downward or emerging strengths.

Results of Standardized Testing

Keep the results of all standardized tests in your child's portfolio (e.g., SAT, ACT, Iowa Test of Basic Skills, Stanford 9s). Be sure to include whether the test was taken with special accommodations: extended time, questions read to student, teacher filled in answer sheet based on verbal answers from student, etc.

Copies of 504 Plans and IEPs

An essential part of your portfolio is copies of all past IEPs and 504 plans. The old ones will give you a basis for creating the new ones, especially when changing schools.

Copy of Federal, Local, and State Regulations

Special education services vary widely depending on the location and size of the school district. Keeping a copy of the regulations and policies that govern your local district in your portfolio alerts educators that you know your legal rights. These can include a copy of The Americans with Disabilities Act and all local and state regulations and policies. You should contact the school superintendent, director of special education, or special education advisory committee to obtain a copy of the school system's procedures for special education ("Notice of Parents' Rights"). Also write to your state Superintendent of Public Instruction to obtain a copy of the state rules governing special education. To get the address, ask the school principal, district superintendent, special education teacher, resource room teacher, or a reference librarian.

Examples of Your Child's Work

It helps to include representative samples of your child's work in the portfolio. For example, if your child has trouble learning long division due to a visual/spatial disability, it helps teachers to see math papers in which the columns drift to the left or right. This visually reinforces the need for using graphing paper so that the child can line up columns and not get lost in long problems. If your child has spelling difficulties, put in a handwritten paper full of spelling errors, and a document written on a word processor with spell check. This can bolster your point that the child needs an AlphaSmart (or similar lap top computer) in class in order to do his best work. Also put in samples of work in areas in which your child excels. The IEP should encourage the child's strengths, as well as address areas in which she needs help.

Copies of Any Correspondence With the School

Whenever you send a letter to a teacher, the principal, or the district, put a copy in your portfolio. This will prevent any misunderstandings about what you asked for and when. Be sure to put in any responses you get to your correspondence. It sometimes helps to collect business cards of all the members of your child's team and put them in the portfolio. Business supply stores sell plastic sleeves with preset holders for business cards.

Your child's academic grade, physical condition, and special needs will determine how elaborate your portfolio becomes. You may just have one portfolio or many over the years. Portfolios help ensure that children gets the education they need to make the most of the life they fought so hard to win. These records should be given to your child when he or she turns 18. They will be essential for testing and accommodations at college or work.

Key Points

- An education portfolio is a collection of documents in a binder that you take with you to all education-related meetings. The information is updated throughout your child's illness and education.

- Examples of items to put in the portfolio are picture of your child, medical summary, all letters to and from the school, copies of state and federal regulations concerning special education, copies of all Individual Education Plans (IEP) or 54 plans, neuropsychological test results, report cards, results of standardized testing, and examples of your child's work.

- Having all necessary information at your fingertips can help give you confidence in meetings with school personnel as well as help you get the most appropriate services for your child.

Parent Perspectives

We have had tremendous resistance from the school district about providing services. They agree in principle that they need to provide services for Ethan, but he is in a unique situation. He goes to a small private grammar school with only 45 children, and is dually enrolled in the school district, so he is eligible for services with them. We have been reluctant to have Ethan out of his classroom for any length of time during the school day, as it makes him 'different' and feeling socially connected has been a struggle for him. As an alternative, we have managed his tutoring as a family, but wanted to get some assistive technology for use in this endeavor at home. The school was not enthusiastic.

I put together my updated portfolio, with articles on the damage that radiation can cause related to learning, an annotated medical history, his IEPs, and the neuropsychological testing done through both the hospital and the school. I was requesting something very specific—I wanted an AlphaSmart (a lightweight and easy to use computer-like device for keyboarding), as well as keyboarding, spelling, and writing programs for use on our home computer. I laid out the situation, referring to my portfolio with regularity, and pointed out all the parts that supported my needs: his school district neuropsychological testing revealed severe spelling problems, and also recommended the keyboarding, his otolaryngologist noted his new and significant hearing loss, and the urgency of intervening in his education early, and the IEP goals that had not yet been met. Amazingly, after three months of foot-dragging and delays, I left the conference with everything I asked for, as well as some additional programs for us to try. Being prepared with a volume of supporting evidence, written at both a lay level and a professional level (you never know what the background of the person you are dealing with is) was invaluable.

✦ ✦ ✦

For organizing the educational records I use a 3-inch, 3-ring binder. I use dividers for:

- *Pending problems and questions. I divide a sheet into columns to summarize the problem/question, who and when I called, their response, a due-by-date, and follow-up. I keep a paper trail of every request.*

- *Current IEP.*

- *Previous IEP.*

- *Neuropsychological test reports.*

- *Current. I use this section for immediate, short-term questions, e.g., things that can be dealt with in a single phone call, but still should have a paper trail to keep people accountable.*

- *Therapists' notes.*

- *Miscellaneous notes.*

- *Work in progress. Some years when we wanted bigger changes in my son's IEP, we have had several planning sessions ahead of time. This section of the portfolio is for long-term, big picture thoughts that are bounced around among us, the learning specialist, and the special education administrator.*

✦✦✦

The treatment (surgery, whole brain radiation, chemotherapy) of the brain tumor of my 5-year-old daughter exacted a high price, including problems with speech, expressive languages, hearing, fine motor control, balance, and processing speed. The first meeting with the school district made it clear to me that they did not have any grasp of how to deal with my child who did not fit neatly into a box they have dealt with before. I decided I was going to have to get educated and organized to be her advocate. Thus was born my educational binder.

I keep a copy of the information that I have given to the school on medical history, neuropsychological exams as well as yearly evaluations in PT, OT, speech, and audiology. This binder is also my portable reference as it contains the best articles I have collected on special education, childhood cancer, and neurocognitive late effects. I have a section on more personal aspects including newsletter articles, pictures and some of her work. Finally, I put in blank pages to write notes and keep phone numbers. I think having this all together helps me feel more confident and competent.

Chapter 17

High School and Beyond

Cecily Betz, RN, PhD, FAAN

Ideally, planning for life after high school begins soon after diagnosis, regardless of the age of the child. This suggestion may sound out of place when you are struggling with the bad news of your child's cancer diagnosis. Or you may think, my child is just too young to be thinking about what he or she will be doing so far in the future. However, as a parent, it is important that your child learn from you that one day he or she will grow up to be an adult and will have to learn to take care of himself or herself. Your child will learn this important lesson from you when you convey positive expectations about the future with comments such as "When you go to college…" or "When you grow up and live on your own…"

Positive attitudes for the future are meaningful only if they are combined with actions needed to help your child achieve his or her dreams. To do this, it will be very useful if you and your child make plans to take advantage of many available federal, state, and local services and programs.

Many survivors of childhood cancer leave high school and go to college or enter the workforce without needing extra support. However, for those who have treatment that affects learning or other ways of functioning, there are many ways to obtain help. This chapter describes some programs and services that help temporarily or permanently disabled survivors transition successfully to adulthood.

Programs covered in this chapter include high school individual education plans (IEP) for special education students and 504 plans for general education students. Other programs are the Department of Vocational Rehabilitation, Disabled Student Services, Social Security Administration Independent Living Centers (ILC), Workforce Investment Act (WIA) One-Stops and strategies for transitioning successfully to adult health care settings.

Ms. Betz is executive editor of the Journal of Pediatric Nursing and director of nursing training, USC University Affiliated Program at Childrens Hospital Los Angeles, CA.

Individualized Education Program (IEP) Transition Plans

Special education students have a right to be prepared for graduation, higher education, and employment in ways that fit their needs. To accomplish this, transition planning should begin in the early years of middle school, when your child's peers are beginning to gain work skills and prepare for high school graduation. IEP transition plans can help students better prepare for entering college, vocational or job training programs after they graduate from high school. The law states that transition services should begin no later than age 14.

To begin transition planning, talk with your child's teacher and special education representatives at his or her school. Although your child's health-related concerns should already be included in your son or daughter's IEP, the transition IEP is developed based on your child's current and future needs. Therefore, your child's previous IEPs will be reviewed to determine what, if any, revisions should be addressed in your child's transition IEPs. Steps for creating the transition plan include:

- Set up a meeting with your child's transition coordinator to discuss with you and your child the plans for the upcoming transition IEP.

- Provide your child's health care provider with information on areas of need that will be discussed in the transition IEP as it relates to employment, training, housing, community skills, and other training that pertains to health care needs.

- Determine what representatives from other agencies to invite to the transition meeting. Examples are the Department of Rehabilitation, community college/college/university Disabled Student Services, One-Stop employment agency, Independent Living Center, Title V Children with Special Health Care Needs Program, and other community agencies such as housing and transportation. You, your child and the educator can discuss what agencies will be needed to provide necessary services.

- Discuss with the transition specialist which staff members from the school should attend the IEP meeting. Depending on your child's needs, you may want to invite the school nurse, school counselor or psychologist, or occupational and/or physical therapist. Discuss whether you would like to have the heath care provider give input at the transition IEP meeting and the reason why.

Be sure to spend time with your son or daughter to discuss the upcoming IEP. It is important that both of you are well prepared for the IEP to ensure that a really effective plan is developed.

The discussion could include:

- Your child's dreams and hopes for the future.
- Plans for making the dreams a reality.
- Questions to bring up with the transition specialist that you need answered before, during and after the IEP meeting.
- Ways for your child to share ideas during the transition meeting.

IEP recommendations that might be appropriate for inclusion in your child's transition IEP are:

- Learning money management.
  - Opening a bank account
  - Learning to budget money
  - Using an ATM machine
  - Learning to make change
  - Learning the value of saving money
- Obtaining a driver's license/identification card.
- Learning to cook and plan meals.
  - Learning to read a recipe
  - Learning to use kitchen utensils
  - Learning to use stove, microwave
- Learning to make retail purchases.
  - Clothes
  - Food
  - Household goods
  - Fun items such as CDs, hobby kits, sports equipment
- Learning to live independently/with support.
  - How to find a place to live
  - How to find a roommate
  - Learning to perform household chores
  - Paying bills on time
  - How to get adaptive equipment to drive an automobile

Transition IEPs should include goals and timetables for reaching those goals.

504 Plans

Many students who have cancer are in general education classes. These students may use 504 plans in much the same way as IEPs, although the available services are different and not as extensive. 504 plans are helpful for students with cancer if their condition interferes with their academic performance. For example, a student who is undergoing chemotherapy treatments may miss days or weeks of school. A 504 plan enables the student to receive the necessary accommodations to ensure that his or her academic performance will not be as severely affected. Whenever the student is unable to attend school, the school will provide the student with other forms of instruction, such as a tutor or packet of learning materials, and make other arrangements for testing. Other 504 accommodations that would be useful to students with cancer include:

- Leaving the classroom to use the restroom without raising his/her hand.
- Using a tape recorder in the classroom.
- Having a note taker.
- Sitting in the front of the class.
- Having more time to complete an assignment or test.
- Performing an alternate school assignment or testing method such as oral presentation rather than written report.
- Excused tardiness for classes as the student may need more time to get to class.

Anyone can make a 504 referral—the student, parents, child's physician, nurse, or teacher. Contact the administration offices at your child's school to find out the name of the 504 coordinator. Contact this person to begin the process of developing and implementing a 504 plan.

Accommodations for Standardized Tests

Students who need accommodations for the Advanced Placement (AP), PSAT/ NMSQT and SAT College Board tests must register with and receive prior approval from the College Board. The registration process begins with contacting the school counselor or other school official. The school counselor will provide both the student and parents with information about the registration process and the necessary forms to complete. The student will need to complete pages 1 and 2 of Services for Students with Disabilities (SSD) Student Eligibility Form (if the student is under 18 years of age, then the parent or guardian must sign it). The form is returned to the school counselor or official who then completes the School Certification section. This form must be returned prior to deadlines listed on the College Board website (*http://www.collegeboard.com/disable/students/html/time.html*).

If the student is approved for accommodations, then an SSD Eligibility Letter will be sent to the student. The SSD eligibility letter includes the approved accommodations and the student's SSD code. A copy of the SSD eligibility letter must accompany registration for the SAT, which should be done in the spring before the year the College Board test is taken. Consult with the school counselor or official about the registration process for PSAT/NMSQT or AP examination. For more information on College Board Testing, access the website: *http://www.collegeboard.com/student/testing/sat/reg.html*

Department of Vocational Rehabilitation

There is a rehabilitation department in every state to help disabled individuals get jobs and live independently. Rehabilitation services are available beginning in high school enabling eligible youth to get work experience and exposure to different types of jobs while in school. Your child's school probably has work-training programs providing opportunities to work in a setting that he or she might desire for a career. You can find out what services are available at your child's high school by contacting your local school district administration.

To obtain services after graduation, your son or daughter should call the local Department of Rehabilitation to find out how to apply. The phone number of the local office of the Department of Rehabilitation is in the Community Services section of the yellow pages. When applying, your child will need to present proof of disability—usually copies of medical and school records. Notification of whether your child is eligible for services will be sent within 60 days from the date of application.

Once it has been decided that the survivor is eligible to receive rehabilitation services, an Individualized Plan for Employment (IPE) is developed. The rehabilitation counselor, survivor and survivor's care providers such as their disability case manager, job developer and employer develop this plan. Before the IPE is finalized, the rehabilitation counselor ensures the survivor's physician or health care provider concurs with the IPE. The IPE contains the individual's job goal, what needs to be done to achieve that goal and what rehabilitation services are required. Rehabilitation services may include:

- Help finding a job.

- Job training.
- Help performing the job.
- Buying supplies, uniforms and equipment needed for work.
- Transportation funding and assistance.

Disabled Student Services

If your child plans to attend college but has academic difficulties due to cancer or its treatment, a helpful campus resource is the Disabled Student Services (DSS) office. DSS offers many services for students who need additional assistance to help them have a positive college experience. These services include:

- Priority with registering for and scheduling of classes.
- Test-taking accommodations.
- Campus transportation services.
- Signing for hearing impairments/deaf students.
- Obtaining audio versions of textbooks.
- Tutoring services.
- Obtaining housing accommodations.
- Obtaining handicapped parking.
- Note taking services.

You and your child should evaluate the services offered by DSS offices for any college he or she is interested in attending. (Another topic to explore is whether the college or university has a tuition insurance plan. This can save thousands of dollars if the student has to drop out due to illness). Some campus DSS offices provide only classroom accommodations and campus access whereas other DSS offices offer additional services such as peer-to-peer support and social activities. Students must show proof of their disability to be eligible for services. You can include a visit to the DSS when you and your child visit prior to applying or as part of your child's college orientation.

Social Security Administration

Supplemental Security Insurance (SSI) provides monthly income checks and health care insurance (Medicaid) benefits for disabled individuals who meet income eligibility and are unable to work. SSI is a federal (U.S.) program administered by the Social Security Administration, and is an entitlement based on family income and assets. Recipients must be blind or disabled, have a low family income and few assets and be a U. S. citizen or legal immigrant eligible to live in the U.S. on a permanent basis. Children under 18 years are eligible for SSI benefits if they meet the disability definition and their family income and assets are low enough. Youth are eligible for SSI benefits up to 22 years of age if they are regularly attending school and are not the head of the household.

Children who receive SSI benefits must reapply when they turn 22 to see if they qualify as adults. Some survivors of childhood cancer qualify as disabled for this program, making them eligible for monthly aid. To apply, look in the phone book under "United States Government" for "Social Security Administration." Call the nearest field office to determine if your child is eligible.

Some programs are targeted specifically to adolescents and young adults who wish to work or continue their education and still be able to receive SSI benefits. The "Plan for Achieving Self Support" (PASS) allows the adolescent/adult to earn money and still receive SSI income. The PASS plan allows the adolescent/adult to save money for education, training or for business purposes to assist him or her achieve a work goal. The money saved must be for the specific purposes identified and approved in the PASS plan. For example, your son or daughter may want to enroll in a training program to become a veterinarian assistant. To achieve this goal, he or she may need financial support for tuition, uniforms, and supplies. Your son or daughter would contact the SSA office to obtain the "Plan for Achieving Self-Support," (SSA-545-BK) form to complete. People who could help your child apply for the PASS plan are vocational rehabilitation counselor, SSA staff, staff from disability organizations, and benefit specialists who work for the SSA supported programs. After your child's PASS plan is written, it is mailed or taken to the SSA office where it is reviewed by the SSA staff. One of three outcomes is possible: it is accepted, revisions are recommended, or it is not approved. An appeal can be filed if the PASS plan is not approved.

The "Student Earned Income Exclusion" program is for SSI beneficiaries who are students. This program enables your son or daughter to earn up to $5,410 per year (total amount is adjusted each year) and not risk losing SSI support. To be eligible, your son or daughter must be under 22 years of age, regularly attending school, and not be the head of household. To be considered a student regularly attending school, your son or daughter must be in either secondary school 12 hours a week, in grades 7 to 12, employment training program from 12 to 15 hours per week, attending a college or university 8 hours per week, or be in a home study course. For more information on this program and other work incentive programs, visit the SSA website and obtain an online version of "*Redbook: A Summary Guide To Employment Support*

For People With Disabilities Under The Social Security Disability Insurance and Supplemental Security Income Programs" at *http://www.ssa.gov/work/ResourcesToolkit/redbook.html#1619A.*

Impairment Related Work Expenses (IRWE) program allows deductions from work earned income for health-related expenses that are needed in order to work. Deductions can be taken for medical equipment and supplies, transportation services, job coaches, attendant care, and home modifications. For more information, visit the Social Security Administration's website at: *http://www.ssa.gov.* There are a number of pages on the SSA website that have good information on SSI benefits and employment programs. The web page address for youth with disabilities is *http://www.ssa.gov/work/Youth/youth.html.* An SSA web page that provides a great deal of information on the SSI work incentive programs is *http://www.ssa.gov/work/ResourcesToolkit/workincentives.html.*

If you feel your child is eligible for SSI but has been denied, a professional organization of attorneys and paralegals called the National Organization for Social Security Claimants' Representatives (NOSSCR) may be able to help. NOSSCR can refer you to a member in your geographic location. The phone number for NOSSCR is (800) 431-2804. NOSSCR has a web page at: *http://www.NOSSCR.org.*

Independent Living Centers (ILC)

ILCs are community agencies, operated and staffed by individuals with disabilities, located in every state. They serve people who have a broad range of disabilities that significantly impact their daily lives. Survivors who have been significantly affected by cancer and its treatment may benefit from an ILC. Many different types of services are offered to individuals with disabilities to enable them to lead independent and productive lives. Each ILC offers the following services:

- Advocacy.
- Help with finding housing.
- Listing of attendants who provide personal assistance.
- Peer counseling and mentoring.

Additional services may be provided by individual ILCs. ILC phone numbers can be found in the Community Services section of the Yellow Pages under the heading of "Disability Services." Parents can call to obtain information but appointments are made only with the person requiring services.

Workforce Investment Act (WIA) One-Stops

In 1998, Congress passed new laws to upgrade job-training programs for adults and youth. As a result, One-Stop employment agencies were created in every state to provide comprehensive employment services to unemployed adults and youth with disabilities. One-Stop employment agencies offer many services to help clients learn work skills, and to find and retain jobs. These services include learning job interviewing skills and writing a resume, case management services, and evaluations to determine work preferences and abilities.

Although the primary focus of One-Stops is employment, many other support services are available for youth such as instruction to obtain GED certificate, leadership training and mentorship programs. To find a One-Stop center in your community, look in the community services section of the yellow pages under the listing of "employment" or "youth and teen services." If you have access to the Internet, go to *www.google.com* and insert the words "(name of your state) Workforce Investment Act" then click on "Google search." If you don't have a computer, a reference librarian at your local library could help you.

Transitioning Successfully to Adult Health Care Settings

Very often the idea of leaving your pediatrician and pediatric specialists for new adult physicians is distressing. You have known these doctors and the other members of the health care team for a long time. Likewise, they know you and your family very well. However the time does come when it is best to confer with adult specialists or primary care doctors who have the medical expertise to care for young adult survivors. Some useful suggestions to assist you and your son or daughter in finding healthcare providers with experience caring for adult survivors of childhood cancer are:

- Ask for a referral from the comprehensive follow up clinic.
- Discuss with other long-term survivors of cancer.
- Ask for opinions at youth and adult support groups for survivors.
- Call national organizations such as Candlelighters Childhood Cancer Foundation.

Begin speaking with your child's pediatric specialty and primary care physicians about the need for finding adult providers before your child reaches that age (it will vary in terms of insurance coverage from 18 years to 21 years). Find out what type of transition program exists at the pediatric medical center where your child receives services.

Your child's nurse practitioner or physician should gradually educate your child throughout his or her teenage years about medical history, including several discussions of the diagnosis, treatment, and possible long-term effects. Your teen should understand the tests necessary to identify any late effects early and should get wellness education at each visit. Areas covered are exercise, diet, not smoking, and sexually transmitted diseases. Before the transfer, you teen should have:

- A detailed summary of his or her medical history.
- Copies of important scans and x-rays.
- Any documentation about medical need for academic accommodations.

Beginning at age 16, discuss plans with the health care provider, agency representative, employer health benefits representative (state Title V Children with Special Health Care Needs Program) for obtaining insurance coverage once pediatric eligibility ends.

Key Points

- Many federal, state, and local programs can help temporarily or permanently disabled survivors transition successfully to adulthood.

- IEP Transition Plans begin at age 14 to help disabled students better prepare for entering college, vocational or job training programs.

- Many students with cancer or survivors of childhood cancer are eligible for accommodations when taking standardized tests such as the SATs (college boards).

- Every state has a Department of Vocational Rehabilitation to help disabled individuals get jobs and live independently.

- Disabled survivors who attend college can find help at their campus Disabled Student Services office.

- The Social Security Administration has several programs that help disabled individuals, including Supplemental Security Insurance (SSI).

- Independent Living Centers provide disabled adults advocacy, help with housing, and peer counseling and mentoring.

- Workforce Investment Act One-Stop employment agencies help unemployed disabled people, learn work skills and find and retain jobs.

- Finding an adult health care provider who has experience helping survivors of childhood cancer is a crucial step towards independent adulthood.

Parent Perspectives

My son Joel was in high school when he was diagnosed with ALL. Communication was the key. I wrote weekly updates and made copies for each teacher, put their names on them, and delivered them to school. I learned that a single copy of a letter didn't get passed around to everyone. Some classes used a tape recorder; they all kept a record of what he'd missed. His math teacher got together with the librarian and arranged to videotape his math classes. They did so much on the board, on overheads, and with discussion in that class that an audiotape would not have helped. All teachers were willing to meet with him after or before school to essentially reteach the concepts that he had missed.

I also told his teachers it was okay to discuss Joel, his leukemia, and his treatment with the other kids in the class. They would never have done it without my okay. I tried to phrase things in my updates so that the kids would understand what was going on. I knew that in the absence of information, there would be rumors flying. This might not work for everyone, but it served us well.

✦ ✦ ✦

My daughter is learning to drive. Besides some attention issues, we worry about multi-tasking, distractibility, and response time. When she started driving, we had to keep the radio off. We still have to watch that the conversation doesn't get too interesting or she makes driving "errors." She decided to wave at a friend who was out for a walk when we were driving by one day, and nearly drove off the road. She couldn't wave and steer at the same time—she was soooo embarrassed! She only got IT methotrexate, not triples or radiation, but had a chemo-related stroke early in treatment, which may have something to do with her status. It is so frustrating to really know what is normal and what isn't and if she is at higher risk than other learners. The good news here is the graduated license, so by law, when she gets the license, she won't be allowed to drive with other kids in the car for several months. That should help with the distraction thing, at least.

+ + +

My son was at the end of his junior year of high school when he was diagnosed with AML, and he had a BMT in July. He missed most of his senior year. He applied to college and got into a bunch of schools. We wanted him to be near home but didn't think he needed to be in the same city. Wrong! To make a long story short, he developed graft-versus-host disease and needed to be in Boston to get treated. He ended up getting into a very good local university as a "special student" at the last minute. The fact that we personally knew one of the admissions counselors and that my husband and I were alumni of that university helped. Anyway, my point is that post-BMT survivors may not be able to go to college full time if they develop side effects. They should be made aware that college may take longer than it does for typical kids.

+ + +

The Department of Vocational Rehabilitation (DVR) in my community is very clear on their policy that any accommodation/specialized assessment that a student needs while in school is the school's responsibility. I work with high school kids with disabilities and have frequently needed a specialized evaluation to determine their ability to take driver's ed/driving. The DVR will not pay for this, saying it is the school's responsibility to provide for all students. We write in the IEP the need and justification for the specialized assessment and write a letter for the director of special education to sign authorizing the funding.

+ + +

I had cranial radiation in 1976 when I was 5. My learning disabilities were identified when I was in third grade. I had problems copying from the board, so the teacher would let me use her notes. But I still had to copy them because it was part of the assignment. It was hard because I got letters transposed and skipped words. But this made less and less of a difference as I went through high school and college, because copying wasn't important anymore. I now use spell check and grammar check and don't have as many problems in that arena.

+ + +

My son was diagnosed with Ewing's sarcoma at age 11. He developed secondary AML at age 15 and was treated with a BMT. The following school year, we switched him to a different school for a "fresh" start where none of the kids knew the details. He managed to find trouble there as well. He would have just as soon home schooled and did much better one on one. Besides not feeling like he fit in, none of the staff were willing to admit that any of his learning/social problems were related to his cancer, although it was clear to his elementary school teachers that "something" had caused the change. This was clearly not the same kid.

Admitting my kid isn't perfect doesn't mean I love them any less or value his life any less. I still find myself bitterly angry many days against my "survivor" son and his cancers, because even though his cancers did not kill him, they have forever changed the person he is. Without going into great detail I will say that he never graduated from high school and after his period of court ordered "house arrest" this summer, he was forced to move out. I am so worried about him. I love him with all my heart and soul and remember the nights of agony when we felt he could easily die.

✢ ✢ ✢

The Texas Commission for the Blind helps people who are in school or looking for work assistance. The state pays tuition for public college, and they pay for a portion of your book costs. It's a free education. They will provide you with any necessary equipment to do your job. Whenever I'm transitioning into school or to a new job they open my case and provide some services.

✢ ✢ ✢

I tell kids who are having a hard time in high school that the world opens up in college. It's such a bigger pool of people. I also think your peers are more mature. You won't be that kid who had cancer anymore. My learning disabilities were not such a big deal in college. No one knew about them, and I had the tools I needed to work around them. The doors really open up in college.

✢ ✢ ✢

One of my best friends is a medulloblastoma survivor. We were very concerned about the number of survivors from the 1970s and 1980s in our area whose social skills had been wiped out by treatment. Many of them live with their parents, are unable to work, and have no life to speak of. So we started a group, and fourteen of us met and talked all weekend. Most of them didn't even know that the others existed. We now meet regularly, plan activities, hold conferences, and help each other out. Many of the most disabled have really blossomed.

✦ ✦ ✦

Nathan was diagnosed in May of his junior year. His school was nice enough to give him his grades as they were up to that point so he did not have to do any more work after that for junior year. That was a good thing because he was in the hospital for six weeks initially. The school (private high school) had a weekly meeting where the whole school got together to learn about an interesting topic. The school devoted one of those sessions to Nathan's illness. They had a girl who had ALL 2 years prior and her mother spoke. The students then had a question and answer session with the nurse. The kids got up and shared their feelings. The administration said that they had never ever seen such a quiet and respectful group of kids as on that day.

Another thing that was great about those kids is that they were not afraid to come and visit Nathan. Before his counts dropped, he would have 6 to 15 kids visiting every evening. The nurses were very liberal and the kids ate, talked, brought presents, walked around, etc. It was a great morale booster for Nathan. As he got sicker from the chemo, the kids naturally dropped off and mostly his closest friends came. His room was decorated to the ceilings with cards and signs from the kids.

The transplant was during the summer. He was supposed to have gone to Israel with the camp group that summer. Those kids kept in touch with him, calling from Israel and sending letters. They brought back sandals for him, and dedicated their trip to him.

The following year, Nathan had a tutor from the public schools. That didn't work out so well because the tutor's attendance wasn't so good. We told the tutor not to come if he had a cold, and he had a lot of colds! Nathan tried to go back to school for three weeks in January but he kept getting sick so he didn't really go to school for senior year. The teacher sent home the work, which he did. The teachers definitely should have been better about communicating with Nathan. Some were great and came to visit, called, emailed, etc. Others, it was like pulling teeth. I wrote some letters to the administration but they weren't very helpful. I was so busy managing Nathan's health and trying to have a life with his three brothers, that I was not able to push the teachers more. One thing we did which really helped Nathan was to get an SAT tutor for math and one for English. Nathan's brain was mushy and he had trouble remembering what he learned. With the help of these tutors, he did well on the SATs. He did take them in his own room because his health was tenuous in those days. His short-term memory is not what it used to be to this day.

Nathan knew he wanted to finish high school with his friends. He was adamant about that. He had lots of time at home to get the work done. They had tried a video hook-up, which never really worked but I think that it would have been ideal. It definitely would have made Nathan feel more involved. He graduated with his class and of course got the biggest round of applause. It was awesome.

✛ ✛ ✛

In searching last year for cancer-related scholarships, I found no "universal" scholarships, that is, ones that any survivor could apply for. There are scholarships available through individual high schools and universities that look for individuals who have "overcome adversity." Tell the high school counselor that you're interested in these kinds of scholarships. There is also a trend at some private schools to have a single scholarship application that the scholarship committee then uses to distribute scholarship funds. These often require an essay. The essay is a good place to write about cancer survivorship issues.

✛ ✛ ✛

I am a long-term survivor of ALL. I had cranial radiation and I process information slower than many other students. Taking untimed tests makes a world of difference for people like me. I took the SATs timed in high school and could only complete half the items. I used to keep close track of the time, and when I only had fifteen minutes left, I'd randomly fill in the rest of the circles. I took the GREs for graduate school untimed and it was great. When I took my licensing exam for social work, I also took it untimed and did well. Being able to relax makes all the difference. I wish I'd known earlier that untimed tests were an option.

✛ ✛ ✛

Yesterday my son graduated from high school—an event I could not even imagine five years ago when he was diagnosed. I was so close to tears as he walked across the stage to get his diploma. He missed graduating with honors by .005 but it's okay. The fact that he got that close is an accomplishment in itself. He made the National Honor Society despite adrenal insufficiency, hypothyroidism, growth hormone deficiency, learning disabilities, left ventricular hypertrophy, central hypoventilation/sleep apnea, renal Fanconi's syndrome, a visual field defect, hand tremors, chronic fatigue, and radiation necrosis of parietal/temporal area.

We had a big celebration and his tree, "Hope," was in full bloom. He is still planning to attend college two hours from home and live in the dorms. I will definitely need my box of tissues then. He also got $5750 in scholarships. For all of you parents who are just starting this journey, don't lose hope. It is a long, rocky road but the rewards at the end are great. There were times I thought this would never happen.

✦ ✦ ✦

Some colleges will accept a local student who will live at home and take only one or two classes, given special situations like cancer/ongoing treatments, which require that a student stay local for college, and prevent him/her from being a full time student. You need to call your local college admission office and speak to a senior admissions person, not just a lightweight! And parents should not expect their kids to take a full time load of classes because sometimes the kids get sick, end up in the hospital and miss too much class time.

Our son took two classes the first semester and three classes the second semester, and it was a challenge because he was weak, had low energy and was hospitalized several times the first year of college.

He was able to take a full load of classes his second year of college, but it was still a challenge because he ended up in the hospital twice. It is very important for your child with cancer to email his/her professor if health issues prevent him/her from attending class, finishing an assignment on time, taking an exam, etc. As long as our son kept his professors informed, they were willing to cut him some slack so that he could complete his course work, even if it wasn't always on time.

It is very important for college students with cancer to take things slowly. They do not have the energy of normal kids, and may find it hard to concentrate for long periods because of chemo or brain radiation which they have had. I encourage our son to do his work when he feels well, to keep up with his work and not count on cramming last minute, because he never knows when he will experience headache/nausea/fatigue for a day or two for unexplained reasons. Also, it is important to get enough sleep and not try to always keep up with other college kids who stay up most of the night to party. Last point: most colleges will not give you any kind of refund after the first month of a semester has passed. You can insure your child's tuition in case he/she becomes medically ill and needs to drop out.

✦ ✦ ✦

I am the parent of an adolescent with cancer and just wanted to comment on a few things. Because the chemo and brain radiation affected our son's concentration and gave him tremors which affected his mechanical ability to write, he was allowed to take his SATs with no time limit. This made a huge difference. It was also easy to arrange: we contacted the College Board and had the oncologist write a letter explaining why it was necessary.

I would strongly urge a planning conference with the principal/teachers/ guidance counselor, etc. when the child is ready to resume some school work. Parents need to actively stay in touch with teachers about the pace and content of the schoolwork. We worked out a plan where our son did most of the work at home. Some teachers were not very good about this and so parents need to be on top of it.

Chapter 18

Physical Activity

Kathy Ruble, RN, PNP, AOCN
Cindy Schwartz, MD

The child who succeeds academically is likely to succeed in the adult world, but for many children, athletics determine childhood success. Muscular growth, bone strength and fitness are the physical manifestations of success, but the interactive skills, balance between interdependency and self reliance, joy of success and acceptance of limitation, combine to develop the skills that contribute to happiness, friendships and productive interactions.

The physical impact of cancer and its treatment affect the ability of a child to take part in physical activity and sports. Yet it is during this stressful time that we must strive harder than ever to provide the child with as many normal experiences as is possible. Spending gym period in the nurse's office can be traumatic, even for the child who never was the first pick on a class team.

Some children define themselves by their physical prowess, from the delicate dancer and robust gymnast to the football team captain and downhill skier. When such children are diagnosed with cancer, limited ability to participate may be devastating. A child who was less athletic before cancer may already enjoy more sedentary activities. Such alternate types of activities can help sustain children during cancer therapy. But even less athletic children often become limited by cancer if they are unable to swim at the beach, bicycle with the family or fish with grandpa.

As in all aspects of life with cancer, the goal must be to help the child or adolescent have as many normal experiences as is possible, maintaining connections to the life that preceded the cancer diagnosis—and to the life that will be resumed after successful treatment. With appropriate encouragement and education, sports teams have allied behind the child, shaving their heads in unity with their teammate and leading charitable events to support the family. Advocacy at the school for appropriate physical education without stigma

> Ms. Ruble is a pediatric nurse practitioner and coordinator of the long-term program for survivors of childhood cancer at Johns Hopkins in Baltimore, MD.

is very helpful. The maintenance of physical activity to the extent feasible helps the child retain physical and emotional strength, improving the child's overall outlook.

The parent who may have struggled to buy a new bike or soccer cleats or to get the child to each lesson, practice or game now has another burden. He or she must determine what the child can realistically continue to do and must encourage the child to maintain a sense of normalcy. This chapter will help parents and teachers encourage physical activity in children with cancer. It covers effects of cancer therapy that may impact physical activity including fatigue, anemia, risk of bleeding, catheters, cardiac or pulmonary dysfunction, cognitive problems, amputation, and loss of a kidney.

Fatigue/Nutrition

Cancer itself can cause fatigue, probably from the energy expended by the rapid growth of tumor cells. Some tumors also produce substances that directly cause fatigue. Once treatment begins these effects may improve, but the therapy itself can be exhausting. Decreased appetite, mouth sores, nausea, vomiting, and diarrhea reduce nutritional intake, causing fatigue. Nutritional supplements may help to some extent, but they usually do not cure fatigue.

Anemia

Chemotherapy and radiation affect the most rapidly dividing cells: cancer and blood cells. Anemia is the result of reduced production of red blood cells that carry oxygen to muscles and other tissues. With fewer red cells, the heart must pump harder to allow sufficient oxygen-laden red cells to reach the muscles. Reduced oxygen delivery and more rapid cardiac pumping of available blood can result in fatigue and headaches.

Transfusions of red cells are common during cancer therapy, but this often does not raise the hemoglobin level (the oxygen carrying protein) to the normal range. In some cases erythropoietin, a hormone that stimulates the production of red blood cells, may be prescribed. Even with such interventions, children with cancer are almost always anemic compared to others their age. They struggle to approach the endurance and energy of peers. Participating in team sports may not be feasible, but physical activity is still important. Planning activities, such as a trip to the amusement park,

Dr. Schwartz is an associate professor of oncology and pediatrics at the Sidney Kimmel Cancer Center and is director of the long-term program for survivors of childhood cancer at Johns Hopkins in Baltimore, MD.

when energy is expected to be greatest can be helpful.

Risk of Bleeding

Therapy also interferes with the production of platelets, a component of the blood that enables blood to clot. Thrombocytopenia (low platelets) significantly increases the risk of bleeding and thus limits the activities that a child can safely perform. Blood proteins that assist in the clotting of blood may also become deficient, increasing the risk of bleeding. This occurs commonly with asparaginase therapy for leukemia. Liver injury can also affect these proteins. Working with the health care team, it is often possible to predict the period of risk so as to plan optimal times for physical activity.

Catheters

Easy access to the blood stream for lab testing and for the infusion of chemotherapy is necessary for the treatment of cancer. Virtually all children now have indwelling catheters for such access. Some catheters, known as "ports," are completely under the skin allowing the child to swim without fear of infection. They are less visible, helping to maintain body image, and are also less likely to be inadvertently damaged or pulled during activity. Some catheters have external plastic tubing that must be stabilized by taping to the skin or wearing snug undergarments during exercise. With careful protection of the tubing, children with external catheters are able to participate in most activities.

Heart

It is unusual for heart (cardiac) problems to directly affect physical activity during treatment. Nonetheless, anthracyclines (doxorubin, daunomycin, and others) damage cardiac muscle cells. This may result in muscle weakness that increases as the cumulative dose increases. The left ventricle of the heart that is responsible for pumping the blood out to the entire body can, in rare cases, lose its ability to squeeze effectively. When this happens, the child or adolescent is likely to avoid strenuous activities. More commonly, the reduction in heart function is minimal and not associated with symptoms.

Medications may be given that reduce stress on the heart by reducing blood pressure or increasing the heart's ability to contract. Those with moderately diminished heart function are told to participate in physical activity to their level of comfort, resting as needed during physical activity. Some cardiologists recommend that such individuals avoid isometric exercise, such as weight lifting, that significantly increases the workload of the heart.

Left ventricular dysfunction is often subtle, and is detectable only by sensitive cardiac evaluations. Clinical effects are usually not apparent until more than 10 years after therapy is completed. Continued routine monitoring is needed so that any change in the ability to take part in physical activities is known.

Lungs

Respiratory function can be affected by radiation, surgery or chemotherapy and can have a significant impact on exercise tolerance. Surgical removal of lung tissue, due either to tumor or more rarely to fungal infection, is sometimes needed. People can live long lives with only one lung. Radiation (and some chemotherapies) may result in the formation of scar tissue, preventing the lung from expanding fully. Scarring (called fibrosis) from bleomycin may interfere with the natural process by which the lung rids the body of carbon dioxide. All of these processes affect the amount of air exchange in the lungs as measured by pulmonary function tests (PFT). Those with declines in their PFT may have shortness of breath, but most will simply find exercise to be uncomfortable.

Scuba diving is not recommended for people who received bleomycin because it causes an increase in pressure on lung tissue. This, along with the effects of breathing high concentrations of oxygen, may further increase the amount of scarring (fibrosis.) There are no interventions known to repair pulmonary damage but avoidance of smoking and second hand smoke is important to prevent further problems.

Behaviors can be modified to compensate for a decline in pulmonary function. Sports that require quick spurts of energy with some periods of rest may be easier for affected children and adolescents. For example, in tennis the child may run after the ball on one play and catch his breath while the ball is returned. Baseball similarly requires only the occasional burst of energy to run the bases. Sports such as long distance running that require constant, high levels of oxygen, are difficult for survivors with damaged lungs.

As with cardiac dysfunction, the best approach for pulmonary dysfunction is to self regulate activity. The child should be encouraged to participate at the level that is comfortable. For instance, if the class is running laps in physical education class, the survivor should be allowed to walk when feeling short of breath. Stamina and endurance may improve over time as the child becomes more physically fit. While those with lungs affected by cancer therapies are unlikely to become professional athletes, most will be able to enjoy normal levels of physical activity throughout their lifetimes.

Nervous System

The nervous system is made up of two parts, the central (CNS) and the peripheral (PNS) nervous systems. Treatment of the CNS with surgery or radiation may affect gait, balance and/or coordination either during therapy or permanently. Team sports clearly become physically difficult. In some instances, neurocognitive changes occur that affect the ability to understand strategies for team play.

Perhaps the most common neurologic effect is that of vincristine on the peripheral nervous system (PNS). Slow transmission of neurologic impulses causes a number of problems including tingling, wide-based gait, muscle aches, and foot drop. Children may stumble more than usual, sometimes falling or tripping when they try to run. Fortunately these effects are temporary and usually go away within a few months of completing therapy.

It is important to maintain safety with activity of any sort. A stationary or tandem bike may be useful when a standard bike could be hazardous. Swimming and golf are usually safe forms of physical activity for those with coordination difficulties.

Amputations/Limb Salvage

Bone tumors are curable only with either surgical removal (osteosarcoma, Ewing's sarcoma) or radiation (Ewing's sarcoma) of the tumor. Surgical removal is accomplished by amputation of the entire extremity beyond the tumor or limb salvage (replacing the malignant bone with either a metal rod or human bone from the individual or a cadaver). Each of the procedures requires adjustments in the performance of physical activities.

Children who undergo amputation are fitted with prostheses. Advances in prosthetic technology allow amputees to take part in most sports and physical fitness activities. With appropriate physical and occupational rehabilitation the amputee can expect to return to favorite activities with some minor modifications. Negative body image issues after amputation are common but can be improved by appropriate rehabilitation, counseling, and integration into physical activities.

Body image issues are less common with limb salvage procedures but other precautions are necessary. Limitations in range of motion are common and the risk of fracture may be high. For these survivors it may be appropriate to avoid activities such as gymnastics that may result in fractures from either falls or high force landings. Specific recommendations from the orthopedic physician are necessary to determine safe and appropriate activities.

Nephrectomy (removal of a kidney)

Children with Wilms tumor usually undergo removal of the affected kidney. Although people can live long healthy lives with one kidney, preserving the remaining kidney becomes critical. Most healthcare providers recommend that children with one kidney avoid boxing, martial arts, football, horseback riding or other sports that involve potential for significant physical trauma. Of greatest concern are injuries directed to the lower back where the kidney is located. For those who do play team sports, a kidney guard may be recommended. It is unclear whether these actually provide important protection, or if they just serve as a reminder to avoid unnecessary risk.

Despite the probability that children with cancer must live with some of these effects of treatment, children can still play and exercise. Reminding the physician of a child's desire to be active may be essential to ensure that appropriate precautions are taken to make physical activity safe and pleasurable.

If a child has problems with physical activities in school, it is probably best to work directly with the physical education instructor or department. Understanding the issues will enable them to tailor activities to the child's needs. For questions concerning the safety of specific activities, a parent should consult the healthcare team. The school may request a letter from the healthcare team that clearly describes activities that are safe for the child and those that should be avoided.

Key Points

- Almost every child with cancer can take part in some form of physical activity.

- Finding an appropriate outlet for physical energy promotes well being while fostering self-confidence, teamwork and independence.

- For those with cancer, successful integration with a sports team, even if the person cannot fully participate, may provide a sense of normalcy.

- Parents often must become the advocate for the child or adolescent, ensuring that the medical team provides the information necessary to make physical activities safe and essential components of life.

Parent Perspectives

The only problem we've encountered in PE so far is with the "Presidential Fitness Tests." My son has a hard time with sit-ups (he can't do more than a few) because of the large abdominal incision he had and the scar tissue. His abdominal muscles are really weak. Also, we found out last week at the long-term survivor's clinic that he will not be allowed to do bench-presses in school weight room activities because of heart issues due to the adriamycin. I will have to inform the schools about this. Personally, I think our kids should get a presidential award just for surviving cancer.

✦ ✦ ✦

My son had Wilms when he was an infant. He is now 10 and a sports fanatic. He plays football, and I got him an abdominal protector that clips to the bottom of his shoulder pads. It is a hard shell with padding inside. It goes all the way around his abdominal area and hooks in the front. When he started wearing it, the other boys all wanted one too. Instead of being the oddball, he began a new fad. I call him "the kid in armor."

✦ ✦ ✦

I was worried about our daughter with leukemia playing sports with her port and low platelets. The PE teacher told me initially not to worry because at her age (8 at diagnosis) kids are not playing true contact sports like tackle football. I was uncomfortable with that so we agreed that she wouldn't do anything that might result in her being hurt. This is what we do: When the class is scheduled to play sports (which is maybe twice a week), they break the class up into 2 groups. Half play the sport and half to another activity such as jump rope, walking, bowling (plastic pins with a tiny ball), Simon Says, or something like that. Our girl is always in the group that does the alternate activity. They break up the class so she isn't the only one doing something different. Many of the kids now actually request to be in the "other" group.

Also, the day after her spinal taps, she does not participate in PE at all. That is only once every 3 months so it isn't a big deal. She helps her homeroom teacher clean the chalkboards or goes to the library on those days.

+ + +

My son's physical limitations from the limb reconstruction, subsequent surgeries, and then the bone marrow transplant prevented him from participating in physical education for several years. The class was always just waived. However, we learned the hard way that you should get it in writing in the IEP and keep a copy at home. We got a new principal my son's senior year and half way through the year he informed us that my son needed to make up his PE credits from 7th grade on.

+ + +

Sports are very important to 17-year-old Steven. We realize we are fortunate that he has few deficits from his treatment of a malignant brain tumor. He has problems with balance and left-sided weakness, primarily. One of the few things he is able to do at this point is golf. His coach applied for and received an exception from the state activities association to allow Steven to use a cart during competitions. None of his teammates or competitors thought anything about it. He is scoring 7 or 8 strokes higher than he was last year and he was disappointed with the season. I was thrilled that he was still able to play and that he chose to make the effort on his own.

I hope Steven's success can be encouraging to others. It has been our decision to not overprotect Steven. We don't suggest what he may or may not be able to do. He will discover these things on his own. We try not to push or pressure. Anything he truly wants to do we try to find a way to encourage and set incremental goals to achieve his desired activity. For instance, he still hopes to play football and/or basketball this fall. Rather than saying it is doubtful, we say, "Then we need to get to work, because it isn't going to happen by simply wanting to." First we have to walk, then jog, then run. He'll need to build strength and endurance and be realistic that it will be difficult to be as proficient at some things as he was prior to diagnosis. If we only make it to the jogging, it's still more than he would have done had that been his only goal. I am tentatively anticipating how he progresses and deals with the challenges, disappointments and successes ahead of him.

+ + +

I took Emma skiing at an adaptive program in New Hampshire, and she absolutely loved it. She isn't walking independently yet, so for her, this was the first time in almost two years that she had the feeling of going fast on her own two feet. She went for 4 two-hour sessions in two days, and was on her feet all but one session (she went in a sit-ski one session so that she could go all the way to the top of the mountain and all the way down fast). She had an instructor on each side and she held on to a ski pole they held between them in front of her. Her skis were tethered together in front, and next time they want to put a spacer between her skis in the back. The eventual goal is to get her skiing independently with out-rigger poles on each side. The program at Loon Mountain is not limited to kids who can't walk. They offer lessons for people of all ages with balance problems, vision problems, weakness from chemo or neurological disorders, Downs syndrome, autism, and anyone who might be at higher risk for injury. Everyone there was terrific. The following link lists adaptive programs across the country. http://www.amputee-coalition.org/inmotion/sep_oct_02/ski.html.

✛ ✛ ✛

Last Friday, Lisa had her dance recital (tap and ballet). For me it was a completely overwhelming experience. In the fall, I looked around for a place that was willing to take her, since she was fairly disabled from her treatment for medulloblastoma. Finally, I found that the YMCA would enroll her in their Saturday morning program. Although she was 6, I put her with the 4- and 5-year-olds. She is tiny and no one really knew the difference.

When we started she did almost everything from a chair and often would just sit and watch. Later, I would kneel behind her and hold her waist as she tried to do the front and back points. Over winter, I had to decide whether she would be in the spring recital. It was hard: getting up to get there by 9AM every Saturday, watching how hard it was for her, hoping that she would be able to go on stage and not be frustrated or embarrassed. During dress rehearsal the doubts multiplied. Would she be too cold in the skimpy outfit (beautiful but sleeveless and very, very short)? Would she slip and fall as she only wore the tap shoes once before? Would she go on in front of 200 people or so? Would the sound system bother her? Would the bright lights make her shield her eyes? When the curtain opened, there she was standing so poised and absolutely stunning. She did the entire routine. She didn't look different than any of the other kids. Most people in the audience had no idea how incredibly fantastic it was, how she could weight shift, point her toes, jump, move side to side and all in tap shoes! It was truly a moving moment.

+ + +

My son is 20, a 15 ½ year brain tumor survivor and a survivor of the school system/post school system. I think the social/emotional effects of all those late physical effects has a huge impact on a survivor's life. Social isolation and depression develop because of balance problems, spinal deformity, learning problems and hearing impairment. Teenagers want to be accepted by their peers, despite any health problems.

My son was a target for the cruelty of teenage boys especially in the gym class where he was easily tripped and laughed at when he fell. They humiliated him by calling him a hunchback. My solution was to approach the gym teacher who knew the core group of "leaders" in the class and give him permission to share some of my son's cancer history with this group. It helped get the message out and the abuse lessened.

Endless parent/teacher relationships and medical documentation and reminders of your child's difficulties to the teachers are necessary throughout school. And start researching resources for post secondary education well before graduation. There are opportunities, but there are also lots of dead ends in your search for life after school.

+ + +

Our 6-year-old son has slower speed than his peers. He also has a visual field cut and partial seizures. Our local Jewish Community center has an excellent swimming and camp program. Our son was assigned an experienced counselor for a swimming buddy at camp. They also provided lessons in soccer, archery, and tennis. Our son sat out any activities when he was too tired. There was no pressure, and it was very supportive. The nurse handled the few partial seizures quite well.

+ + +

My son had a Port-a-cath for three years, from age 14 to 17. During that time, he played basketball, football, softball, and threw the shot in track. His port was placed on his left side just below his armpit. For football, I worked with the trainer and we developed a special pad that went into a "custom" pocket I sewed into some t-shirts. That way the port had a little extra padding. We also found shoulder pads that had a sidepiece that covered the area. He never had any problems or soreness from the port.

+ + +

We decided against adaptive PE for our pre-teen son who had a brain tumor over two years ago, even though he still needs to use a cane (unless he is just around the house with walls to reach for when his balance waivers). The adaptive PE program at our junior high is geared toward mentally challenged kids. The teachers thought that he would not be comfortable taking this class. His regular PE was scheduled for the second period. However, after the first week of junior high his PE teacher phoned me concerned because of our son's exhaustion level. After PE he was wiped out for the rest of the day. We discussed it and she excused him from PE because she wanted him to just concentrate on making it through the day. She felt his other classes were more important. They recorded that period as classroom aide and let him do a study hall/rest period. This semester PE, which for him is still a study hall/rest period, was switched to 7th period so that really helps him. He gets most of his homework done then and can rest when he is home in the evenings. He never has regained his pre-diagnosis energy level.

✢ ✢ ✢

Our son skipped PE in middle school while on treatment for a brain tumor due to fatigue. After treatment, he took regular PE. Due to some balance problems and fatigue, he was graded on just what he was able to do. If the class was running laps, he ran at his own pace and could rest if needed. Since he is banned from all contact sports he would be scorekeeper or referee. This fall he was to start gym two weeks after his second craniotomy. He chose to take personal fitness for gym in which the kids write their own exercise programs and learn lifetime sports like weight lifting, bowling, walking, yoga, and aerobics. He enjoyed it. They were willing to waive gym or have him in adaptive PE but he wanted to be like everyone else. We were very fortunate that we had a PE department that was willing to work with us. I think it was good for him.

✢ ✢ ✢

Our son's main problem during treatment (aside from all the yucky side effects) was the fact that he was weaker than the other boys and he was made fun of by some mean kids as a result. We had many meetings with the teacher and principal over this. The problem was that most of the meanness took place outside the purview of the PE teacher e.g., kids saying to others that they didn't want the weakling on their team. Even now, a year off treatment, he feels weaker, although I sometimes think he just is scared to try new things and really push himself physically. The bottom line is that he feels excluded from the other boys and that causes all kinds of problems socially.

✛✛✛

I wanted my daughter to be involved in physical activities because I thought it was healthier emotionally to be with other kids in a "normal setting" rather than going to the hospital for therapy all the time. Our school is a Quaker school for kids with learning differences so they emphasize inclusion, participation, co-operation, and striving to do one's best. The kids learn to be supportive and encouraging to one another. In her first grade, she has yoga everyday. When it snows the class goes sledding at recess (truly a challenge to walk back up the slippery, uneven snow to the top for my unsteady brain tumor child). They also have six sessions of ice-skating where the whole school participates. This is not something that I do (so would not have encouraged it), however, they have walker-like devices. She loves it and is out on the ice for the whole time.

✛✛✛

Emma (8 ½) has been riding at a therapeutic riding center for more than a year and a half. She could barely sit upright and couldn't hold her head up for long when she started about four months after her surgery. Now she is off lead (steers the horse herself), can post while walking and is working on trotting. She works with a physical therapist who determines what she needs. One day, while working on balance, they had Emma stand on her horse's back with just a sheep skin under her feet. Emma told them to let go of her hands, which they did, and she stood there for quite a while studying herself in the mirrors they have lining one side of the riding barn. And this is a kid with significant ataxia and hypotonia who is still not able to walk more than two steps on her own! Beyond the physical benefits, which have been tremendous, Emma has developed a very special bond with her horse.

✛✛✛

As a result of our son's graft-versus-host disease he no longer sweats well. That means he can overheat easily and the PE teacher certainly needs to be aware of it. Also, because of the chemo he received, he is at risk for heart problems. Our oncologist said that as long as he isn't pushed beyond what he can do, then there shouldn't be a problem. I remember our oncologist saying that weight lifting is a particular problem. The other thing I can think of is sun exposure. Kids on chemo or antibiotics (such as TMP/sulfa) have a harder time with that than the average child.

Chapter 19

Helping Siblings in the Classroom

Kathleen A. Ingman, PhD

A child's diagnosis of cancer affects every member of the family, including brothers and sisters. The diagnosis has a different meaning for each family member and each person will react in his or her own way. These reactions will vary with time, the age of the siblings, and the course of the disease. Siblings of children diagnosed with cancer have special needs both at home and in the classroom. It is critical that parents and educators alike understand the unique impact that cancer has on siblings and the helpful steps they can take to ensure that siblings' emotional and educational needs are addressed.

How Siblings Feel

Parents and other adults often assume that the other children in the family may not be aware of their sibling's illness or are not impacted by it. They may even be reluctant to share information about the illness in an effort to "protect" their other children. But the reality is that even very young children will be aware that something serious is happening and will notice that their family has changed. They may experience some of the following emotions:

Worries and fears: Siblings of children with cancer often worry about their brother or sister's health. They may be afraid that the ill child will die. They may also worry about their own health, thinking that they too might "catch" cancer. In addition, children worry about how their parents are coping or whether their family will ever get back to normal. They might not talk about their fears in an effort to protect their parents or other family members from further stress.

Dr. Ingman is a licensed clinical psychologist and coordinator of psychological services at the Childrens Center for Cancer and Blood Diseases at Childrens Hospital Los Angeles, CA.

Guilt: Brothers and sisters may wonder if

something they thought, said, or did caused the cancer. They might also feel angry at or jealous of the ill child, and then feel guilty later because they think their reactions to the ill child's being sick are wrong.

Jealousy: Because the ill child is receiving extra attention, special privileges, or gifts, brothers and sisters might feel left out and jealous. Since parents cannot give them as much time and attention, they may feel that they are not important. In addition, parents' expectations and discipline are often different for the ill child, which may cause further feelings of jealousy and resentment toward the sibling. In fact, some brothers and sisters have even wished that they would get sick too so that they could have some of this special treatment.

Loneliness: Brothers and sisters miss their parents and ill sibling when they are away at the hospital or at the clinic. They may miss their friends too if they need to go away to stay with another relative or if visits are restricted because of low blood counts.

Anger and resentment: When a child becomes sick, it may seem as if the entire world has been turned upside down. Brothers and sisters may feel angry or resentful because their routines are disrupted, and they miss out on fun events or activities. In addition, they don't get as much time with their parents, they may have extra chores, and they don't know what to expect from one day to the next.

Embarrassment: Siblings of a child with cancer may feel embarrassed because their brother or sister looks different or because their family has changed. They may not want to tell anyone that someone in the family has cancer, or they may not want to be seen with their sick brother or sister at school or in public.

How These Feelings May Be Expressed

Depending on their age, children may not be able to tell you what they are feeling, or may not be fully aware of how their sibling's illness is impacting them. Even if they are aware of their feelings, they may keep their feelings to themselves in an effort to protect their parents or prevent further "burden" to their family. Sometimes changes in a child's behavior are the only clues that they are suffering.

Some common behavior changes to look for include seeking attention by misbehaving. They can become overactive, impatient, and irritable. They might withdraw from others and cry more often than usual. They might have somatic symptoms such as headaches and stomachaches, or they might complain of symptoms that are similar to those that the child with cancer is experiencing. They might have difficulty sleeping or sleep more than usual, or their appetite might change. They might compete with the ill child for attention, or they might express jealousy or hostility toward their sick sibling or their parents. Younger children might exhibit regressive behavior such as bedwetting, thumb sucking, or clinging to their parents.

Changes at school can also be due to difficulties coping with the cancer diagnosis. Things to watch for include poor grades, difficulty concentrating, daydreaming, aggression on the playground, or social withdrawal.

Positive changes in behavior can also be a warning sign. Brothers and sisters may neglect their own feelings and needs and try to be on their best behavior or take on more responsibility (for example, acting like an adult or doing extra chores). They may become overachievers at school, devoting themselves to their work in an effort to forget stressors at home.

What Parents Can Do

There are many things that parents can do to help their children adjust to a cancer diagnosis within the family. The following is a discussion of some strategies that can help prevent or alleviate any emotional or behavioral problems that your children might experience.

Keep the school informed about what is happening: A child's world revolves around his or her family, friends, and school. It is important for your children's school to have up-to-date information so that they are aware of your children's special emotional needs. Teachers can help provide emotional support, and can watch out for any changes in behavior or academic progress. Since you may be busy caring for your sick child, your other children may turn to their teacher with questions or concerns. If you feel too busy or overwhelmed to keep in touch with the school yourself, you might consider asking another family member or friend to help you with this task. Be sure to let the school know that you have given permission for them to talk to the person you designate.

Ask someone at the school to look out for the needs of your children: Consider identifying a specific person at the school who is willing to keep an eye on each child's emotional health and academic performance. This advocate can be a teacher, principal, counselor, or secretary whom your child knows and trusts. Let your child know that he or she can turn to this person for help. Whenever it is needed this person can give your child a little extra support, and can also keep in touch with you to let you know if there are any problems. You might want to give the advocates a copy of this chapter so they will have a better understanding of what they can do to help and why it is important.

Find out if there are resources at your medical center for helping with school issues: Some hospitals have staff members who are specially trained to help with school issues for children with cancer and their siblings. Ask your child's social worker, nurse, or doctor if there is a program like this available at your hospital.

Keep your children informed: Even though it can be tempting to "protect" children from difficult information, it is important to tell them what is happening to their brother or sister. Even very young children will benefit from having information in simple terms that they can understand. Keep in mind that children are very sensitive and will know that something bad has happened even if you don't tell them. If they are not given accurate information, they will be left to their imaginations. Often what they imagine is much worse than the actual situation. Give brothers and sisters information in as much detail as they want and can understand. Explain what is happening with the ill child and keep them up to date. It may help to arrange a conference for the whole family with your child's doctor.

Try to keep things as normal as possible for all of your children: Establish a daily routine and stick to it as much as possible. This will provide much-needed reassurance that everything is going to be all right. If you can't be there to do usual activities (such as make breakfast or help them with their homework), it is helpful to enlist the help of a friend or family member who is familiar with the routine and can help keep things as normal as possible.

Give your children opportunities to talk about their feelings: It may help for you to verbalize your children's unspoken concerns, such as "you may experience a lot of different feelings about your brother's sickness, like feeling sad, scared, angry, or jealous." When they share their feelings with you, it is important to listen carefully and let them know that their feelings are normal. Although you may not approve of how your children express their feelings (by acting out, for example), it is important to let children know that the feelings themselves (such as anger and jealousy) are normal. You might be able to help your children express their feelings in a healthy way by setting an example for them. When your child says that he or she feels angry, you could say "I feel that way too sometimes, but I always feel better if I … talk about it, take a walk, listen to music, etc."

Take them to visit the hospital or clinic: What children imagine happening at the hospital can be worse or better than the reality. If you reduce the unknown, they are likely to be less fearful or jealous. As brothers and sisters grow, you will need to adapt information to their changing age and understanding.

Give brothers and sisters some guidance about their activities and relationship with the ill child: What you suggest will depend on the particular circumstances of your child's illness and your family. In some cases you will encourage them to act the way they always have around their brother or sister. In other cases you will need to explain to them why they need to behave differently. Even if they are separated from their sick brother or sister, you can suggest activities that will help them maintain their special sibling relationship. Some examples are talking on the phone, writing a letter, making something to decorate the hospital room, or entrusting them with a task that will be meaningful to your sick child such as feeding the dog that your sick child adores.

Try to spend some time alone with each child during the week: This time can be to talk about feelings or it can be just to have fun together. This will help all of your children feel secure that their relationships with you have not changed. It might also be an opportunity for you to have a break from caring for your sick child. If it is impossible for you to find time to do this, ask a family friend or relative to do it instead. Any special attention from a caring adult will help children feel good about themselves.

Ask for help if you or your children need it: You cannot do everything; just do the best you can. It is important to ask for emotional support from friends, family members, hospital staff, or mental health care providers. The same can be said for your children. If their emotional difficulties are interfering too much in their lives (for example, poor grades at school, disruptive behavior at home, or depression or anxiety), they may need support from a professional. Ask your ill child's doctor or social worker about programs for siblings of children with cancer. There may be a support group or camp for brothers and sisters, or there may be a psychologist or counselor who can help.

What Teachers and Other School Personnel Can Do

Teachers and other school personnel are in a unique position to be able to help children learn to cope with life's challenges. Since parents may be overwhelmed with caring for a sick child, the school may need to take an active role in supporting the sibling of a child with cancer. Some strategies to consider are discussed below.

Watch for signs that the sibling is having trouble coping with what is happening in their family: Because children are aware of the extraordinary stress that their family is under due to their brother or sister's illness, they may choose to act out their emotional responses at school rather than at home. Typical symptoms that they are having trouble coping include social withdrawal, crying, low frustration tolerance, rebellion, poor academic performance, inattention, and disruptive behavior.

Communicate your concerns to the child's parents and to other school personnel: Just because parents are busy caring for a sick child doesn't mean they don't want to know about problems with their other children. If you sense that the parents are having difficulty juggling these competing demands, ask whether they would prefer that you talk to another family member that they designate. It is also important to keep other relevant school personnel such as counselors, psychologists, and the principal, informed about how the student is doing. If you become particularly concerned about the student, it might be helpful to organize a meeting where the child's parents, teachers, and other school personnel can discuss ways to help the student cope.

Ask the parents for updates about the sick child: It is important for you to be aware of what is happening in the family so that you will know when your student needs extra support. For example, if the sick child is hospitalized or her medical condition worsens, you might need to check-in with that child's sibling and provide support during this difficult time.

Get permission to share information with other students and parents if needed: Talk to the parents of the child with cancer about whether they are comfortable with you disclosing information about their child to other concerned parents and students. It is likely that other students and parents will learn of the illness and will want more information about how to address this issue in their own families.

Provide tutoring, counseling, or other support if needed: Siblings of children with cancer have special needs and may need extra help in order to thrive academically and emotionally during this difficult time. Assist the child's family in accessing any resources that may be available to help the child at your school.

Let the child know that you are there to help them: If you feel comfortable doing so, let the child know that you share their concern about their sibling and that you know they may be having a difficult time. This will help the child feel supported by you and may help to prevent any maladaptive emotional or behavioral problems in the classroom.

Maintain a normal classroom routine as much as possible: This will be reassuring to all of the children since it sends a message that things are okay. For the sibling of a child with cancer, a normal classroom routine may allow him to forget his stress temporarily and feel like a normal child again.

Help other children in the class be supportive: If other children know that their friend has a sibling with cancer, be sure to correct any misconceptions (for example, that cancer is contagious or that children get cancer because they did something bad) that could lead to teasing or hurt feelings. Children often feel ashamed of their sibling with cancer, and teasing or peer rejection can make this feeling worse. Discuss positive ways to help, such as sitting with the sibling at lunch or inviting her to play during recess.

Key Points

- Siblings of children diagnosed with cancer have special needs both at home and in the classroom.

- Even very young children will be aware that something serious is happening to their sibling and will notice that their family has changed.

- Siblings may experience some of the following emotions: worries, fears, guilt, jealousy, loneliness, anger, resentment, and embarrassment.

- Sometimes changes in a children's behavior are the only clues that they are suffering. Signs to watch for include difficulty concentrating, poor grades, aggression, social withdrawal, and changes in sleep pattern or appetite.

- What parents can do to help:
  - Keep the school informed about what is happening.
  - Ask someone at the school to look out for the needs of your children.
  - Find out if there are resources at your medical center for helping with school issues.
  - Keep your children informed.
  - Try to keep things as normal as possible for all of your children.
  - Give your children opportunities to talk about their feelings.
  - Take them to visit the hospital or clinic.
  - Try to spend some time alone with each child during the week.
  - Ask for help if you or your children need it.

- What teachers and other school personnel can do to help:
  - Watch for signs that the sibling is having trouble coping with what is happening in their family.
  - Communicate your concerns to the child's parents and to other school personnel.
  - Ask the parents for updates about the sick child.
  - Get permission to share information with other students and parents if needed.
  - Provide tutoring, counseling, or other support if needed.
  - Let the siblings know that you are there to help them.
  - Maintain a normal classroom routine as much as possible.
  - Help other children in the class be supportive.

Parent Perspectives

Lindsey was in kindergarten when Jesse was first diagnosed. Because we heard nothing from the kindergarten teacher, we assumed that things were going well. At the end of the year, the teacher told us that Lindsey frequently spent part of each day hiding under her desk. When I asked why we had never been told, the teacher said she thought that we already had enough to worry about dealing with Jesse's illness and treatment. She was wrong to make decisions for us, but I wish we had been more attentive. Lindsey needed help.

✦ ✦ ✦

My son had Ewing's sarcoma and then leukemia, treated with a bone marrow transplant. His twin brother Brian was devastated. Brian's English teacher sent his missing assignments stapled to a biweekly report (which is a form to show progress at our school.) At the bottom of the report she wrote, "Behavior and academics are no longer an issue for Brian and it shows. My heart goes out to him at this time but he can be so insolent and disruptive. Some days I can't hold class with him in the room. I have 27 other students in the room who are entitled to some attention!" It still upsets me when I think about it. Instead of trying to help, she complained.

✦ ✦ ✦

I am not sure what to credit in all of this, but we have stopped fixating on what the school can do for our son who had a medulloblastoma. We have taken on the major areas of weakness he has educationally as a family—currently handwriting, reading, and keyboarding. There are five of us total (two parents, three brothers) to do the tutoring, and we can offer consistency in a way that is hard for anyone else to do. We do three sessions with Ethan daily—7 days a week. We have a chart on the fridge, and the kids make sure they cover their "shifts." We (the parents) negotiate for coverage if we cannot do ours, and we are actually having some good times with it (now that we are all used to it, which took some time and parental persuasion).

Again, maybe it is coincidence, but Ethan had made very little progress over a year in reading until we started the home tutoring last summer. Over the three months of summer, he progressed a full grade and has made another grade of progress this fall. I have been very worried about cognitive issues, and was funneling that worry into arm-wrestling with the school for services. Now, I at least am feeling less frustrated and feel like we can take some credit and pride in what he has accomplished this past six months, and feel a bit more like we can influence our destiny (probably falsely, but it feels good).

There have been a number of unexpected pluses to this besides his progress. My boys have become more aware of the long-term effects that treatment has had on Ethan. They are more forgiving of the "extras" that he gets, and more patient with him overall. Additionally, it has helped them to feel more like a team—they have been more likely to help each other with homework, as well as helping Ethan. They see more clearly that they are not only siblings but part of a support system. They complained a lot at the beginning, but it has become a routine. Last week when I decided to give them a day off from these responsibilities, they called me at work to find out what they were supposed to do that day—when I said I was giving them a day off, they said no, they would do their usual routine, that it was better for Ethan and they were used to it.

I have been most pleased with this approach. It really made home a lot more fun, and our son has made much more progress.

+++

We have been straight with all the kids from the beginning about the diagnosis and treatment, using the words "leukemia" and "cancer." We have not really discussed prognosis. I don't find that a useful concept anyway, since there is such individual variation. They know that Chris will be in and out of the hospital, that he might feel tired, vomit, lose his hair, need to sleep more, and that the chemo is strong and Chris is susceptible to infections. They've picked up the hand washing routine! I think the kids can understand and accept more than we give them credit for. Kids naturally live in the moment (another reason to limit discussion of prognosis) and that's the key to coping with living with cancer. What has helped us is:

- *Giving the sibs simple, age-appropriate, but accurate information.*
- *Focusing on the present day's events.*

- *Staying calm but talking about feelings (rather than "showing them" by crying or screaming).*

- *Keeping to some routines/traditions at home (e.g., I rearranged my work hours so that I could be home to do homework and have dinner with the kids several nights a week).*

- *Making time for the sibs while another relative or friend stays with the kid in the hospital (a treat for the hospitalized child too!).*

- *Encouraging the kid with cancer to share some of the gifts/goodies (or deliberately planning the sharing yourself. My son received some toys that were not interesting to him but I knew his brother would love).*

- *Reminding people to remember the sibs with cards, dollar-store gifts, and special treats too.*

- *Accepting help (e.g., a prepared meal might not be my favorite thing to eat, but it frees me up to spend more time with all the kids).*

I was able to arrange with the oncology social worker at the hospital for her to visit Chris' class and talk to the classmates about leukemia (she may have visited the sibs' classes as well; I was in too much of a daze at the time to remember). We also borrowed a copy of the Leukemia & Lymphoma Society's video about leukemia, "Why, Charlie Brown, Why?" and that made the rounds of some of the classes. In addition, the vice-principal of the children's school was friends with a family in the district whose daughter was just finishing chemo for ALL (Chris has AML). Whenever she'd be at clinic, she stopped by to visit Chris—they are pretty close in age. Her family brought a goodie basket for all of us, including Chris' sibs. This young lady also visited the classes and talked about her own experiences with leukemia.

Our other children are eight and six. I told their teachers what was happening and asked them to keep in touch with me about any signs of stress. I also had the school psychologist meet with both of them in the very beginning, so I could get his assessment of their understanding and coping. I know the school nurse also kept an eye on them, looking for any physical symptoms of stress.

I had been a homeroom mom in each of their classes, and I chose to relinquish my duties immediately. I was disappointed that I had to miss out on their activities, but I early on decided that I could only do so much.

They really missed very little school; I felt the routine was important. They missed one day, early on, to see their brother in the hospital and know he was okay; another day was spent getting the HLA typing done, followed by a hospital visit. We kept the hospital visits to the weekend so the kids could have more time together but not miss school.

✝ ✝ ✝

When Kara was diagnosed with neuroblastoma, Jim was a high school senior, Dana was an 8th grader, and David was in 6th grade. We contacted all the teachers that Jim and Dana saw as well as their counselors. We contacted David's teacher, counselor and principal. My husband always put out email updates on Kara and these were also emailed to the teachers so they would know when times were particularly difficult. I was very fearful that I wouldn't be aware if my other children started having academic or social problems in school and I didn't want that to occur. We asked teachers to please let us know if they started seeing homework not being turned in, grades slipping or other problems.

If I were to give any advice to teachers, I think I would say to listen to the sibling when they need to talk, even if it doesn't make a great deal of sense to you. I was talking to David's grade school counselor one time and she told me that David went on and on about how Kara wouldn't eat chocolate and that's all he would talk about. She indicated that she didn't think that was very relevant. Kara considers herself a "chocoholic" and is always in the mood for chocolate. So for her to be so ill that she didn't want to eat chocolate was a sign of how sick she was and David recognized this and was very worried.

We gave each of our three children phone cards to carry and also the number of the oncologist's office and the hospital where Kara was. They could call us anytime with that phone card and could even call from school if they felt the need to. That helped, but it still wasn't the same as having Mom and Dad around. Siblings do have some really hard times and face some really tough issues.

✝ ✝ ✝

Our eldest, Jake, was in junior high when Ethan was diagnosed, and so it is not just one teacher, but a number of them. We stumbled upon a great option by accident. Jake missed the orientation for school because he was at sibling oncology camp, and I called his guidance councilor to arrange a make-up. Lo and behold, his counselor is a testicular cancer survivor, who said immediately that he wanted to be a resource as well as a source of support. The guidance counselor talked to Jake's teachers about what it is like to have cancer, to be in a family with cancer, and how they could support Jake. I really liked his approach of "what can you do to help" rather than "what are signs of trouble." I would never have thought to ask to have a cancer survivor involved with my kids, but found that there were a number of teachers who had cancer as adults who were able to help with a proactive plan to avoid obstacles, rather than repairing the damage created from running into them.

✝ ✝ ✝

Our daughter was 15 at the time of our son's diagnosis and should have been starting her sophomore year at high school. She was still reeling from losing her uncle to cancer six months before; they were very close. She had spent the last three months of his life with him and watched him die. Now our son was sick and she was scared and angry. She began cutting school, running away and hanging out with kids who did drugs. At first the school would call when she didn't show up but after a few months they stopped. They kept her on the enrollment to save her place but that was all they could do.

Our son's treatment was out of county and we were gone a lot. My mom would come and stay with her but the reality was I was not there to be on top of where, when and who she was with. We talked to the social workers where our son was being treated and they offered no help or resources at all.

She was on the edge, out on the streets or worse most of the time by her 16th birthday. Fortunately, we have good insurance and were able to send her out of state to a behavioral rehab facility for a month. They put her on mood stabilizers and anti depressants and she received intensive counseling. I truly believe it saved her life. She stayed on the medication for a year and continued counseling at home. By now she was 17 and emotionally no longer a teenager. The school offered to let her return but she knew she could not go back. When she was younger she was identified as gifted, but with only the freshman year of high school under her belt she could not pass the GED.

She finally got one break. The psychologist I had been seeing used to be the head of the counseling department at the local community college (and still worked there part time). He met with her, signed a waiver, we got her high school to sign a waiver and she started attending college the next semester. It's been a long hard road for her, but today she is doing great. She is finishing community college this semester and has applied to the local university for a degree in horticulture. She is 21, smart, beautiful and with a wonderful guy who she plans to marry this summer.

✦ ✦ ✦

One of the biggest and most painful eye-openers for us was watching how frightening, heartbreaking and anger-producing cancer and bone marrow transplant could be on the sibling of a patient. For us, it was the feeling of helplessness as little (then 4 years old) Spencer was pulled along—almost like the rug was completely pulled out from under him—again and again and again. Suddenly, all the attention was on Travis; we were known as "Travis' mom and dad;" gifts and cards and mail poured in for Travis; and hours on end were spent with Travis at doctor appointments, many of which Spencer attended with us at the hospital 30 minutes away.

Spencer was uprooted out of his preschool and moved into a new school in a new city with us where he knew no other children; lived in temporary housing (the Ronald McDonald House), all the while watching the horrors of his brother getting poked, prodded, medicated, getting thinner, getting bloated and moody.

Spencer could not understand all that was going on around him, nor the conflicting emotions he was experiencing, changing from moment to moment. Spencer made a good friend at the Ronald McDonald House, and then had to be told one day that his new good friend died after fighting leukemia. Four-year-old Spencer endured the discomforts of wearing a mask in Travis' hospital room day after day, even though the rest of our family didn't have to wear one. He washed his hands like a surgeon every time he set foot into Travis' room, touched the floor or went to the bathroom or ate a treat. His little hands were raw. He came along on 2-hour car rides and daylong clinic visits, sometimes even three times a week. He endured our sharp reprimands if he came too close during sterile procedure dressing changes, as we were trying to be hyper-vigilant about safety and germs.

And during all this, Spencer has been doing his best to cope and carve out his own identity. Yes, there have been many moments of beauty for Spencer throughout this time, but maybe for him, it has been hardest of all, to stand by so helplessly and not be able to control one stinkin' thing having to do with his best friend, his brother. I still believe that this experience will affect him in many unknown ways for the rest of his life. A few weeks ago in our kitchen, Travis said to Spencer, "You are a hero, Spencer, because you played with me every day and you never let me give up." There are three main heroes in our miracle journey—Travis, his bone marrow donor and Spencer. Travis says he couldn't have gotten through his cancer or transplant without his brother. At one point, a TV reporter spoke with the boys, and I wouldn't have traded a million dollars for the look on Spencer's face—pure pride and innocent joy— at being "the center of attention" for that fleeting 8 seconds or so that he saw himself on TV. This young child had been through so much that was unrecognized (as have all the siblings of these kids and parents with cancer), that whatever genuine recognition, support, and comfort he receives is a vital boost to his self-development. It will be a long time before I get over the pain and guilt of what he has been through. Cancer is a dangerous thing—trying to tear away at more than just the patient. So, Spencer, and all the siblings of kids with cancer, You ARE special people in and of yourselves—true heroes in this journey and this world.

✦ ✦ ✦

I was 9 years old when my 7-year-old sister was diagnosed with AML. I remember my mother telling me these strange new realities in the rush between hospital runs—and I remember being so frightened. Naomi was not only my best friend, she was also my violin partner on the concert stage. I was afraid that she was going to die. I was frightened for myself as well, when I was told that I was going to be her donor for a bone marrow transplant. I wanted to be the one to save her life but what if it didn't work? Would it be my fault? Would people blame me?

Our family life changed dramatically too. I was bopped all around during the year that she was in hospital. Sometimes I would stay with neighbors, sometimes with friends, and sometimes with other family members. It was unsettling to be left at so many places. Often I didn't know where I was going to be sleeping that night. I would just have my pillow and toothbrush ready in my backpack and hope for a familiar face. My mother had moved to another city to be with my sister during her transplant. She was gone for months. I suppose I had lost touch with what family really was.

I remember one particularly bad day at school. Kids in my class had been laughing about my sister's lack of hair. Not being a particularly violent person, I could not believe where all these new feelings of anger were coming from. In defense of my sister, I yelled the timid kids away and fought the persistent ones off as best as a school-boy knows how. After that, school had lost its charm. I didn't want to be around anyone anymore, so I just walked off the school grounds one day and then all the way home. It wasn't until later, months later I presume, that I forgot about the insults.

There was one teacher though that did help me during this difficult time. She came to my house on weekends and would take me out to do cool things with her. She made up a deck of cards with activities that I could choose from whenever I felt like I needed a friend or someone to talk to. She promised that she would immediately be there for me and that we would do whatever I had chosen to do on the cards—things like fossil hunting, going to her brother's farm, and eating at McDonalds were among the few that I treasured.

It's been seventeen years since the day I found out that my sister had cancer. My bone marrow did save her life and she's still my best friend. She's now a University senior completing a double major in biology and psychology, while also working in a research lab on cancer vaccines. I returned to school, of course, and am finishing up a double degree in economics and music. Ah, and those cards—I still have them, somewhere. Maybe I'll give that teacher a call some day and see if I can still take her up on that offer for a 'Big Mac.'

Chapter 20

Grief in the Classroom

Avi Madan-Swain, PhD
Heather Austin, MS, PhD
Patricia Taylor-Cook

For many children and even their teachers, the loss of a student is their first experience with death. Everyone's grief experience is different, and each time we grieve over the loss of someone precious to us, the experience is varied. How we experience grief depends mainly on what type of relationship we had with the person who died.

Children, including siblings of the deceased child, are no different from adults in the wide variability of their responses. The way a young person views death changes as the child grows and matures cognitively. Preschoolers' understanding of reality is based on their physically observable world, circumscribed by their own experiences. They recognize death in terms of lying-down immobility but may not recognize that being dead and alive are mutually exclusive. Children of this age do not see death as irreversible. Because preschoolers see themselves as the center of the universe and engage in magical thinking they are particularly vulnerable to feeling responsible for events, including the death of a sibling (e.g., even just wishing in a moment of jealous frustration, that an ill sibling would "get lost") is sufficient cause for young children to feel responsible for the sibling's subsequent death. These youngsters interpret very literally what is told to them, and thus, their understanding of death is quite limited. Children in this age group require repeated simple explanations, reassurances, and much physical contact.

By the age of seven, most children will have acquired a concept of death that recognizes that death is not reversible. They are learning that old age and illness are causes of death. At this age, children are asking why things happen rather than what things are, and are increasingly concerned with rituals surrounding death, such as funerals and burials. Siblings and their classmates, as well

> Dr. Avi Madan-Swain is assistant professor of pediatrics and director of the hem/onc psychosocial program at University of Alabama, Birmingham, AL.

as peers of the deceased child need to be given opportunities to plan, organize and participate in any events planned by the school.

Teenagers, having developed the capacity for abstract reasoning, are better able to understand the physiologic systems of the body and comprehend illness and disease. They are able to speculate on the implications and ramifications of death in a way that younger children cannot.

A number of other factors influence children's understanding of death. Support from their families, prior experiences with death, ethnic and cultural issues, and spirituality are just some of the factors that can also influence a child's level of maturity while mourning. While the focus of this chapter is on helping classmates of the deceased child, special attention needs to be paid to the bereaved siblings. They also will have an individual reaction based in part on their age, personality, experiences, and relationship with the brother or sister who has died. Their reactions also may be shaped by the behavior of parents and others including how news of the sibling's death is communicated, and how the family is coping with the grief.

The main role of the school after the death of a student is to acknowledge the death and to participate actively in bereavement rituals in order to create an atmosphere of warmth, support, reassurance, and reliable routines. Teachers and school personnel need to be particularly aware and sensitive to the needs of the grieving sibling(s). It is critical that the sibling's classmates be informed of the loss prior to the sibling returning to the classroom. This will prevent any embarrassing moments of silence when the sibling returns and encourage expressions of grief by classmates.

Teachers need to be attuned to their own feelings and be willing to express them in a direct, open, and honest manner. Such openness will encourage students to feel safe expressing their own emotions. By denying feelings, teachers may stifle the natural responses of their students. Such unresolved feelings may ultimately resurface in a far less positive manner.

Children's Responses to Grief

Classmates and siblings of the deceased child exhibit grief reactions in many different ways. The most frequently occurring behaviors in bereaved siblings include acting out (e.g., arguing, disobedience), sadness and depression, feelings of loneliness, anxiety, and guilt, and poor schoolwork. Psychophysiological behaviors

Heather Austin is a post-doctoral psychology fellow in the division of pediatric hematology/oncology at the University of Alabama, Birmingham, AL.

(e.g., aches and pains, sleep disturbance, bed wetting, eating disturbance) also are common. The following list is by no means comprehensive, and it is important to remember that individual students will not exhibit all of these reactions. However, each of the following can cause pain and confusion for the student and may be misunderstood by those who care for this young person.

Acting younger than their age

When someone they love dies, children may wish to go back to a time when they felt a sense of security. Thus, they may engage in behaviors such as being over-dependent on adults and talking "baby talk." Typically, these behaviors are temporary and are an indicator of the child's emotional needs. Offer support, care and nurturance, and provide a trusting presence for the child.

Worry, disorganization, and difficulty concentrating

Many children struggle with anxiety and depression during the grieving process, causing them to become disorganized, inattentive, impulsive, and even hyperactive. Often the symptoms mirror those of children diagnosed with Attention-Deficit/Hyperactivity Disorder (ADHD). However, such behaviors are typical coping responses for children who are grieving.

Children may have many questions about life and may be experiencing very intense feelings related to the death. They may think frequently of the death, how it occurred, and what this means for themselves. Be supportive and comforting during this time and answer questions that they have honestly. If a child continues to have persistent difficulties with these behaviors in school several months after the loss, refer the child to the guidance counselor. In addition, consider scheduling a meeting with the parents to discuss whether a referral to a local mental health specialist, such as a psychologist, may be helpful.

Physical ailments

Our physical well being is directly connected to our mental health. Children who are grieving often have physiological responses to their grief. These can include but are not limited to: lack of energy, sleep or appetite disruption, shortness of breath, headaches, stomachaches, shaking, and skin rashes. The aches, pains, and medical symptoms are very real. Offer support and encourage the child to discuss feelings related to the loss. Talk about how feelings can make bodies react by hurting more or feeling tired. Engage in relaxation techniques with the

> Patricia Taylor-Cook is a doctoral student in the medical psychology program at the University of Alabama Birmingham, AL.

children in class, such as deep breathing exercises to help relieve stress.

Apathy

Apathy can be defined as withdrawal from life. Bereaved students may not be able to enjoy themselves because the life they shared was taken from their friend. They may still attend activities that they formerly enjoyed, but the zest and fun are missing. Some school-aged children and teenagers withdraw from family and friends.

Acting out

Acting out behaviors in the classroom include being disruptive, fighting with other students, showing disrespect for authority figures, and cutting class. Students may exhibit a general "I don't care" attitude. Children who express their grief in this way may have underlying feelings of insecurity, abandonment, or low self-esteem. As a teacher, just acknowledging that these frustrating behaviors are rooted in emotional difficulties is sometimes helpful. This does not mean that you should excuse the child for this behavior because she is grieving. Discuss appropriate limits and negative consequences for inappropriate behavior. Do this without anger or harshness. In addition, maintaining structure within the classroom is comforting to students whose primary need is a sense of security. Above all, showing care and affection for them despite negative behaviors helps during the grieving process.

Poor academic performance

Decline in grades sometimes indicates that a student is experiencing difficulty coping with loss. Going through the grieving process is tough on children, just as it is with adults. Initially, you should expect students who have just lost a close friend to have difficulties with attention, concentration, and motivation to complete their work. Let your students concentrate on their grief, rather than their schoolwork, and provide them with opportunities to do this within the classroom setting. If academic problems persist, address them.

Guidelines for Teachers Working with Grieving Children

Given that a large part of a child's day is spent at school, teachers are in an excellent position to model feelings and effective ways of coping with grief. Teachers need to express their grief and feelings openly. This sends the message that it is all right to express feelings and it validates the grief and sadness that students may be feeling as well.

Listen and honestly answer questions

As a teacher, children look to you as a supporter, role model, friend, and confidant. This gives you a unique opportunity to help your students through the grieving process. Children may not talk about death, but be prepared to listen and understand when they tell you what they are feeling. Answer even the hard questions honestly. A good response for questions such as, "Am I going to die too?" would be something like, "We're all going to die; we just don't know when. That's why it is important that we enjoy the time that we have. I hope that you will not die for a long time."

Remember that children, especially teens, may not engage in easy, open conversations about feelings. It is more likely that there will be bursts of interaction when the children share their feelings. Be prepared to listen during these times, rather than force communication. Having people available to listen, as many times as they wish to share their story, is helpful.

It is important to keep in mind that young children in particular can take in only so much information at a time, so that they, or you, may have to repeat or emphasize various aspects of previous discussion over time. As children reach new developmental stages and their concept of death evolves they will have additional questions to ask from the perspective of each new phase. What seems like the "same old questions," may sound the same, but the answers will need to be altered so that they fit with the child's new level of understanding.

Give children choices and encourage consistency and routine

Giving children choices gives them a sense of control in their environment. This is especially helpful at times when students may feel insecure and out of control. Consistency and routine also provide structure and comfort to grieving students.

Find teaching moments

Use everyday occurrences, such as the change in seasons, death of a famous person, or book that discusses death to make children aware of the cycle of life. These moments allow you to incorporate exploration of loss in the classroom.

Encourage students to talk about their deceased classmate

Teachers need to provide their students with some basic information regarding death in order to dispel any potential misperceptions. During the discussion the following elements should be addressed.

- A dead person does not experience anything. They cannot feel hot, cold, or pain.

- The physical reality of death is forever.
- Death is universal.

During the discussion, teachers need to keep in mind their students' understanding of death and dying. For example, school-aged children need to be reassured that they are not responsible for the child's death, nor can they revitalize the dead child through magical thinking or positive behavior. They require reassurance of their own safety, and of the rarity of that which happened to their peer. This should be followed by free and open discussion about the student who has died. It may also be helpful to create a scrapbook or collage of pictures to commemorate their friend.

Respect differences in grieving styles

Each child will have a unique way of handling emotional pain associated with the loss. These differences are determined by age, maturity, and prior experiences with death. Culture and ethnic background also play a role in handling grief. It is important to obtain information about your students' ethnic/cultural background and religious beliefs and understand how these may impact the expression or repression of grief.

Provide emotional support for the students

Part of working with children who are grieving includes recognizing that grief and the loss of someone that they loved is a root cause of irritability and acting out behavior. Allow children to express their emotions in an appropriate way, while providing them with much needed support.

Respond in a feeling rather than a thinking way

Connecting with a child through emotions will do a much better job of allowing them to talk freely with you than trying to lecture about the grief process. Talk with them, not at them. By observing facial expressions, body language, and reoccurring themes in play, parents and teachers can note children's feelings and talk to them about how they are feeling (e.g. "You look really sad right now").

Resist being overprotective

Some people deal with difficult situations by pretending that they did not occur. Others do not discuss grief because they do not want to cause anyone pain by addressing the issue. Despite good intentions, this may send the message that hiding feelings is an accepted way to handle grief and may not allow students the opportunity to work through their grief, an important step in accepting their loss and healing.

Resist asking too many questions

Asking questions automatically places you in a position of directing interactions that you have with the child. Allow children to lead you and teach you about their own experience with grief.

Therapeutic Activities in the School Setting

Based on clinical experience and research findings, the following is a list of some suggested activities that may be utilized by teachers as they deal with the loss of a student in the class. When selecting an activity, keep in mind the developmental age of the children in the classroom and that the activity may need to be modified to make sure it is age appropriate.

Acknowledge the death

Both students and school personnel should be informed as soon as possible about the student's death. Large group presentations such as a school assembly are almost always less beneficial for individual students. Whenever possible, students should be informed about the loss in their classroom by an adult who they are familiar with and trust. Special attention should be given to ensuring that classmates in the bereaved siblings class are informed. If the classroom teacher is not comfortable performing such a task individually then the guidance counselor, principal, or school nurse may participate and remain in the classroom to assist the teacher in answering any questions and addressing feelings and reactions. Some typical questions children ask regarding the death of a peer include:

- Did it hurt?
- Where is the child now?
- Can I get the same disease the child had?
- What will happen at the funeral?
- What will happen to the body?
- How will the child's brothers and sisters react?
- Should I mention _____'s name to his brother or sister, or should I talk about something else and never mention his/her name?

It is important to create a supportive atmosphere and keep the message simple and consistent for all students. Don't be afraid to use the words "death" and "dead" in the message, since using euphemisms such as "gone away" or "sleeping" will likely be confusing, especially for younger children. Also, provide information about when and where the family would like to receive friends, and the date, time, and location of the funeral services.

Sometimes it also is helpful to send a letter home to the parents of classmates informing them about the death.

Crisis response teams

Many public schools have developed crisis response teams to address tragic events that occur within the school or the community. The primary goal of these teams is to provide practical guidelines when a tragic event, such as the death of a student occurs. These teams also can facilitate the mourning process for the school community and offer referrals for those who would benefit from more long-term support.

Individual/group grief time with the school counselor

Students and teachers may benefit from meeting individually with the school counselor to explore feelings surrounding the loss of a student. Sometimes the counselor will meet with small groups of students on a regular basis to provide additional support.

Tell personal stories

It is helpful for teachers to share their prior experiences with the loss of a loved one, including how they felt and how they handled the situation. It may also be helpful to open this topic for class discussion by inviting students who have had someone close to them die talk about their experiences. Open communication about these experiences sends the message to students that the feelings they are having about their loss are normal.

Create a safe zone

It helps to create an area in the classroom or find one outside the classroom (e.g. counselor's office) where students can go to deal with any difficult emotions that they are having. Make this area comfortable, and include books about feelings, loss, and grief.

Memory circles

Memory circles can provide children an outlet for sharing their memories with other children and teachers. After the death of a classmate, it is important to gather all the children who have a personal tie to the child together to provide them a chance to share personal stories. Everyone attending the circle should have had a personal relationship with the child so they can participate or at least benefit from the stories shared. Each individual in attendance should be given an equal opportunity to share stories and memories of the child. Such an outlet provides the students an opportunity to share their grief among other grieving people. This may help prevent the student from internalizing the grief and trying to deal with it on his own.

Explore, identify, and validate feelings

Feelings such as shock, sadness, guilt, anger, and forgiveness are common after the death of a classmate. Encourage the attitude in the classroom that all feelings are okay, and give students the opportunity to express these feelings both verbally and nonverbally. Art, dance, and music are examples of mediums for expressing feelings without words. Sometimes younger children will have more difficulty labeling their emotions (e.g. saying, "I am sad."). When you observe a child having difficulty expressing an emotion, label it for him.

Learn to say goodbye

Children may need the closure that attending a funeral provides. Funerals can make the death more real and gives children a chance to say goodbye. It may also be helpful to set aside some time in the classroom to say goodbye to the child who died. Writing letters to the family expressing sympathy and recalling good memories, or writing letters to the child who died and hanging them up in the classroom, are ways to remember and say goodbye.

Include students/staff from the entire school community

Children throughout the school who had a personal relationship with the child, regardless of age or grade, will benefit from participating in a school-based program addressing bereavement. Children are more likely to open up to friends who also share their grief rather than adults, parents, and teachers. Providing support may help children cope with their grief and return to a more normal life quicker. In addition, different children recover from grief at varying times. Offering groups over a longer period of time to those children who are having difficulties dealing with the loss of a close friend may be helpful.

Classmates, teachers, and school personnel also should attempt to maintain contact with the family. Parents and particularly siblings are most appreciative of cards sent by teachers and their child's friends. Whenever possible, with the parents consent, plan an activity that acknowledges the deceased child's importance to the school community. This will enable the family to achieve closure and move forward in the grief process.

Additional creative age-appropriate activities

Following are a few activities for early elementary students:

- Encourage students to draw a picture of something they did with their classmate, or something they remember about him or her. When appropriate, these pictures can be shared with the child's family as a sign of support and condolence.

- Read a story with the entire class that involves the loss of a pet or a loved one.

- Share a special object (e.g., a bright colored kite) with the students and then put it away. Ask the children to recall the special characteristics of the object. Use this to draw parallels to memories of their classmate. Stress that although they may like to keep the object they cannot do so. The ability to remember the object keeps it special in their hearts and minds.

- Plan and conduct a school memorial service. During the memorial service consider including a special activity the student enjoyed (e.g., reading favorite poem, playing favorite song, releasing balloons).

Following are some activities for later elementary students:

- Help children devise a plan to raise money to purchase a memorial tree to plant on the school campus.

- Encourage students to keep a journal about their feelings. This can provide a valuable emotional outlet.

- Encourage the students to express their feelings through art.

- As a class the students may make a memory book about the child that they can give to the family.

Following are some activities for junior high and senior high students:

- Offer students the option of attending funeral services, either as a group or individually.

- The class may decide to dedicate a yearbook or class publication in memory of their classmate.

- Private schools may elect to set to a trust fund to be given to an incoming freshman.

- Set aside time to view an appropriate movie or read and discuss a suitable book.

- Establish a fund raising event or blood drive in the child's name.

- Participate in an act of regrowth, such as the planting of a tree, or refurbishing a special spot on the school campus.

- Hold a special memorial service.

- Keep in touch with the student's family, especially at significant events such as graduation.

In the weeks and months following the death of a classmate teachers will need to provide ongoing opportunities for students to express grief. Creating a photo or artwork display on a centrally located bulletin board will help all the school's students acknowledge the reality of the death. Hang blank sheets of poster board throughout the school on which students can jot down some thoughts and feelings about their loss, whenever they feel moved to do so.

Community resources

School personnel should make community resources, such as local counselors and grief support groups, available to teachers and students.

Summary

Grief is a process not an event. Even more than adults, children, will have ups and downs related to the loss of a friend. Typically, children demonstrate a "short sadness span" because they have difficulty staying with painful feelings for long stretches of time. Children may exhibit short, intensive, but sporadic outbursts followed by periods where they appear unaffected by the loss. In addition, although it is commonly accepted that we work through the stages of grief, grieving children may go back and forth from acceptance to anger to sadness all in a short period of time. Teachers need to assess the degree of intrusiveness created by the grieving in the child's life. If the grieving interferes with the child's social, emotional, or physical development, then grieving may be considered disabling and additional services from a trained professional may be necessary. Because children spend so much time at school, it is essential that their teachers be emotionally available to help them on this journey.

Key Points

- Children's responses to grief:

    - Acting younger than their age.

    - Worry, disorganization, and difficulty concentrating.

    - Complaints of physical ailments.

    - Apathy.

    - Acting out.

    - Poor academic performance.

- Guidelines for teachers working with grieving children:

    - Listen and honestly answer questions.

    - Give children choices when possible and encourage consistency and routine.

    - Find teaching moments.

    - Encourage students to remember and talk about their deceased classmate.

    - Respect differences in grieving styles.

    - Provide emotional support for the students.

    - Respond in a feeling rather than a thinking way.

    - Resist being overprotective.

- Therapeutic activities for the school setting:

    - Acknowledge the death.

    - Provide crisis response teams.

    - Include children from the entire school.

    - Creative age appropriate activities.

    - Encourage individual/group grief time with the counselor.

    - Tell personal stories.

    - Create a "safe-zone" and memory circles.

    - Explore, identify, and validate feelings.

    - Learn to say goodbye.

Parent Perspectives

Jody was lucky because he went to a private school, and there were only sixteen children in his class. Whenever he could come to school, they made him welcome. Because children worked at their own pace, he never had the feeling that he was getting behind in his classwork. He really felt like he belonged there. Sometimes he could only manage to stay an hour, but he loved to go. Toward the end when he was in a wheelchair, the kids would fight over whose turn it was to push him. The teacher was wonderful, and the kids really helped him and supported him until the end.

✦ ✦ ✦

When Katie was in the hospital, many of her classmates sent cards both personally and from a class she was in. The best though, was a poster board with pictures of kids in her government class covered with personal messages to Katie. It was done with a digital camera and printed on copy paper, then pasted on the poster board in a collage format. The class included a copy of that day's school announcements and a picture of the hot lunch served that day. We taped it on the door to her bathroom, and I don't think a day went by that she didn't see something new on the poster. It appeared to be a great deal of fun for the class, and it was immeasurable fun for Katie.

Katie was able to go home for ten days after her first round of chemo. In that time, she was able to attend her high school graduation. She walked across the stage to a standing ovation from a standing-room-only crowd. It was awe-inspiring.

When Katie died during her second round of chemo only eleven days later, her classmates filled the funeral home for both the wake and the funeral. Some of her closest friends brought small gifts that they placed in her casket. The standing ovation and the support after her death, that's what they did for Katie.

Katie
01/06/84 ~ 06/13/02
She dances through our hearts and thoughts every moment of the day.

By the start of second grade, sadly Olivia could not attend (wheelchair, partial paralysis, etc.) so the school district provided a tutor. This was very important to Olivia because she loved school. The tutor came daily for a few hours and Olivia kept up with her classmates easily. Olivia's teachers came to see her several times, and the school bought her a teddy bear with a school shirt that all the teachers signed.

After Olivia died, her dad and I attended the second grade graduation (magnet school preschool through second grade). During the ceremony one little girl stood up and said, "Olivia Patton would have been in our class and she would have loved second grade. Olivia was my best friend." Then each of those second graders got up one by one and said things like "Olivia would have loved reading" and "Olivia would have love recess," etc. Wow. The kids painted a planter with all their names and handprints to leave at the school and they painted Olivia's name with a heart and wings. The school also has a plaque with Olivia's picture and name that says, "Always in our hearts." They are raising money for a much needed playground that will have a plaque that says: "Olivia's Playground."

June 27, 1994 ~ November 12, 2001
Olivia Mackenzie Patton
We love you peanut, all the way to the moon and back.

✦✦✦

Just before Nikki died, the class lost a young man in a car accident. Gosh I felt so bad for the class, two kids in four months, right before high school graduation. They opened the school the next day (Saturday) so the kids could all congregate in the gym and console each other. It's something the kids needed to do and it also gave them a safe place to do it. The parents hung out in the hallway and the kids took care of each other. I think there were a couple of admired teachers who sat with them and just kept an eye on things.

After Nikki passed, the school framed and gave us her 'home' soccer jersey (soccer was a great love). Her 'away' jersey was also framed and hangs in the gym. I have yet to go see it, but it means a great deal to us. Her number is officially retired. The school has done a few other things, (dedicated the school play etc.), but what I really wish is that the teachers were more educated on grief for the siblings. I really don't know exactly what I'm looking for here (and that's part of the problem). The siblings really suffer.

December 30, 1983 ~ August 14, 2002
Angel Nikki, forever 18 & now gracing heaven with her sweet soul and sweeter smile.
~love you babes~

✝ ✝ ✝

When Connell died, my oldest son Joseph was in 3rd grade. Each of his classmates made him a card, and the teacher sent them to our home. I think that sometimes the siblings are the silent grievers. I think that getting the cards made Joseph feel that he mattered too and that his loss was huge. Having the surviving children acknowledged is very important. Everyone seems to immediately migrate to the parents, while the surviving children stand in the wings wondering if anyone realizes how much they love and miss their dead sibling!

July 21, 1998 ~ March 20, 2001
Connell, you are always on our minds and forever in our hearts. We long to kiss your face and hug you tightly. Please know you are loved and missed more than words can say!

✝ ✝ ✝

My daughter Lisa was 12 years old when she was diagnosed with acute lymphoblastic leukemia in 1996. Lisa died the weekend before her high school's homecoming, when she was 15 years and a sophomore in high school. Needless to say, family and friends were devastated. Then, I was asked by Lisa's friends to attend the homecoming football game the next Saturday. I was still in a state of shock then, but agreed to go.

When we got there, one of the Moms was passing out lengths of yellow ribbons to be tied around everyones' arms in memory of Lisa. They also had two bunches of yellow balloons they released later on after her dear friends paid tribute to her memory on the sound system. The boys on the team all had the yellow ribbons with Lisa's name on them tied to their wrists with tape over them. There was no stopping them, and they were determined to win—and they did—46-0! After the game they gave me the winning homecoming football, signed by the whole team.

The West Chicago Community High School also awarded Lisa an honorary diploma and announced her name when her class graduated. Lisa and our family were surrounded with sympathy, compassion, and kind acts from so many at her school through the years. I just want to say that it meant so much more to Lisa and us then anyone involved will ever know, and Thank You to Each One of You!!!

December 5, 1983 ~ October 3, 1999
My sweet Angel Lisa. You are, and continue to be an inspiration to all of us! We love and miss you so very much! I can't wait to see your beautiful smile again!

✛ ✛ ✛

Michelle died on a Saturday, and by Monday morning, the school had lined up bereavement counselors for any students who needed to talk. One girl who was at school and on the same softball team as Michelle, had borrowed Michelle's slider during a previous game (a slider is a fabric covering that goes over the knee area for when you slide into home plate: we didn't allow Michelle to slide anymore). This girl wore this slider every day to school for weeks after Michelle's death because it gave her some comfort. The school let her wear it.

For Michelle, the school planted a tree outside the front door where most of the students go in and out, and they placed a small plaque telling who the tree was in remembrance of. Megan (Michelle's twin) was very involved in the committee that selected of the tree. They also did an assembly for Megan. The principal got up before the students and told how she had lost her best friend in grade school, and how much it hurt. She encouraged everyone to talk about Michelle and remember what a brave and cheerful little girl she was, especially to Megan.

Michelle's band teacher dedicated the first concert after Michelle's death, to Michelle. He was going to say more, but he got choked up and couldn't say everything he'd planned. And that first year, the school dedicated two pages to Michelle in the yearbook, and Michelle's yearbook (which I had bought for her before she died) was passed around to all the teachers who had taught Michelle, and they wrote sweet and funny memories about her in it for me.

August 10, 1984 ~ September 13, 1997
Michelle Cambria Rief
We miss your courage, your strength and your sense of humor.
We love you sweetie.

✞ ✞ ✞

I am a teacher, so I have seen it from both sides—having lost my own 4-year-old son almost 6 years ago and having two of my students die (one just last year) in my 18 years of teaching. I teach at a small Christian school and the way we handle death may be a bit different from how a large public school may do things.

From my own experiences, it is always best to acknowledge the death rather than pretend it didn't happen or that it's not worth mentioning. Last year a 7th grader named Nick was hit by a car on his way to school and was on life support for 24 hours. The morning of his accident, all kinds of stories were being rumored, so once we got all the correct information we immediately had an all-school assembly, told the story the right way and took time to pray. Ministers and counselors were available throughout the day if kids needed to talk. A prayer service was held in our school in the evening. When he was taken off life support the next day, midmorning, we had another assembly with just the 7th graders meeting in the gym with additional parents and counselors. They were all given an hour to grieve, to cry, to hug, to talk, to pray, to remember Nick. The 8th graders were told in their classes that Nick had died and that ministers and counselors would be available the rest of the day, but they were not part of the assembly.

I put out a table with some poster boards, markers and stick-it notes so kids could write a note to Nick's family or put something on his locker. The two nights of the visitation we teachers took turns being at the funeral home, in case kids needed a welcoming face and someone to talk to. I stayed in line with several girls who had never been to a visitation before and needed extra reassurance of what Nick would look like and what was appropriate to say to his folks.

The afternoon of the funeral, anyone who had a note from their parents were allowed to miss school to attend and we had bussing available to and from the nearby church, although many students left with their parents to attend together as a family.

Our principal hired a Christian counseling team to come to school a few weeks after Nick died. It was an after school staff in-service, meant to be a kind of "wrap-up" session which gave us time as a staff to rethink the whole situation, talk about what we did as a school in meeting the needs of the students and what we would do differently next time, targeting kids who we felt were exceptionally at risk for grief. It also gave us time as a staff to grieve with each other. We all shed tears thinking about the experience and sharing our feelings and our faith. It was well worth the time and money to have done this.

4/29/93 ~ 7/22/97
Remembering my Michael who makes my life a continuous lesson and me a better teacher.

✦ ✦ ✦

Danny's high school had an electronic announcement board both outside in the Quad and in the lunchroom. They displayed "Get Well Danny Klancher" for a while after he relapsed. After he died, they posted "In memory of Danny Klancher" with his birth and death dates.

Kids held an onsite memorial at the high school the Monday after Danny died. It was wonderful, and kids called my older son, Stephen, and asked him to bring his parents to the memorial after school to see the photos, flyers, etc. They did a balloon release after kids signed messages to Danny. More importantly for our family, there was a huge piece of butcher paper hung up at the school where kids wrote poems and other messages to Danny, and to his family. I treasure this.

Several high school teachers and administrators attended the memorial, along with many students. I think that is very important. Other things that help are:

- *Let family members know in advance if anything is being done in memory of their son or daughter. Lots of times these things occur and the family never knows. Parents frequently wrestle with whether to attend graduation, particularly if the deceased child was in her/ his senior year. At graduation, for example, let the parents know if a chair will remain empty, a rose left on the chair, the child's name announced, and/or a moment of silence during the ceremony. These things are easy and appropriate to do, but parents often go to graduation and there is no mention of the child who should be there, who lost his/her life in a battle most people cannot fully understand.*

- *Do an article about the child and his/her life for the school newspaper or put a tribute in the yearbook, maybe even each year that the child would have been there. I designed a yearbook ad for Danny's sophomore class (this past May), only to have the administration forget about it and leave it out. I had already told many of Danny's friends to "look for a message from Dan each year."*

- *Other memorials or tributes can include plaques, a tree dedication, etc. Danny's elementary school planted a crepe myrtle and planted a rose garden in his name, four years after he was in school there.*

- *Keep in touch with the parents about surviving siblings. I had several teachers e-mail me on a regular basis about Stephen.*

Danny Paul Klancher
5/27/87 ~ 3/15/02
We continue to be inspired by the beauty of your life, the courage of your fight, and the dignity of your death.
http://www.dannyklancher.com

✢ ✢ ✢

When my son passed away there was no formal acknowledgement from the school. The principal came to the wake, a couple of teachers, and about three kids. Anthony was only in 1st grade so there wouldn't be a big circle of friends at that age, but I've heard of other schools where the whole class went to the wake or the funeral, but I suppose it's up to an individual family how to handle that. His home tutor approached the PTO committee, and they did have a fundraiser for a scholarship in his name the year he would be graduating, which is in four years. But we never did get a card or flowers sent from the school, which I think should have been done.

Anthony J. Quartarone
4/30/89 ~ 4/12/98
We miss your smiling face and will never forget you.

✢ ✢ ✢

Our son Gavin was in the 9th grade when he died after a BMT. His classmates had a very hard time and the 9th grade counselor worked with many of them. The thing that those classmates ultimately did really touched us deeply. When they were seniors and had the class meeting about graduation and the ceremony, they asked the principal if they could include Gavin somehow in the ceremony. With our permission, they had his name included on the list of graduates (with deceased indicated) and they placed an empty chair on the stage where he would have sat. It was very moving and helped us to know that they had not forgotten him.

Our daughter, as the BMT donor and surviving sibling, was only 12 at the time and struggling to fit in as an adolescent. She had a very difficult time that year in 7th grade and we asked one of her teachers whom she liked very much to be a special friend to her that year. That teacher did special things for her and found times to just take little walks and have talks with her at school. She also encouraged her to write about her feelings. I think the surviving siblings are still not well understood.

May 30, 1971 ~ January 29, 1986
Gavin, our son, who continues to inspire us and point us in new directions.

✦ ✦ ✦

My 4-year-old son is being treated for leukemia. A little boy named Ben at my son's preschool died one year ago. The school's director got in touch with some social workers familiar with children and grief, and compiled a packet of photocopies for each family about helping their children cope with grief. I found the information very timely and helpful.

My son's nonchalance and many of his questions were upsetting to me. But the handouts explained that preschool kids usually don't grasp that death is forever and might not be very upset by it, and that young kids are very concrete and ask a lot about the details. Since I knew my son's questions were normal I didn't feel the need to escape those conversations. The information also made me feel brave enough to bring my kids to the funeral, which I was later glad I had done.

They closed the preschool for the day for the funeral. One of Ben's teachers talked at the funeral, and told a hilarious story about how Ben loved this one pink polka-dotted frilly shirt he found in the extra clothes box. The school also got several children's books about death and grief from the library and shared them with children and families. The school organized meals for the family for a month, until the family said they didn't need meals anymore.

The school has set up a beautiful memorial garden next to the school, and we plan to put in a bench with a tile photo of Ben wearing the polka-dotted shirt. All the families in the school have been working on the garden, and the process of clearing out cactus and thorns has been symbolic. Ben's mom is going to help do a big art project of a clay tree with a leaf with the name of every kid who goes to the school. The tree will grow bigger each year as new kids come to the school.

Ben's brother went to a different school and they too were really helpful. One thing they did was have the students make art that can hang from trees, and they decorated the trees where we had Ben's funeral. At Ben's family's house they still have many of the artworks hanging from their trees—very beautiful things with crystals and beads.

✦ ✦ ✦

Five months into our new life (after our daughter's death), we attended several parent teacher meetings for our son Douglas (16) at the school. Douglas is very smart but has definitely lost some drive this year and had a few discipline issues, nothing serious. At one meeting the teacher said, "I think he's still grieving." Thankfully I was in such shock when she said this that I couldn't respond. I did manage at the end of the meeting to say, "This is something we will never get over; we will always live with this."

✦ ✦ ✦

Our school was excellent in the first week or two. First of all, they closed school so that the teachers and kids could go to the funeral. We are a small private school (this year we have 130 kids). They allowed Yenti Frost from "Caring Children" to come in and speak with the kids. She talked to his classmates, and to my kids' classmates. She covered a lot of ground, like what to say and what not to say. They had a counselor from Jewish Family Services speak to the teachers on how to deal with the death of a classmate. They also made the counselor available to any students who wanted to speak with her on the day of the funeral.

They are working on a library that will be named after my son even though I did not reach my total fund raising goal. It is so important to me as a bereaved mom to see my son's name somewhere. It sort of says, he was here and he was alive.

Yossi Chaim
born 4/14/88 passed away in my arms on 3/10/01
BLEE AYIN HORA

✦ ✦ ✦

The night 9-year-old Sarah died my sister was here with us. In the wee hours of the morning Sue and I gathered Sarah's stuffed animals, which she called 'stuffies.' She had so many from when she was in the hospital. We wrote a little card for each of her classmates. We attached the card to a stuffy with a purple ribbon (Sarah's favorite color). We tried to pick an appropriate stuffy for each child and make the notes personal. Sue took them to the school and left them on the children's desks before the students and teacher arrived. At Sarah's service a number of her classmates carried their new 'friend' with them.

The school lowered the flag to half-mast and the next day Sarah's classmates released balloons out in the schoolyard. Each child was allowed to say a little something if he or she wanted. The teacher invited the parents and notified them this would be happening.

A few weeks after Sarah died, her school planted a flowering cherry tree in their front garden. Sarah died at Easter time. Each year since then, one of her classmate's moms has arranged to have the tree decorated for Easter. She hangs hollow Easter eggs/ornaments on the tree and any children who want to write a little letter or note puts it inside the ornaments. Donna has given me the notes, but I haven't been able to read them.

I went to the grade 7 graduation for Sarah's class. It was hard. Sarah's friends looked so grown up that I didn't recognize some of them. As part of the ceremonies, her class presented almost $600 to a representative from the Make A Wish Foundation. They had held a hot dog sale earlier in June to raise the money for a tribute to their friend Sarah. I had been forewarned of this but it was still very hard. During the ceremony, there were many tears from many of the moms, so mine weren't out of place. They had a slide presentation to end the morning—a baby picture of each of the students followed by a current one. The show included our Sarah and her pictures were followed by much whooping and hollering. Lucky thing it was the end of the event and I had found a chair near the back door. I had a feeling I might need a quick escape, and I did. I was so very pleased to see that Sarah has not been forgotten by her friends.

Sarah
November 14, 1990 ~ March 28, 1999
Love you forever darling, big as the sky.

Appendix A

Sample: Communicable Disease Letter

This appendix contains a sample letter about the dangers of communicable diseases. This version is sent from the school principal to parents of the child's classmates. It can be modified as necessary to fit the child's special circumstances. For example, some parents want to have their child's name included, while others don't. Discuss the letter with school administrators to make sure it is accurate and reflects your wishes.

You might wish to also send this note to the classmates of any siblings, or to all children who ride the bus with the ill child or her siblings. Some parents may wish to inform all of the families at the school.

Teachers and staff members are usually asked many questions about the ill child. While these questions arise out of concern and caring, they may infringe on the child's privacy. It is helpful for staff to talk with the family about what information they are comfortable sharing with other parents.

The sample letter is on the next page.

Dear parents,

As you may have heard, _____ , a classmate of your child, has been diagnosed with cancer. While this is sad news, we are encouraged because there are excellent treatments for this illness. Treatment will be intensive but the family is hopeful that _____ will soon return to school.

We are writing this letter for three reasons:

- We want to reassure you that cancer is not contagious. Children and adults cannot "catch it."

- We want to let you know that we are discussing the illness at school. A nurse from the hospital will present a short program, and will answer all of the children's questions in a sensitive and caring manner. *[Only put in previous sentence if this will happen]*. You may find that your child has concerns or questions that you may wish to discuss at home.

- Because _____'s immunity is lowered by treatment, he/she is at greater risk from infections than other children. Illnesses such as chicken pox, measles, the flu, and strep throat are dangerous for him/her and can be life-threatening.

Please let us know as soon as possible if your child becomes ill. We will inform _____'s parents so that they can take appropriate action. Treatment must be given within 72 hours of exposure to be effective. If your child becomes ill over the weekend or on a vacation, please call _____'s parents at *[insert phone number]* so they can determine if she has been exposed. With your help, we hope to protect _____ from illnesses while she is being treated for cancer.

Thank you for your understanding and cooperation. Please call if you have any questions or concerns, or if you wish to attend the class presentation.

Sincerely,

Principal

Appendix B

Glossary of Educational Terms

Accommodation: alteration to the classroom or format of materials, testing, or presentation for a student with disabilities such as seat placement, a second set of books at home, or oral rather than written testing.

Advocate: a professional (lawyer, psychologist) or lay person with knowledge and training about special education services and children with special health care needs who helps parents request and receive appropriate services for their children.

American with Disabilities Act (ADA): a federal law to protect individuals with disabilities that requires public and private institutions to provide reasonable accommodations.

Attention deficit disorder (ADD): a condition characterized by difficulty focusing and sustaining attention.

Attention deficit with hyperactivity disorder (AD/HD): a condition characterized by hyperactive behavior and difficulty focusing.

Assessment: gathering and evaluating information about a child's educational, cognitive, psychological, behavioral and/or physical strengths and needs. It can include standardized testing, interviews, and information from other sources such as parents or teachers. The information gathered during the assessment is used to create the IEP.

Assistive technology: a product or a piece of equipment that is used to compensate for functional limitations, such as a communication device for someone who is unable to speak.

Audiology: a related service that includes testing for the ability to hear sounds and fitting and maintaining any necessary assistance devices.

Behavior intervention plan: A plan of positive behavioral interventions contained in the IEP of a child whose behaviors interfere with his or her learning, or that of others.

Child Find: a provision of the Individuals with Disabilities Act which mandates state and/ or local agencies to identify persons with disabilities between birth and age 21 and direct them to appropriate services.

Consent: a requirement that the parent be informed of all information that relates to any action that school wants to take about the child and that the parent understands that consent is voluntary and may be revoked at any time.

Due process: a procedure that parents or school officials use to help settle disagreements about needs or services to be provided to a child in the school setting. Due process can include informal meetings, mediation, and hearings.

Early intervention (EI): federally required services for children under five years of age who have physical disabilities or developmental delays.

Executive functions: term for cognitive abilities that are needed for self-directed, goal-oriented behavior such as organization, mental flexibility, insight, creativity, and abstract thought.

Extended school year (ESY): extension of the school year or related services through the summer if the child is likely to regress significantly and will be unable to regain those skills in a reasonable amount of time during the next school year.

Evaluation: an assessment to help determine eligibility for a program or set or services.

Free, appropriate public education (FAPE): the right of every child with a disability to a free, appropriate public education, as described in IDEA and section 504.

Full Scale IQ: a combined result of verbal and performance IQ scores.

General education: the regular school program attended by children without special needs.

Homebound instruction: tutoring given by school district teachers at a student's home when the student is unable to attend school.

Home schooling: a private educational option in which parents choose to educate their child themselves outside the public system.

Inclusion: placing a child with special education needs into a classroom environment with non-disabled peers. It is often referred to as "mainstreaming."

Individuals with Disabilities Education Act (IDEA): the federal legislation that defines services and protections for individuals with disabilities in obtaining a free, appropriate public education.

Individualized education program (IEP): a process of developing a plan that specifies the child's strengths and educational needs. This is a contract between the school district and the parent/guardian that defines what the school district will provide to help the child achieve his/her educational goals. The plan itself is also commonly known as an IEP (individualized education plan.

Individualized family service plan (IFSP): a written plan for providing early intervention services to infants and toddlers age birth to three years with, or at risk of having, a developmental disability and their families.

Individual transition plan (ITP): outlines services necessary to transition to higher education or vocation.

Least restrictive environment (LRE): the classroom environment that is closest to what the child would need if he/she did not have a disability.

Local educational agency (LEA): the institution or agency charged with evaluating and providing services to special needs children. This is usually the school district.

Mainstreaming: regular classroom placement of disabled students.

Mediation: procedural safeguard to resolve disputes between parents and schools. It must be voluntary, cannot be used to deny or delay right to a due process hearing, and must be conducted by a qualified and impartial mediator.

Modification: alteration of educational requirements for a student with disabilities; may include changes in instruction, content, or performance; for example, requiring that only every other math problem be completed.

Nonverbal learning disability (NVLD): learning deficits in nonverbal areas such as coordination, mental flexibility, organization, and social skills.

Occupational therapy: Related service that includes therapy to improve fine motor skills.

Other health impaired (OHI): under IDEA, an eligibility category used for students with a condition that causes reduced vitality, strength, or alertness that affects the child's educational performance.

Performance IQ: results of several subtests regarding a person's ability to perform manipulation tasks and analysis (e.g. block design, object assembly, symbol search).

Physical therapy: related service that includes therapy to improve gross motor skills.

Procedural safeguards: the "rules" in IDEA that promote and protect a parent's right to participate in decision-making regarding their child's education.

Procedural safeguards notice: requirement that schools provide comprehensive but easy to understand explanations of procedural safeguards that describe the parent's right to an independent educational evaluation, to examine records, and to request mediation and due process.

Rehabilitation Act of 1973: civil rights statute that protects individuals with disabilities from discrimination and maximizes employment, economic self-sufficiency, independence, inclusion and integration into society.

Resource room: a classroom with a special education teacher where a student receives additional instruction for part of the day.

Related services: services that are necessary for child to benefit from special education; includes speech-language and audiology services, psychological services, physical and occupational therapy, early identification and assessment, counseling, rehabilitation counseling, orientation and mobility services, school health services, social work services, and parent counseling.

Section 504: a part of the Rehabilitation Act of 1973 that prohibits groups that receive public funds (e.g. schools) from discriminating against individuals with disabilities. It requires reasonable accommodations for the child with a disability, whether or not that child receives special education services.

Self-contained classroom: a class of students with disabilities who have little or no interaction with students without disabilities.

Special education services: services to meet the unique needs of students whose needs cannot be met with modification of a regular instructional program, and related therapies such as physical, speech or occupational therapy.

Special health care needs: those health care needs that are beyond those typically required by children.

Transition services: activities to assure the successful movement of a child from high school to college, work, or vocational education.

Transportation: related service that includes transporting children with disabilities. Can specify use of specialized equipment such as special or adapted buses, lifts, and ramps.

Traumatic brain injury: damage to the brain from an external force that can result in disabilities.

Verbal IQ: The results from six subtests that evaluate the use and understanding of oral language.

Appendix C

School Accommodations

Following are check off lists, grouped by disability, that parents who contributed to this book obtained to help their children learn. Teachers and parents can use this appendix to help devise the best Individual Education Plan for each unique survivor of childhood cancer.

General For Students With Cancer

- ❑ Apply infection precautions
- ❑ Adjust attendance policies
- ❑ Allow a reduced day
- ❑ Provide personalized course selection
- ❑ Limit number of classes taken
- ❑ Provide homebound or hospital tutor
- ❑ Adjust activity level and expectations in classes based on physical limitations
- ❑ Help student maintain involvement in extracurricular activities
- ❑ Provide appropriate assistive technology
- ❑ Shorten day and provide home tutor if necessary
- ❑ Send set of textbooks and assignments home or to the hospital
- ❑ Tape lessons
- ❑ Modify schedule to include rest breaks
- ❑ Educate classmates
- ❑ Provide awareness training for staff
- ❑ Provide counseling or create a peer support group
- ❑ Provide counseling to classmates as appropriate
- ❑ Adapt physical education
- ❑ Provide access to school health services
- ❑ Modify workload and/or homework
- ❑ Provide a free pass system from the classroom (to go to a rest area or the health office)

- ❑ Furnish a peer tutor
- ❑ Allow student to wear hat or other head covering
- ❑ Allow student to drink fluids during class
- ❑ Instruct student in preferred learning mode
- ❑ Involve parents in teacher selection
- ❑ Provide teachers and student teachers reading materials on cognitive and social late effects from cancer treatment

Lesson Accommodations

- ❑ Write key points on board
- ❑ Use visual aids
- ❑ Provide access to computer-assisted instruction
- ❑ Check student understanding of directions
- ❑ Provide written outline of material
- ❑ Use multi sensory methods of instruction
- ❑ Provide small group instruction
- ❑ Pair students to check work
- ❑ Allow student to tape record lessons
- ❑ Provide classroom aides and/or note takers
- ❑ Allow calculator use after mastery demonstrated
- ❑ Provide daily one-to-one tutoring with a certified special education specialist

Environmental Accommodations

- ❑ Provide preferential seating
- ❑ Seat near a role model
- ❑ Maintain physical proximity when giving directions or presenting lessons
- ❑ Avoid distracting stimuli
- ❑ Increase distance between desks
- ❑ Use FM trainer
- ❑ Provide access to a separate bathroom
- ❑ Provide elevator privileges
- ❑ Allow student to leave class early to go to next class in uncrowded hallways
- ❑ Travel between classes with adult/responsible peer
- ❑ Provide convenient locker
- ❑ Provide transportation to and from services or school
- ❑ Schedule accommodations to permit time to walk service dog outdoors

Processing Disabilities

- ❏ Modify assignments, e.g., do every third problem
- ❏ Give extra time to complete tasks
- ❏ Eliminate timed tests
- ❏ Simplify directions
- ❏ Provide written directions
- ❏ Allow typewritten or computer printed assignments
- ❏ Use self-monitoring devices
- ❏ Reduce homework assignments
- ❏ Allow use of laptop for note taking, assignments, and homework
- ❏ Provide Alpha Smart keyboard (www.alphasmart.com)
- ❏ Provide study skills training
- ❏ Teach learning strategies
- ❏ Reduce reading level of assignments/homework
- ❏ Give clear one or two step directions
- ❏ Help student break long-term assignments into small, more manageable tasks
- ❏ Provide a quiet place for student to repeat directions
- ❏ Provide a structured routine in written form
- ❏ Create study groups with discussion for learning/memory
- ❏ Provide copy of peer notes to increase listening in class and reduce writing
- ❏ Provide copy of teacher's planning notes prior to instruction
- ❏ Reduce writing requirements
- ❏ Provide computer for written assignments
- ❏ Provide keyboard training (kindergartners are not too young to learn)
- ❏ Provide software for written language

Fine Motor Skills Problems

- ❏ Use a word processor (e.g. Alpha Smart) rather than handwriting
- ❏ Provide occupational therapy
- ❏ Provide a note taker or tape recorder
- ❏ Administer written tests orally
- ❏ Allow student to give reports orally
- ❏ Verify that all homework assignments have been copied from blackboard
- ❏ Provide preprinted homework assignments
- ❏ Shorten written assignments

- ❏ Allow student to write answers to standardized tests in test booklet
- ❏ Base handwriting grade on effort; do not penalize student for poor handwriting
- ❏ Use visuals and verbal directions in addition to written instructions
- ❏ Reduce pencil/paper tasks
- ❏ Shorten assignments/tests

Visual Impairment; Visual/Spatial Difficulties

- ❏ Provide preferential seating
- ❏ Provide aide for class changes
- ❏ Provide aide to take notes
- ❏ Use large type
- ❏ Keep page format simple
- ❏ Avoid use of distracting graphics
- ❏ Use materials in Braille
- ❏ Provide books on tape for reading assignments
- ❏ Provide slant board for visual issues
- ❏ Provide visual tracking systems for dealing with print

Hearing Impairment

- ❏ Place child in a seat close to teacher
- ❏ Have teacher stands next to child when speaking
- ❏ Use state-of-the-art FM device (feeds teacher's voice directly to student)
- ❏ Arrange periodic visits from an audio therapist to assess student in class
- ❏ Teach sign language
- ❏ Provide speech/language therapy

Modified Testing Procedures

- ❏ Use open book exams
- ❏ Arrange for oral testing
- ❏ Give take-home tests
- ❏ Provide practice questions for study
- ❏ Give multiple choice questions rather than short answer or essay
- ❏ Give frequent short quizzes; avoid long exams
- ❏ Permit breaks during tests
- ❏ Allow extra time for exams
- ❏ Let resource teacher administer tests

- ❑ Allow student to take test in a quiet, distraction free place
- ❑ Read test items to student
- ❑ Adjust grading criteria
- ❑ Allow use of computer for test taking
- ❑ Allow use of dictionary or calculator during test
- ❑ Do not grade handwriting

Grades

- ❑ Base grades on improvement rather than test results
- ❑ Base grades on IEP objectives
- ❑ Base grades on effort as well as achievement
- ❑ Mark correct answers, not mistakes, on classwork and homework

Organization and Study Skills

- ❑ Provide AM check-in to prepare for day
- ❑ Provide PM checkout to organize homework
- ❑ Provide a clear, predictable schedule
- ❑ Post or provide an individual daily assignment sheet
- ❑ Provide a weekly syllabus, in advance, of upcoming week's assignments and lessons
- ❑ Give time to organize desk during class
- ❑ Assist student to set up and maintain a color-coded organizational system
- ❑ Provide homework assignment book
- ❑ Check off assignments in homework assignment book
- ❑ Provide an extra set of books at home
- ❑ Send daily or weekly progress reports home
- ❑ Provide study skills class
- ❑ Provide time management training
- ❑ Provide training in how to take notes or provide note taker
- ❑ Teach student to identify key words in text and operational signs in math
- ❑ Develop a reward system for schoolwork or homework completed
- ❑ Shorten assignments
- ❑ Break assignments into short, sequential steps
- ❑ Provide organizational strategies, e.g., charts, timelines
- ❑ Ask student to repeat/discuss plan before beginning task
- ❑ Allow student to observe task first
- ❑ Use a day timer to plan long assignments

❑ Provide volunteer homework buddy

Behavior Management

❑ Praise specific behaviors
❑ Increase frequency of feedback
❑ Teach self-monitoring strategies
❑ Keep classroom rules simple and clear
❑ Allow for short breaks between assignments
❑ Use a non-verbal signal to cue student to stay on task
❑ Mark student's correct answers, not mistakes
❑ Monitor student closely on field trips
❑ Use a buddy system during field trips
❑ Allow movement during class
❑ Make a behavior contract with student
❑ Make rewards immediate
❑ Give corrections in private
❑ Provide public recognition for accomplishments
❑ Implement time out procedures
❑ Develop strategies for transitional periods (cafeteria, PE, library, etc.)
❑ Provide advance notice for changes in routine, e.g. field trips, changes in class schedule
❑ Monitor behavioral plan at school and home for consistency

Social Interventions

❑ Monitor playground interactions
❑ Teach conflict resolution skills
❑ Monitor lunchroom interactions
❑ Provide social skills training from outside professional

Communication with Parents

❑ Schedule periodic parent/ teacher meetings
❑ Provide duplicate set of textbooks for home use
❑ Send weekly progress reports home
❑ Mail a schedule of class and work assignments to the student's parents

Appendix D

Resources

Many resources exist for families of children with cancer. This appendix contains a sampling of some especially helpful organizations, books, videotapes, and websites dealing with educating the child who has or had cancer. To find additional resources, refer to the appendices of the books *Childhood Leukemia*, *Childhood Cancer,* or *Childhood Brain & Spinal Cord Tumors* listed below. You can find them in your local public library, at your local bookstore (if not on the shelf, they can order one for you), or from an online bookseller like *www.amazon.com* or *www.bn.com.*

Books

General

Keene, Nancy. *Chemo, Craziness, and Comfort: My Book About Childhood Cancer.* Candlelighters Childhood Cancer Foundation, 2002. Provides clear explanations and practical advice for children ages 6 to 12 with cancer. Warm and funny illustrations by Trevor Romain help the child (and parents) make sense of cancer and its treatment. Free to families of children with cancer.

Keene, Nancy. *Childhood Leukemia: A Guide for Families, Friends, and Caregiver.* 3rd ed. O'Reilly & Associates, 2002. Provides comprehensive, accurate, and up-to-date information for families of children with leukemia. Includes the stories of over 100 parents, children with leukemia, and their siblings.

Keene, Hobbie, Ruccione. *Survivors of Childhood Cancer: A Practical Guide to Your Future.* O'Reilly & Associates, 2000. A user friendly comprehensive guide on late effects after treatment for childhood cancer.

Klett, Amy. *The Amazing Hannah, Look At Everything I Can Do!* Candlelighters Childhood Cancer Foundation, 2002. Photographs and clear messages help preschoolers make sense of cancer and treatment. Free to families of children with cancer.

Janes-Hodder, Keene. *Childhood Cancer: A Parent's Guide to Solid Tumor Cancers.* 2nd ed. O'Reilly & Associates, 2002. Provides comprehensive, accurate, and up-to-date information for families of children with solid tumors (except brain and spinal cord tumors). Contains stories from dozens of families of children with cancer.

Shiminski-Mahar, Cullen, Sansalone. *Childhood Brain & Spinal Cord Tumors: A Guide for Families, Friends, and Caregivers.* O'Reilly & Associates, 2002. Provides comprehensive, accurate, and up-to-date information for families of children with brain and spinal cord tumors. Includes stories from dozens of families of children with brain and spinal cord tumors.

College

Peterson's Guides. *Peterson's Guides to Colleges with Programs for Learning Disabled Students or Attention Deficit Disorders.* 6th ed. Princeton, NJ: Peterson's Guides,. 2000. Excellent reference, available at most large libraries.

Coping in school

Krisher, Trudy. *Kathy's Hats: A Story of Hope.* Concept Books, 1992. (800) 255-7675. A charming book for ages 5 to 10 about a girl whose love of hats comes in handy when chemotherapy makes her hair fall out.

Romain, Trevor. *Bullies are a Pain in the Brain.* Minneapolis, MN: Free Spirit Publishing, 1997. Full of warmth and whimsy, this book teaches children skills to cope with teasing and bullying.

Schultz, Charles. *Why, Charlie Brown, Why?* New York: Topper Books, 1990. Tender story of a classmate who develops leukemia. Available as a book or videotape. For video availability, call the Leukemia & Lymphoma Society. (800) 955-4572.

Grief in school

Gliko-Braden, Majel. *Grief Comes to Class: A Teacher's Guide.* Centering Corporation, 1531 N. Saddle Creek Rd., Omaha, NE 68104. (402) 553-1200. Comprehensive guide to grief in the classroom. Includes chapters on grief responses, the bereaved student, teen grief, developmental changes, sample letter to parents, and sample teacher/ parent conferences.

The Compassionate Friends. *Suggestions for Teachers and School Counselors.* P.O. Box 3696, Oak Brook, IL 60522. (630) 990-0010.

Romain, Trevor. *What on Earth Do You Do When Someone Dies?* Minneapolis, MN: Free Spirit Publishing, 1999. Warm, honest words and beautiful illlustrations help children understand and cope with grief.

Hearing loss

Poitras Tucker, Bonnie. *IDEA Advocacy for Children Who Are Deaf Or Hard of Hearing: A Question and Answer Book for Parents and Professionals.* Singular Publishing Group, 1997.

IEP advocacy

Seigel, Lawrence. *The Complete IEP Guide: How to Advocate for Your Special Ed Child.* Harbor House Law Press, 2001. Spells out the IEP process for families and includes helpful sample letters and forms.

Anderson, Winifred, Stephen Chitwood, and Deidre Hayden. *Negotiating the Special Education Maze: A Guide for Parents and Teachers.* 3rd ed. Bethesda, Maryland: Woodbine House, 1997. Excellent, well-organized text clearly explains the step-by-step process necessary to obtain help for your child.

Susan Gorn, Editor. *Special Education Dictionary.* LRP Publications, 1997. (215) 784-0860.

Wright, Peter, and Wright, Pamela. *Wrightslaw: Special Education Law.* Hartfield, VA: Harbor House Law Press, 1999. Text of key laws and regulations.

Wright, Peter, and Wright, Pamela. *Wrightslaw: From Emotions to Advocacy: The Special Education Survival Guide*. Hartfield, VA: Harbor House Law Press, 2001. Full of essential information on special education law, advocacy tactics, and IEP tips.

Learning disabilities

Levine, Mel, MD. *All Kinds of Minds*. Cambridge, Massachusetts: Educator's Publishing Service, Inc., 1993. Highly readable book about different learning styles. Written for grade-school-aged children, but parents benefit from reading it, too.

Levine, Mel, MD. *Keeping a Head in School: A Student's Book About Learning Abilities and Learning Disorders*. Cambridge, Massachusetts: Educator's Publishing Service, Inc., 1991. Book about different learning styles for junior high and high school students.

Levine, Mel, MD. *The Myth of Laziness*. New York: Simon & Shuster, 2003. Discusses children who do poorly in school due to neuro-developmental weaknesses and contains tips for parents and teachers.

Levine, Mel MD. *A Mind at a Time*. Touchstone Books, 2003. Levine defines eight specific mind systems (attention, memory, language, spatial ordering, sequential ordering, motor, higher thinking, and social thinking) and ways to use them to enhance education.

Silver, Larry, MD. *The Misunderstood Child: Understanding and Coping with Your Child's Learning Disabilities*. 3rd ed. Times Books,. 1998. Comprehensive discussion of positive treatment strategies that can be implemented at home and in the school to help children with learning disabilities. Excellent chapters on psychological, social, and emotional development, evaluation, and treatment.

Tanguay, Pamela, Sue Thompson. *Nonverbal Learning Disabilities at School: Educating Students with NLD, Asperger Syndrome and Related Conditions*. Jessica Kingsley Publishers, 2002.

Thompson, Sue. *The Source for Non-Verbal Learning Disabilities*. East Moline, IL: LinguiSystems, 1997. Explains non-verbal learning disabilities and how to provide appropriate interventions at home and in school. (800) PRO-IDEA.

School re-entry

Chai Lifeline. *Back to School: A Handbook for Educators of Children with Life-threatening Diseases in the Yeshiva/Day School System*. Write to: 151 West 30th St., New York, NY 10001, or call (212) 465-1300. Covers diagnosis, planning for school reentry, infection control in schools, needs of junior and senior high school students, children with special educational needs, and saying good-bye when a child dies. Includes a bibliography and resource list. *http://www.chailifeline.org*

Leukemia & Lymphoma Society. *The Trish Greene Back-to-School Program for Children with Cancer* was designed to increase communication among healthcare professionals, parents, patients and school officials to assure a smooth transition from active treatment back to school and daily life. Materials, videos, and other printed inventory are available at all local LLS chapters. *http://www.leukemia-lymphoma.org* or (800) 955-4572 (4LSA).

Nessim, Susan, and Ernest Katz. *Cancervive Teacher's Guide for Kids with Cancer*. (310) 203-9232 or (800) 4-TOCURE, or *http://www.cancervive.org*.

Social skills

Duke, Nowicki, Martin. *Teaching Your Child the Language of Social Success*. Atlanta, GA: Peachtree, 1996. Easy-to-use guide which helps assess children's strengths and weaknesses and incorporates exercises for teaching and improving non-verbal skills to increase social success.

Speech and language

McAleer Hamaguchi, Patricia. *Childhood Speech, Language and Listening Problems: What Every Parent Should Know.* John Wiley & Sons Inc., 1995.

Schoenbrodt, Lisa, ed. *Children with Traumatic Brain Injury: A Parent's Guide.* Woodbine House, 2003.

Schwartz, Sue, and Joan E. Heller Miller. *The New Language of Toys: Teaching Communication Skills to Special-Needs Children.* Rockville, MD: Woodbine House, 1996.

Videotapes

Hairballs on My Pillow. CARTI. (800) 482-8561 or (501) 664-8573. Interviews children with cancer and their friends about friendship and returning to school. $35 for video and newsletters for students, exercises and activities for students, and a teacher's notebook of information about cancer, its treatment, and dealing with returning students.

Welcome Back. 14 minutes. Produced by the Child Life Department at Johns Hopkins Medical Center. Children with cancer talk about their fears, expectations, and experiences when they go back to school. Explains cancer and dispels myths in terms children understand. Aquarius Healthcare Videos: (888) 420-2963. *http://www.aquariusproductions.com.* ($112)

Why, Charlie Brown, Why? Tender story of a classmate who develops leukemia. Available as a book or videotape. For video availability, call the Leukemia and Lymphoma Society, (800) 955-4572 (4LSA).

Cancervive Back to School Kit. A comprehensive package of materials developed to assist children and adolescents re-entering the school setting. The kit contains a "Teachers Guide for Kids with Cancer" and two award-winning documentary videos: "Emily's Story: Back to School After Cancer" and "Making the Grade: Back to School After Cancer for Teens." *http://www.cancervive.org/sfbv.html.* Item No. 123. ($79.95)

Drying Their Tears. Produced by CARTI. For information, call (800) 482-8561. Video and manual to help counselors, teachers, and other professionals help children deal with the grief, fear, confusion, and anger that occur after the death of a loved one. Has three segments: one about training facilitators, one for children ages 5 to 8, and one for ages 9 to teens. Each section includes interviews with children and video from children's workshops.

Back to School: Teens Prepare for School Re-entry. Produced by Starbright Videos with Attitude. *http://www.starbright.org.* Teens who have been there share their stories and advice on how to get back into the groove of school. Also discusses how teens can get the extra help they may need to make returning to school a successful experience.

The Learning Disabilities Association of Massachusetts has several videos on different aspects of coping with learning disabilities including: *Einstein & Me: Talking About Learning Disabilities, Meeting with Success: Ten Tips for a Successful I.E.P., Planning for Success: The College Application Process for Students with Learning Disabilities, Portraits of Success: Fostering Hope and Resilience in Individuals with Learning Disabilities, and Stop and Go Ahead with Success: An Integrated Approach to Helping Children Develop Social Skills.* For more information, visit *http://www.ldam.org.*

Organizations

American Speech-Language-Hearing Association
10801 Rockville Pike
Rockville, MD 20852
(301) 897-8682 or (800) 638-8255
http://www.asha.org

ASHA's mission is to ensure that all people with speech, language, and hearing disorders have access to quality services to help them communicate effectively. Canadian organization at *http://www.caslpa.ca*

Candlelighters Childhood Cancer Foundation
PO Box 498
Kensington, MD 20895-0498
(800) 366-CCCF
http://www.candlelighters.org

Founded in 1970, Candlelighters' National Office has more than 50,000 members. Some of the free services provided by Candlelighters include a toll-free information hotline, a quarterly newsletter, various childhood cancer guides to help families of children with cancer, local support group chapters, and national advocacy.

Childhood Cancer Ombudsman Program
http://www.childhoodbraintumor.org/ombuds.html

This is a service of the Childhood Brain Tumor Foundation that provides information and research options to make decisions in treatment, schooling, rehabilitation, and employment. They also provide complaint investigation.

Children's Hemiplegia and Stroke Association
Suite 305, PMB 149
4101 W. Green Oaks
Arlington, TX 76016
(817) 492-4325 (volunteer will return phone calls)
www.hemikids.org

A non-profit organization that offers support and information to families of infants, children, and young adults who have hemiplegia, hemiparesis, hemiplegic cerebral palsy, childhood stroke, infant stroke, or in utero stroke.

George Washington University Heath Resource Center
2121 K Street NW Suite 220
Washington DC 20037
(202) 973.0904 or (800) 544.3284
http://www.heath.gwu.edu

A national clearinghouse on postsecondary education for individuals with disabilities. Support from the U.S. Department of Education enables the clearinghouse to serve as an information exchange about educational support services, policies, procedures, adaptations, and opportunities at American campuses, vocational-technical schools, and other postsecondary training entities.

Home Education Magazine
P.O. Box 1083

Tonasket, WA 98855
(800) 236-3278
www.home-ed-magazine.com

Organization that publishes a magazine for home schooling families. The website contains newsletters, a discussion board, a networking list and more.

Leukemia & Lymphoma Society
1311 Mamaroneck Avenue
White Plains, NY 10605
(914) 949-5213 or (800) 955-4LSA
http://www.leukemia-lymphoma.org

This organization provides financial assistance to families (up to $500/year for outpatients), funds research, sponsors a national program in education for the public and the medical community, and publishes a large number of booklets on cancer-related topics.

National Association of Private Special Education Centers
http://www.napsec.com

NAPSEC is a non-profit association whose mission is to represent private special education programs and affiliated state associations and to ensure access for individuals to appropriate private special education programs and services. The association consists of private early intervention services, schools, residential therapeutic centers, and adult living programs that serve both privately and publicly placed individuals with disabilities.

National Information Center for Children and Youth with Disabilities
P.O. Box 1492
Washington, DC 20013
(800) 695-0285
www.nichcy.org

NICHCY is the national information center that provides information on disabilities and disability-related issues with a special focus is children and youth (birth to age 22). Anyone can use these services-families, educators, administrators, journalists, students. NICHCY publishes *Transition Planning: A Team Effort* in print or on the Web at *http://www.nichcy.org/pubs/transum/ts10txt.htm*

Super Duper Publications
Department SD 98
P.O. Box 24997
Greenville, SC 29616-2497
(864) 288-3536 or (800) 277-8737
http://www.superduperinc.com

SuperDuper has a huge catalog of speech and language learning materials, games, videos, books, and tests. It also includes items related to augmentative communication, social skills, and sensorimotor activities.

SuperSibs!
1566 West Algonquin Road, Suite 224
Hoffman Estates, IL 60195
(866) 444-SIBS (7427)
http://www.supersibs.org

SuperSibs! mission is to support, honor and recognize brothers and sisters of children with cancer. They provide numerous "Advocacy and Support" services, including journals for siblings, guides, scholarships and a monitored teen chat internet room. SuperSibs! also sponsors "Surprise and Delight" services such as special sibling activities and giveaways for siblings ages 4 to 18. Services are provided free of charge.

Online Support Groups

ACOR, The Association of Cancer Online Resources, Inc.
http://www.acor.org

ACOR offers access to 131 mailing lists that provide support, information, and community to everyone affected by cancer and related disorders. It hosts several pediatric cancer discussion groups, including PED-ONC (a general pediatric cancer discussion group), ALL-KIDS (childhood acute lymphoblastic leukemia), and PED-ONC SURVIVORS (for parents of survivors).

Apraxia-Kids mailing list
Listserv@Listserv.syr.edu
http://www.apraxia-kids.org

This website and mailing list covers oral motor apraxia and related disabilities. To subscribe, send an email with the message "subscribe apraxia-kids FirstName LastName."

Home Schooling Special Needs Children
http://groups.yahoo.com/group/special-needs-homeschool

This group is interested in supporting parents who chose to home school their children with special needs. Most members have medically fragile children dealing challenges in speech, motor development and learning disabilities and home school full time or part of the time. Topics include: curricula, speech, feeding issues, OT, PT, siblings, and a host of other issues.

Hydrocephalus (HYCEPH_L)
http://www.geocities.com/HotSprings/Villa/2020/listserv.html

This list is open to all people interested in hydrocephalus.

IEP Guide and Listserv Yahoogroup
http://groups.yahoo.com/group/IEP_guide

This is a very large listserv of more than 1600 people that offers special education support and has a free IEP guidebook.

Educating Brain Tumor Kids
http://groups.yahoo.com/group/EducatingBTKids

A group with links and files dealing with neuropsychological testing, school re-entry, school options, late effects, etc. There is an associated listserv with archives.

Websites

Pediatric Oncology Resource Center
http://www.acor.org/ped-onc

Edited by Patty Feist-Mack, this site contains detailed and accurate material on diseases, treatment, family issues, activism, and bereavement. Also provides links to helpful cancer sites. The direct link to the school section of the website is *http://www.acor.org/ped-onc/cfissues/backtoschool/backtoschool.html*

Bandaids and Blackboards-When Chronic Illness Goes to School
http://www.faculty.fairfield.edu/fleitas/sitemap.html

Wonderful, fun, and informative website about ill children and school.

Behavior

Behavior Problems of Children who have undergone Treatment for Brain Tumors
http://www.childhoodbraintumor.org/BehaviorProblems02rev.htm

An article written for Childhood Brain Tumor Foundation.

Cerebellar mutism

Cerebellar Mutism and Posterior Fossa Syndrome
http://groups.yahoo.com/group/cerebellarmutism

There is an annotated bibliography from a medline search on cerebellar mutism, a bibliography on radiation and cognitive effects, and several articles from a speech pathologist.

Charter schools

Charter Schools
www.uscharterschool.org

U.S. Department of Education website with lots of information on charter schools.

Disabilities

Council of Educators for Students with Disabilities, Inc. (CESDI)
www.504idea.org

CESDI provides Section 504 and special education training and resources to educators.

Protection and Advocacy
http://www.pai-ca.org

Group that works to advance the human and legal rights of people with disabilities. Website includes a page on assistive technologies.

Pacer Center Parent Advocacy Coalition for Educational Rights
http://www.pacer.org

A national coalition of parents working for educational rights.

Family Village: A Global Community of Disability Resources
www.familyvillage.wisc.edu

A huge site that provides informational resources on specific diagnoses, communication connections, adaptive products and technology, adaptive recreational activities, education, health issues, disability-related media and literature, and much, much more.

Distance learning

Talia Seidman Foundation
www.talzee.org

An organization dedicated to using technology to bring hospitalized and homebound chronically ill children back into the classroom.

Hearing impairment

Hard of Hearing and Deaf Students: A Resource Guide to Support Classroom Teachers
http://www.bced.gov.bc.ca/specialed/hearimpair/toc.htm

Higher education

The Student with a Brain Injury: Achieving Goals in Higher Education
http://www.heath.gwu.edu/PDFs/Brain%20Injury.pdf

Single copies of this and other papers are free-of-charge and can be obtained by visiting the HEATH web site, http://www.heath.gwu.edu/, or calling 800-544-3284 (V/TTY).

Homeschooling

A to Z's Cool Homeschooling
http://www.gomilpitas.com/homeschooling

Huge site with information on beginning to homeschool, curricula, homeschooling laws, support groups, methods, and philosophies.

National Home Education Network
http://www.nhen.org

A source for homeschooling information, support group listings, homeschool news, and related resources.

Nonverbal learning disabilities

Nonverbal Learning Disabilities
www.nldontheweb.org

A comprehensive site on nonverbal learning disabilities.

Siblings

The Sibling Support Project
http://www.thearc.org/siblingsupport

A national program dedicated to the interests of brothers and sisters of people with special health and developmental needs. Includes a listserve for younger brothers and sisters.

Siblings of People with Disabilities
http://www.iidc.indiana.edu/cedir/sibbib.html

A list of books and videos that help siblings of people with disabilites.

Special education law

Consortium for Appropriate Dispute Resolution in Special Education (CADRE)
www.directionservice.org/cadre

CADRE provides support and materials that can help parents and educators implement the mediation requirements under IDEA 97. The web site features articles, resource directories and other information on alternative dispute resolution.

Questions and Answers about IDEA
http://www.nichcy.org/pubs/newsdig/nd21txt.htm

Very clear answers to common questions about the Individuals with Disabilities Education Act.

Wrights Special Education Law
www.wrightslaw.com

This extensive and very well organized site is probably the best place to start to gather information. There are sections on advocacy, law, specific topics, books and other resources.

Educational Rights/Educational Law
www.edlaw.org

This site provides publications and services for attorneys, advocates, and parents who need to know about educational law. There is a section that deals with transportation and another for finding a lawyer.

Americans with Disabilities Act Homepage
http://www.usdoj.gov/crt/ada/adahom1.htm

National Information Center for Children and Youth with Disabilities
http://www.nichcy.org

Includes helpful resource sheets for every state.

Healthy and Ready to Work Network
www.mchbhrtw.org

The Healthy and Ready to Work initiative promotes a comprehensive system of family-centered, culturally competent, community based care for children with special health care needs who are approaching adulthood and may need assistance in making the transition from pediatric to adult health care and to postsecondary education and/or employment.

Half the Planet
http://www.halftheplanet.com

A disability community where people with disabilities can access reliable services and products, connect with peer support, and keep up with disability-related news and information all day every day.

Speech and language

IntelliTools
http://www.intellitools.com

This firm has a great catalog of assistive technology and communication devices.

Sports

Disabled Sports USA
http://www.dsusafw.org

An organization that gives people with physical, neuromuscular and developmental impairments the opportunity to participate in a variety of activities including water/snow skiing, camping, and whitewater rafting. Adaptive equipment information available. Some scholarships available.

American Hippotherapy Association
http://www.americanequestrian.com/hippotherapy.htm

Hippotherapy is therapeutic riding for those with motor disturbances.

North American Riding for the Handicapped
http://www.narha.org

An organization that promotes the benefits of horseback riding for those with physical, emotional or learning disabilities.

Skating Association for the Blind and Handicapped
http://www.sabahinc.org

An organization dedicated to allowing all to experience the joy of being on the ice. There are products including special skates and walkers available.

Student financial aid

Financial Aid for Students
http://www.heath.gwu.edu

Produces *Creating Options: A Resource on Financial Aid for Students with Disabilities.* The 2003 edition features up-to-date information about federal financial aid programs, describes the relationship between state vocational rehabilitation agencies and the financial aid process, and lists organizations that offer disability-related grants and scholarships for postsecondary education. It also includes a list of 29 sponsors of scholarships specifically designated for students with disabilities. You may also wish to request a copy of *Vocational Rehabilitation Services: A Post Secondary Student Consumer's Guide.*

Scholarships for Survivors of Childhood Cancer
http://www.acor.org/ped-onc/scholarships/index.html

A list of scholarships is available.

Vocational rehabilitation

American Congress of Community Supports and Employment Services
http://www.accses.org

A national, nonprofit organization of vocational rehabilitation service and community supports committed to maximizing employment opportunities and independent living for individuals with mental and physical disabilities.

Teleconferences

Surviving a Brain Tumor: Understanding Changes in Thinking, Behavior and Memory
http://www.cancercare.org/TeleconferenceArchive/
teleconferenceArchive.cfm?ID=2663&c=412

A lecture by a neuropsychologist that explains brain function and cognitive remediation.

Returning to School after Treatment for Childhood Cancer
http://www.cancercare.org/TeleconferenceArchive/
TeleconferenceArchive.cfm?ID=2652&c=407

An archived lecture on Cancer Care with Dan Armstrong and Barbara Gannon.

School Re-entry After Diagnosis and Treatment of your child's Brain Tumor
http://www.pbtfus.org/informedparent3.htm

This is a one-hour archived lecture by Dan Armstrong for the Pediatric Brain Tumor Foundation of the U.S.

Colophon

Candlelighters Childhood Cancer Foundation is a 501c3 nonprofit, licensed in the District of Columbia. Our federal tax-exempt ID number is: 52-1071862. Candlelighters name is derived from an old Chinese proverb, "It is better to light a candle than to curse the darkness." The proverb expresses the organization's decision in 1970 to identify the problems associated with childhood cancer and to take steps towards change. Informed families are better able to make decisions regarding their child's treatment and on-going care. Informed children with cancer and their siblings are better prepared to understand the disease that they are fighting and the long-term impact of the treatment. Informed teachers are better equipped to educate children on treatment and to survivors of childhood cancer. This book was written to guide parents and teachers as they work together to provide the best possible education for children who have or have had cancer.

The cover for *Educating The Child With Cancer: A Guide for Parents and Teachers* was illustrated by Trevor Romain, an author and Candlelighters' National Board member. The interior layout was created by Shannon Schaffer using Adobe PageMaker 6.5. Fonts include: Garamond, Times and Arial. Candlelighters National logo is produced using PMS 872 Gold and PMS 274 Purple.

Ruth Hoffman, Executive Director of the National office of Candlelighters Childhood Cancer Foundation, did the interior layout and copyediting.